MATHEMATICAL FOUNDATIONS OF THE CALCULUS OF PROBABILITY

HOLDEN-DAY SERIES IN PROBABILITY AND STATISTICS

E. L. Lehmann, Editor

MATHEMATICAL FOUNDATIONS OF THE CALCULUS OF PROBABILITY

By JACQUES NEVEU
Faculty of Sciences, University of Paris

Translated by AMIEL FEINSTEIN

Foreword by R. FORTET

HOLDEN-DAY, INC.
San Francisco, London, Amsterdam
1965

This book is translated from *Bases Mathématiques du Calcul des Probabilités*, 1964, Masson et Cie, Paris

Library of Congress Catalog Card Number: 66–11140

Printed in the United States of America

FOREWORD

In its present state, the calculus of probability and, in particular, the theory of stochastic processes and vector-valued random variables, cannot be understood by one who does not have, to begin with, a thorough understanding of measure theory. If one is to prepare for participation in the future development of the calculus of probability, it is not sufficient to know the fundamental concepts and results of measure theory; one must also be experienced in its techniques and able to use them and extend them to new situations.

Again, one often hears—and quite justifiably in a certain sense—that the calculus of probability is simply a paragraph of the theory of measure; but within measure theory, the calculus of probability stands out by the nature of the questions which it seeks to answer—a nature which has its origins not in measure theory itself, but in the philosophical and practical content of the notion of probability.

The advanced course in the calculus of probability is aimed at those students having the body of knowledge which in France is called "licence de Mathématiques"; this body of knowledge covers mathematics in general. It naturally encompasses the theory of measure and integration, but is necessarily limited to an introduction to the subject. It is thus necessary that this question be taken up again and developed in advanced studies; it is still more necessary that its exposition be oriented specifically toward applications to probability theory.

Since 1959, Professor Neveu has been given the task of presenting this course at the Faculty of Sciences of Paris. It is not necessary to introduce him to the specialists in probability theory. In a short number of years he has gained their attention by brilliant work; but not all can know as well as I how much our students and young researchers appreciate his lively and clear method of teaching. The course which he has taught, enriched by this pedagogic experience, constitutes the subject matter of the present work.

To be sure, there are already books, some of them more extensive, on the theory of measure and several of them are excellent. However, I have already stated why probabilists have need of a text written especially for their use; and for beginners, a text of limited size is preferable.

In such a domain, Professor Neveu has naturally sought to write an expository book, not one of original work, in the sense that he does not pretend to introduce new concepts or to establish new theorems. The fact that he has, very usefully, enriched each chapter with Complements and Problems underlines the essentially pedagogic objective of his book, concerning which I can with pleasure point out two non-trivial merits: he avoids an overburdened notation, and, in a subject which is by its nature abstract, he does not hesitate to insert whenever necessary a paragraph which interprets, which states the reason for things, or which calls attention to an error to be avoided.

The exposition nevertheless proceeds with profound originality. First, by its contents: To the classical elements of measure and integration, the author adds all the theorems for the construction of a probability by extension; from an algebra to a σ-algebra, from a compact subclass to a semialgebra, from finite products of spaces to infinite products of spaces (theorems of Kolmogorov and Tulcea), etc. He treats the measurability, separability and the construction of random functions; conditional expectations, and martingales. He illustrates general results by applications to stopping times, ergodic theory, Markov processes, as well as other problems, all of these rarely included in treatises on measure theory, some of them because of their recent development, others because, while they are of major importance in probability theory, they are perhaps of less interest in general measure theory.

The originality appears equally in the presentation; I particularly appreciate the simple but systematic way in which Professor Neveu has set forth from the first the algebraic structures of families of events which intervene (Boolean algebra and σ-algebras, etc.), while avoiding the premature introduction of topological concepts, whose significance is thereby even better understood.

Throughout, he has succeeded in establishing the most concise and elegant proofs, so that in a small number of pages he is able to be remarkably complete; for example he treats, at least briefly, L_p spaces and even, by a judicious use of the Complements and Problems, decision theory and sufficient statistics.

As a text for study by advanced students, as a reference work for researchers, I can without risk predict for this book long life and great success.

R. Fortet

August, 1965
Geneva

TRANSLATOR'S PREFACE

In comparison with the French original, this translation has benefited by the addition of a section (IV.7) on sequences of independent random variables, as well as by certain additions to the Complements and Problems. Also, the proofs of a few results have been modified. For these improvements, and in particular for the full measure of assistance which I have received from Professor Neveu at every stage of the translation, it is a pleasure to record here my deep gratitude.

A. Feinstein

DEFINITIONS AND NOTATION

Definitions of the terms *partially ordered set* (*or system*), *totally ordered set*, *lattice*, *complete lattice*, *generalized sequence*, *vector space*, *Banach space*, and *linear functional* (among others used in this book) may be found in Chapters I and II of the treatise *Linear Operators*, Part I, by N. Dunford and J. T. Schwartz.

A *real vector lattice* is a set which is both a lattice (under some partial ordering) and a real vector space, and such that $x \leqslant y$ implies $cx \leqslant cy$ for every real $c > 0$, and also $z + x \leqslant z + y$ for every z. A linear functional f on a vector lattice is said to be *positive* if $x \geqslant \mathbf{0}$ implies $f(x) \geqslant 0$. A partially ordered set E is said to be *inductive* if it satisfies the hypothesis of Zorn's lemma (Dunford and Schwartz, p. 6), i.e., if every totally ordered subset of E has an upper bound in E. A *pre-Hilbert space* is a space satisfying all the axioms of a Hilbert space except the axiom of completeness.

The symbol $\Rightarrow$ indicates logical implication; ▮ denotes the end of a proof; $\{x: \cdots\}$ denotes the set of all objects x which satisfy the conditions $\cdots$; * marks difficult sections or problems, for whose understanding or solution concepts not discussed in the text may be needed; finally, $\doteq$ has occasionally been used for "equality by definition."

AUTHOR'S PREFACE

The object of the theory of probability is the mathematical analysis of the notion of chance. As a mathematical discipline, it can only develop in a rigorous manner if it is based upon a system of precise definitions and axioms. Historically, the formulation of such a mathematical basis and the mathematical elaboration of the theory goes back to the 1930's. In fact, it was only at this period that the theory of measure and of integration on general spaces was sufficiently developed to furnish the theory of probability with its fundamental definitions, as well as its most powerful tool for development.

Since then, numerous probabilistic investigations, undertaken in the theoretical as well as practical domain, in particular those making use of functional spaces, have only served to confirm the close relations established between probability theory and measure theory. These relations are, incidentally, so close that certain authors have been loath to see in probability theory more than an extension (but how important a one!) of measure theory.

In any case, it is impossible at the present time to undertake a profound study of probability theory and mathematical statistics without continually making use of measure theory, unless one limits oneself to a study of very elementary probabilistic models and, in particular, cuts oneself off from the consideration of random functions. Attempts have been made, it is true, to treat convergence problems of probability theory within the restricted framework of the study of distribution functions; but this procedure only gives a false simplification of the question and further conceals the intuitive basis of these problems.

The book reproduces the essentials of a course for the first year of the third cycle (which corresponds roughly to the first or second year of graduate work in the United States) which is addressed to students who already have some elementary notions of the calculus of probability; it is intended to furnish them with a solid mathematical base for probability theory. Only a reader with a sound mathematical development could consider this book an introduction to the theory of probability.

Our first aim in this course is therefore to teach the reader how to handle the powerful tools provided by measure theory and to permit him subsequently to deal with any chapter of probability theory. Numerous problems complement the text; given the very "technical" nature of the subject being treated, it would seem to us indispensable for the reader to try to read and solve the greater part of these problems. (To help the reader in this task, we have frequently sketched a solution of a problem.) In accordance with a presently well-established French tradition concerning introductory treatises, we have not deemed it worthwhile to insert bibliographical references in the text, or, with rare exceptions, to attribute the results obtained to their various authors. The reader will find, at the end of the book, a concise bibliography relating to the text or to the complements; most of the problems, in particular, arise out of the works listed in this bibliography.

We would not wish to conceal from the reader the fact that measure theory is not the unique tool of probability theory, even though it is its principal tool; we could not too strongly advise him to learn, if he has not already done so, the precise notions of topology, the theory of metric spaces, and the theory of Hilbert and Banach spaces. This book could not contain within its limited confines any introduction to these theories. Certain problems, and even certain portions of the text,† make use of notions borrowed from these theories; the beginner can ignore them without fear of losing the thread of the presentation, while the more advanced reader will be able to find connections with outside fields which may interest him.

I wish to take this opportunity to thank Professors R. Fortet, M. Loève and A. Tortrat for their suggestions and encouragement. The form of this book also owes much to the reactions of the students who have taken my course.

Finally, my thanks go equally to Dr. A. Feinstein for his excellent work of translation.

J. Neveu

† We have marked them with an asterisk.

TABLE OF CONTENTS

CHAPTER I

PROBABILITY SPACES

The fundamental concepts of the theory of probability are those of *events* and of *probabilities*: Axiomatically, events are mathematical entities which are susceptible of combination by the logical operations "not," "and," "or" (according to the rules specified in Section 1 of this chapter), while a probability is a valuation on the class of events whose properties are by definition analogous to those of a frequency (see Section 3).

Another notion, which is in fact frequently introduced as the first notion of the theory of probability, is that of a trial, that is, the result of a random experiment. From the natural condition of considering only events and trials relating to the experiment which is being studied, every trial necessarily determines, by its definition, either the realization or non-realization of every event which one wishes to consider. We are thus led to introduce the ensemble Ω of trials (or possible results of the experiment being considered) and to identify each event with the subensemble of trials which realize this event; a probability thus becomes a set function, similar to a volume defined on certain subsets of a Euclidean space. The preceding ensemble point of view is that of measure theory, which we shall develop in the first chapter.

With regard to probabilities, we have defined them first on Boolean algebras (or, as in Section 6, on Boolean semialgebras), following which we extend them to σ-algebras and thus construct probability spaces. This procedure has the advantage of exhibiting a very important extension theorem of measure theory; moreover, in the construction of probabilities on Euclidean spaces or on product spaces (see Chapter 3), probabilities turn out to be defined naturally, at the outset, on algebras or semialgebras.

I.1. EVENTS

The first concept of the theory of probability is that of an event; we shall consider events only from the point of view of their occurrence or non-occurrence. The analysis of this concept will lead us to endow the ensemble of events, which we wish to consider relative to a definite problem, with the structure of a Boolean algebra.

We consider first two special events: *the impossible event*, denoted by $\varnothing$, and the *certain event*, denoted by Ω.

With every event A we associate the *contrary event*, denoted by A^c; by definition the latter event is realized if and only if the event A is not realized. The following properties of this operation (which are "intuitively" evident) are then set down as axioms:

$$(A^c)^c = A; \qquad \varnothing^c = \Omega; \qquad \Omega^c = \varnothing.$$

With every pair A, B of events we associate, on the one hand, the *event "union of A and B,"* that is, "A or B," denoted by $A \cup B$ or $\sup(A, B)$; and on the other hand, the *event "intersection of A and B,"* that is, "A and B," denoted by $A \cap B$, AB or $\inf(A, B)$. By definition the event $A \cup B$ occurs if and only if at least one of the two events A and B occurs, while the event $A \cap B$ occurs if and only if both of the events A and B occur. The operations of union and intersection are commutative and transitive:

$$A \cup B = B \cup A; \qquad A \cap B = B \cap A;$$
$$(A \cup B) \cup C = A \cup (B \cup C); \qquad (A \cap B) \cap C = A \cap (B \cap C)$$

so that every finite nonempty family $\{A_i, i \in I\}$ of events has a union $\bigcup_I A_i = \sup_I A_i$ and an intersection $\bigcap_I A_i = \inf_I A_i$. The following formulas are again set down as axioms:

$$A \cup A = A, \qquad A \cap A = A;$$
$$A \cup \varnothing = A, \quad A \cap \varnothing = \varnothing; \qquad A \cup \Omega = \Omega, \quad A \cap \Omega = A;$$
$$A \cup A^c = \Omega, \qquad A \cap A^c = \varnothing;$$

as are the following relations which we write for a finite nonempty family $\{A_i, i \in I\}$ of events:

$$\left(\bigcup_I A_i\right)^c = \bigcap_I A_i^c, \qquad \left(\bigcap_I A_i\right)^c = \bigcup_I A_i^c.$$

Finally, the operations of union and intersection are distributive relative to each other:

$$B \cap \left(\bigcup_I A_i\right) = \bigcup_I (B \cap A_i); \qquad B \cup \left(\bigcap_I A_i\right) = \bigcap_I (B \cup A_i).$$

The structure which is established on the ensemble of events by the preceding definitions and axioms is called the structure of a Boolean algebra. The following auxiliary notions which are defined on such a Boolean algebra are no less important.

Two events A, B such that $AB = \varnothing$ are said to be *exclusive* or *disjoint*; in this case we call their union their *sum* and write $A + B$ instead of $A \cup B$. Given a finite nonempty family $\{A_i, i \in I\}$ of events which are pairwise disjoint, we similarly call their union the "sum of the A_i $(i \in I)$" and write $\sum_I A_i$ instead of $\bigcup_I A_i$.

The difference of two events A, B, denoted by $A - B$, is defined by $A - B = AB^c$, while their *symmetric difference*, denoted by $A \triangle B$, is defined by $A \triangle B = (A - B) + (B - A)$. The event $A - B$ occurs if and only if the event A occurs and B does not; the event $A \triangle B$ occurs if and only if one, but not both, of the two events A and B occurs.

It is convenient to extend the notation $\bigcup_I A_i$, $\bigcap_I A_i$, $\sum_I A_i$ to the case of an empty family of events by setting

$$\bigcup_I A_i = \varnothing, \qquad \sum_I A_i = \varnothing, \qquad \bigcap_I A_i = \Omega \quad (I \text{ empty}).$$

By means of this natural convention, all the formulas written earlier relative to a finite family of events are valid even if the family is empty. This convention also permits us, for example, to write in a simple form the formula which constitutes the following elementary lemma.

LEMMA I.1.1. *Given a family* $\{A_i, 1 \leqslant i \leqslant n\}$ *of* n $(\geqslant 1)$ *events, we have*

$$\bigcup_{i=1}^{n} A_i = \sum_{i=1}^{n} \left(A_i - \bigcup_{j=1}^{i-1} A_j\right).$$

This lemma is proved by induction on n. For $n = 1$ it is obvious. Consequently (on setting $A = \bigcup_1^n A_i$, $B = A_{n+1}$), it suffices to prove that $A \cup B = A + (B - A)$ for every pair A, B of events; but this identity is an easy consequence of the definitions. ∎

Let us remark that the preceding lemma states simply that one of the events of the sequence $A_1, \ldots, A_n$ is realized if and only if there exists a first event of this sequence which is realized. (The event $A_i - \bigcup_{j=1}^{i-1} A_j$ is in fact realized if and only if A_i is the first event of the sequence to be realized.)

The event A is said to *imply* the event B (which implication is denoted by $A \subset B$ or $B \supset A$) if $A = A \cap B$, or equivalently, if $B = A \cup B$. Two events A and B such that $A \subset B$ and $B \subset A$ are said to be *equivalent* ($A = B$); we shall never distinguish between two such events. The relation of implication is an order relation on the ensemble of events, that is:

$$A \subset A;$$
$$A \subset B, \quad B \subset A \Rightarrow A = B;$$
$$A \subset B, \quad B \subset C \Rightarrow A \subset C.$$

Moreover, the union $A \cup B$ (the intersection $A \cap B$) of two events A and B is the supremum (infimum) of these two events under the order relation:

$$A \subset C, \quad B \subset C \Leftrightarrow A \cup B \subset C;$$
$$A \supset C, \quad B \supset C \Leftrightarrow A \cap B \supset C.$$

Finally, we note that

$$A \subset B \Rightarrow B^c \subset A^c.$$

Complements and problems

I.1.1. Starting from the definitions and axioms above, show that the following identities are valid for any events A, B, C, D:

$$A - B = A - (A \cap B) = (A \cup B) - B; \qquad A \triangle B = (A \cup B) - (A \cap B);$$
$$(A - B) \cap (C - D) = (A \cap C) - (B \cup D);$$
$$(A \triangle B) \cap (A \triangle C) = A \triangle (B \cup C);$$
$$(A \triangle B) + (A \triangle B^c) = \Omega.$$

I.1.2. Show that for the two operations $\triangle$ and $\cap$, every Boolean algebra is (in the algebraic sense) a commutative ring with a unit (Ω) such that $A \cap A = A$ for all A; for this reason the operation $\triangle$ of symmetric difference is also called the *Boolean sum*, and the operation $\cap$ of intersection is called the *Boolean product*. Conversely, given a commutative ring $\mathscr{A}$ with a unit, say Ω, such that $A \cdot A = A$ for all A, the operations

$$A \cap B = A \cdot B; \qquad A \cup B = A \dot{+} B \dot{+} A \cdot B; \qquad A^c = A \dot{+} \Omega$$

define a Boolean algebra structure on $\mathscr{A}$. (The signs $\dot{+}$ and $\cdot$ here denote the operations of addition and multiplication, respectively, in the ring $\mathscr{A}$.)

I.2. TRIALS

A second concept which is generally introduced at the beginning of the theory of probability is that of a *trial*. One thinks of a trial as an experiment in which chance intervenes, or rather as the outcome of this random experiment. As a consequence, every trial related to the model being considered necessarily implies either the realization or non-realization of every event given a priori and relative to the model in question. We shall now make precise in mathematical terms this relation between the concepts of trial and event.

Let us first consider the ensemble of all trials related to a given model; we shall substitute the consideration of this ensemble for that of the model being studied. Let us therefore associate with every event A that part A' of the space of trials consisting of the trials which realize A; it is then natural to seek to "identify" A and A'. To this end, we shall first suppose that the correspondence $A \to A'$ is one-to-one, that is, that the space of trials is large enough that, given two distinct events, there is at least one trial which realizes one of these events to the exclusion of the other.

Let us turn next to the definitions of Section I.1. To the certain event Ω corresponds the ensemble Ω' consisting of all the trials, while to the impossible event $\varnothing$ corresponds the ensemble $\varnothing'$ containing no trial; in other words Ω' is the space of trials and $\varnothing'$ is the empty set in Ω'. If to the event A corresponds the set A' in Ω', then to the event A^c, which is realized if and only if A is not, there will correspond the set $(A')^c$ which is complementary to A' in Ω', that is, which consists of those points in Ω' (trials) not belonging to A'. Similarly if A and B are two events and A' and B' are the sets in Ω' consisting of the trials which realize A and B respectively, the set $(A \cup B)'$ $[(A \cap B)']$ in Ω' is made up of those trials belonging to A' or B' [to A' and B'].

In short, if we denote by ^{c}, $\cup$ and $\cap$ the operations of complementation, union and intersection, respectively, defined in the sense of set theory on Ω', the preceding can be written as:

$$(A^c)' = (A')^c; \qquad (A \cup B)' = A' \cup B'; \qquad (A \cap B)' = A' \cap B'.$$

The reader can now verify that the various axioms of Section I.1 go over, under the correspondence $A \to A'$, into axioms of set theory. We shall say that the correspondence $A \to A'$ establishes an isomorphism of the

Boolean algebra of events *into* the Boolean algebra $\mathscr{P}(\Omega')$ consisting of all the subsets of the space Ω' of trials. (In general there exist subsets of Ω' which do not correspond to any event.)

It is thus permissible to identify the event A and the set A' of trials which realize it. (We shall in future suppress the sign $'$.) To the various notions of Section I.1 relative to events, there correspond the classical notions of set theory. This explains, in particular, the dual terminology of Section I.1, namely:

A or B,	union of A and B;
A and B,	intersection of A and B;
A and B are incompatible,	A and B are disjoint;
the certain event Ω,	the space Ω;
the impossible event $\varnothing$,	the empty set $\varnothing$.

From the preceding we shall, in essence, carry over the following notions for the sequel:

(a) *the specification of a set* Ω (*or space of trials*),

(b) *the specification of a Boolean algebra of sets in* Ω (*or events*)*; that is, by definition, a class of sets in* Ω *containing* $\varnothing$, Ω, *and closed under the operations of complementation, finite union and finite intersection.*

(A class $\mathscr{C}$ of subsets of a set Ω is said to be closed under an operation on sets if this operation, applied to any subsets of Ω belonging to $\mathscr{C}$, yields a subset of Ω belonging to $\mathscr{C}$.) Note that by virtue of the identities:

$$A_1 \cap \cdots \cap A_n = (A_1^c \cup \cdots \cup A_n^c)^c;$$
$$A_1 \cup \cdots \cup A_n = (A_1^c \cap \cdots \cap A_n^c)^c$$

it suffices, for $\mathscr{A}$ to be a Boolean algebra, that $\mathscr{A}$ contain $\varnothing$, Ω, and be closed under complementation and finite union (alternatively, under complementation and finite intersection).

Given an arbitrary class $\mathscr{C}$ of subsets of a set Ω, there exists a smallest Boolean algebra $\mathscr{A}$ of subsets of Ω which contains $\mathscr{C}$. To see this, it suffices to define $\mathscr{A}$ as the class of subsets of Ω belonging to all Boolean algebras (of subsets of Ω) containing $\mathscr{C}$. (Such algebras exist; for example $\mathscr{P}(\Omega)$.) The Boolean algebra thus defined is said to be *generated* by $\mathscr{C}$. The reasoning which shows its existence is of greater generality: it shows that when one considers a certain number of operations on sets (in the above, complementation, finite union and finite intersection), for every class $\mathscr{C}$ of subsets of Ω there exists a smallest class of subsets of Ω containing $\mathscr{C}$ and closed under the set operations considered.

Proposition 2 below will give us a more explicit construction of the Boolean algebra generated by a class $\mathscr{C}$. First we will study the particularly simple example of finite Boolean algebras.

Definition I.2.1. A FINITE PARTITION $\mathscr{P} = \{A_i, i \in I\}$ OF A SET Ω IS A FINITE FAMILY OF NONEMPTY SUBSETS OF Ω, PAIRWISE DISJOINT AND WITH UNION Ω.

A finite partition $\mathscr{P}'$ of Ω is said to be *finer* than a finite partition $\mathscr{P}$ if every subset of Ω in $\mathscr{P}$ is the union of subsets of Ω in $\mathscr{P}'$ or, as one can easily show to be equivalent, if every subset of Ω in $\mathscr{P}'$ is contained in some subset of Ω in $\mathscr{P}$. We note that if $\mathscr{P}_1$ and $\mathscr{P}_2$ are two finite partitions of Ω, then there always exists a finite partition $\mathscr{P}$ of Ω which is finer than both $\mathscr{P}_1$ and $\mathscr{P}_2$; in fact, if $\mathscr{P}_1 = \{A_i, i \in I\}$ and $\mathscr{P}_2 = \{B_j, j \in J\}$ it suffices to take for $\mathscr{P}$ the family of nonempty $A_i \cap B_j$ $(i \in I, j \in J)$.

PROPOSITION I.2.1. *The Boolean algebra $\mathscr{A}$ generated by a finite partition $\mathscr{P}$ of Ω is made up of the set of unions of all subfamilies of $\mathscr{P}$ (if $\mathscr{P}$ consists of n elements, $\mathscr{A}$ consists of 2^n). Conversely, if $\mathscr{A}$ is a finite Boolean algebra of subsets of Ω, the ensemble of its atoms (nonempty subsets A of Ω such that $\varnothing \neq B \subset A$, $B \in \mathscr{A} \Rightarrow B = A$) constitutes a finite partition of Ω which generates $\mathscr{A}$.*

CONCISE PROOF. The verification of the first part of the proposition is simple and is left to the reader. To prove the second part, we note that if $\mathscr{A} = \{A_i, i \in I\}$ is a finite Boolean algebra of subsets of Ω, then every subset B of Ω of the form $B = \bigcap_I B_i$, where $B_i = A_i$ or A_i^c $(i \in I)$, is either empty or an atom of $\mathscr{A}$. Since two nonempty sets B are necessarily disjoint and since every $A \in \mathscr{A}$ (in particular Ω) is the union of nonempty sets B which it contains, the set of nonempty B indeed forms a finite partition of Ω which generates $\mathscr{A}$. Finally, it is clear that every atom of $\mathscr{A}$ is equal to a set B. ▮

PROPOSITION I.2.2. *Let $\mathscr{C}$ be an arbitrary class of subsets of a set Ω. We form successively:*

(1) *the class $\mathscr{C}_1$ consisting of $\varnothing$, Ω and the $A \subset \Omega$ such that A or $A^c \in \mathscr{C}$;*
(2) *the class $\mathscr{C}_2$ of finite intersections of subsets of Ω in $\mathscr{C}_1$;*
(3) *the class $\mathscr{C}_3$ of finite unions of pairwise disjoint subsets belonging to $\mathscr{C}_2$.*

Then $\mathscr{C}_3$ is simply the Boolean algebra generated by $\mathscr{C}$.

PROOF. It is first of all evident that:

(a) $\mathscr{C} \subset \mathscr{C}_1 \subset \mathscr{C}_2 \subset \mathscr{C}_3$ and that $\varnothing, \Omega \in \mathscr{C}_1$;
(b) $\mathscr{C}_1$ is closed under complementation;
(c) $\mathscr{C}_2$ is closed under the operation of intersection.

Let us show that $B \in \mathscr{C}_2 \Rightarrow B^c \in \mathscr{C}_3$; to this end we note that if $B = C_1 \cap C_2 \cap \cdots \cap C_n$ where $C_1, \ldots, C_n \in \mathscr{C}_1$ $(n \geqslant 1)$, then

$$B^c = \sum C_1' \cap \cdots \cap C_n' \qquad \text{where} \qquad C_i' = C_i \quad \text{or} \quad C_i^c \quad (1 \leqslant i \leqslant n)$$

and where the preceding sum is taken over all possible combinations of values of C_i', excluding $C_i' = C_i$ $(1 \leqslant i \leqslant n)$; since $C_i' \in \mathscr{C}_1$ $(1 \leqslant i \leqslant n)$, we have $C_1' \cap \cdots \cap C_n' \in \mathscr{C}_2$ and finally $B^c \in \mathscr{C}_3$.

To show that $\mathscr{C}_3$ is closed under the operation of intersection, i.e., that $A_1 \cap \cdots \cap A_n \in \mathscr{C}_3$ if $A_1, \ldots, A_n \in \mathscr{C}_3$, we represent the subsets A_i in the form

$$A_i = \sum_{j \in J_i} B_i^j$$

where $\{B_i^j, j \in J_i\}$ is, for each i, a family of pairwise disjoint subsets of Ω in $\mathscr{C}_2$; then

$$\bigcap_i A_i = \sum_{J_1 \times \cdots \times J_n} B_1^{j_1} \cap \cdots \cap B_n^{j_n} \in \mathscr{C}_3$$

since $\mathscr{C}_2$ is closed under the operation of intersection.

To show that $\mathscr{C}_3$ is closed under complementation, we observe that if $A = \sum_J B_j \in \mathscr{C}_3$ where the B_j are in $\mathscr{C}_2$ and pairwise disjoint, then $A^c = \bigcap_J B_j^c$; by virtue of the preceding, $B_j^c \in \mathscr{C}_3$ $(j \in J)$ and $A^c \in \mathscr{C}_3$. The class $\mathscr{C}_3$ is thus a Boolean algebra containing $\mathscr{C}$. Conversely, it is easily seen that every Boolean algebra containing $\mathscr{C}$ also contains $\mathscr{C}_1$, $\mathscr{C}_2$ and $\mathscr{C}_3$; the proposition is therefore proved. ▮

Complements and problems

To solve the following two problems, one uses the distributivity formula

$$\bigcup_{j \in J} \bigcap_{i \in I_j} F_i^j = \bigcap_{\{i_j\} \in K} \bigcup_{j \in J} F_{i_j}^j$$

where $K = \prod_{j \in J} I_j$ (the set of all sequences $\{i_j, j \in J\}$).

I.2.1. We denote by $\mathscr{F}_s$, $\mathscr{F}_\sigma$, $\mathscr{F}_d$, $\mathscr{F}_\delta$, respectively, the class of finite unions, countable unions, finite intersections and countable intersections of subsets of Ω contained in some given class $\mathscr{F} \subset \mathscr{P}(\Omega)$; these are also the classes generated by $\mathscr{F}$ for each of the operations considered. Show that the classes $\mathscr{F}_{sd} = (\mathscr{F}_s)_d$ and $\mathscr{F}_{s\delta}$ ($\mathscr{F}_{ds}$ and $\mathscr{F}_{d\sigma}$) are closed under finite union (finite intersection); deduce from this that the classes $\mathscr{F}_{sd}$ and $\mathscr{F}_{ds}$ are identical and equal to the smallest class, closed under finite union and intersection, which contains $\mathscr{F}$. Show by counterexamples that in general neither $\mathscr{F}_{\sigma d}$ nor $\mathscr{F}_{\sigma\delta}$ ($\mathscr{F}_{\delta s}$ and $\mathscr{F}_{\delta\sigma}$) are closed under countable union (countable intersection).

*I.2.2. **The Souslin operation** is the operation which associates, with a family $\{F_{(n_1,\ldots,n_k)}\}$ of subsets of Ω indexed by the collection of all *finite* sequences $(n_1, \ldots, n_k)$ of positive integers, the subset $F = \bigcup_\nu F_\nu$, where $\nu = (\nu_1, \nu_2, \ldots)$ runs through all *infinite* sequences of positive integers and where $F_\nu = \bigcap_{k \geq 1} F_{(\nu_1,\ldots,\nu_k)}$. We denote by $\mathscr{F}_S$ the class of all sets F obtained by the Souslin operation, starting from families $\{F_{(n_1,\ldots,n_k)}\}$ contained in a given class $\mathscr{F}$ of subsets of Ω; if $\mathscr{F}$ is closed under finite intersection, the class $\mathscr{F}_S$ is not restricted by considering only families $\{F_{(n_1,\ldots,n_k)}\}$ such that

$$F_{(n_1,\ldots,n_k,n_{k+1})} \subset F_{(n_1,\ldots,n_k)}.$$

Show that the operations of countable union and countable intersection are both special cases of the Souslin operation. Show that the class $\mathscr{F}_S$ is closed under the Souslin operation. (Use the above distributivity formula.) Deduce from this that the class $\mathscr{F}_S$ contains the σ-algebra generated by $\mathscr{F}$ whenever $F \in \mathscr{F} \Rightarrow F^c \in \mathscr{F}_S$, in particular whenever the complement F^c of every $F \in \mathscr{F}$ is a countable union of sets from $\mathscr{F}$.

*I.2.3. **The Stone representation space.** Given an abstractly defined Boolean algebra $\mathscr{A}$ (see Section I.1), one gives the name *filter* to a nonempty subset $\mathscr{F}$ of $\mathscr{A}$ such that (a) $\varnothing \notin \mathscr{F}$, (b) $A \in \mathscr{F}$, $A \subset B \Rightarrow B \in \mathscr{F}$, (c) $A, B \in \mathscr{F} \Rightarrow AB \in \mathscr{F}$. In order that a filter be maximal, that is, that it not be contained in any other filter, it is necessary and sufficient that for every $A \in \mathscr{A}$, either A or A^c belong to $\mathscr{F}$. (Observe that if $\mathscr{F}$ is a filter and if $A \in \mathscr{A}$, the ensemble $\{C\colon C \supset AB \text{ for a } B \in \mathscr{F}\}$ is either a filter, or else equal to $\mathscr{A}$.) Every filter is the intersection of the maximal filters which contain it. (Use Zorn's lemma to show that if $\mathscr{F}$ is a filter and if $A \notin \mathscr{F}$, there exists a maximal filter not containing A, but containing $\mathscr{F}$.)

The maximal filters will be called trials and denoted by $\mathscr{E}$, and the set of all such will be denoted by E. Show that the mapping $A \to A' = \{\mathscr{E}\colon A \in \mathscr{E}\}$ is an isomorphism of $\mathscr{A}$ onto a Boolean algebra $\mathscr{A}'$ of subsets of E. In order that A be an atom of $\mathscr{A}$, it is necessary and sufficient that A' consist of a single trial. If $\mathscr{A}$ is isomorphic to a Boolean algebra of subsets of a set Ω, the mapping φ of Ω into E such that $\varphi(\omega)$ is the trial $\{A\colon \omega \in A\}$ has the property: $\{\omega\colon \varphi(\omega) \in A'\} = A$ for every $A \in \mathscr{A}$; but it is in general false that $\varphi(A) = A'$, in particular that $\varphi(\Omega) = E$.

With every finite partition $\{A'_i, i \in I\}$ of E in $\mathscr{A}'$ we associate the subset $\sum_I A'_i \times A'_i$ of $E \times E$. These subsets of $E \times E$ form a fundamental system of neighborhoods of a uniform structure of E for which E (the Stone representation space is compact and totally disconnected, and $\mathscr{A}'$ consists of those subsets of E which are both open and closed. (Show that E is complete and precompact.)

I.3. PROBABILITIES

Definition I.3.1. A PROBABILITY P ON A BOOLEAN ALGEBRA $\mathscr{A}$ OF SUBSETS OF A SET Ω IS A MAPPING OF $\mathscr{A}$ INTO THE REAL INTERVAL $[0, 1]$ SATISFYING THE FOLLOWING THREE AXIOMS:

(a) $0 \leqslant P(A) \leqslant 1$ FOR EVERY $A \in \mathscr{A}$, AND $P(\Omega) = 1$;

(b) (ADDITIVITY) $P(\sum_I A_i) = \sum_I P(A_i)$ FOR EVERY FINITE FAMILY $\{A_i, i \in I\}$ OF PAIRWISE DISJOINT EVENTS;

(c) (MONOTONE SEQUENTIAL CONTINUITY AT $\varnothing$) FOR EVERY SEQUENCE $\{A_n, n \geqslant 1\}$ OF EVENTS DECREASING TO $\varnothing$, THAT IS, SUCH THAT $A_1 \supset A_2 \supset A_3 \ldots$ AND $\bigcap A_n = \varnothing$, ONE HAS $\lim_{n\uparrow\infty} \downarrow P(A_n) = 0$.

The following properties of a probability are easy consequences of axioms (a) and (b); they are thus also valid for set functions which do not satisfy axiom (c).

(1) $P(\varnothing) = 0$;

(2) (monotonicity) $P(A_1) \leqslant P(A_2)$ if $A_1 \subset A_2$ in $\mathscr{A}$;

(3) (strong additivity) for any A_1, A_2 in $\mathscr{A}$ one has the equality

$$P(A_1) + P(A_2) = P(A_1 \cup A_2) + P(A_1 \cap A_2);$$

(4) (subadditivity) $P(\bigcup_I A_i) \leqslant \sum_I P(A_i)$ for every finite family $\{A_i, i \in I\}$ of events; more generally, if $\{A_i, i \in I\}$ and $\{B_i, i \in I\}$ are two finite families of events such that $A_i \supset B_i$ for all $i \in I$, then

$$P\left(\bigcup_I A_i\right) - P\left(\bigcup_I B_i\right) \leqslant \sum_I [P(A_i) - P(B_i)]$$

and

$$P\left(\bigcap_I A_i\right) - P\left(\bigcap_I B_i\right) \leqslant \sum_I [P(A_i) - P(B_i)].$$

In fact, property (1) results from the additivity of P and from $\varnothing + \varnothing = \varnothing$; property (2) is a consequence of the identity $A_2 = A_1 + (A_2 - A_1)$ which is valid when $A_1 \subset A_2$; property (3) follows from the decompositions $A_1 = A_1A_2 + A_1A_2^c$, $A_2 = A_1A_2 + A_1^cA_2$, $A_1 \cup A_2 = A_1A_2 + A_1^cA_2 + A_1A_2^c$. The subadditivity of P follows from the monotonicity property of P and from the formula of Lemma I.1.1; finally, this subadditivity and the formulas

$$\bigcup A_i - \bigcup B_i \subset \bigcup (A_i - B_i),$$
$$\bigcap A_i - \bigcap B_i \subset \bigcup (A_i - B_i),$$

which hold when $A_i \supset B_i$, imply the last properties (4).

The following three lemmas, which are essentially a consequence of axiom (c), are fundamental. Note that we write $A_n \downarrow A$ ($A_n \uparrow A$) when $n \uparrow \infty$ to indicate that $A_n \supset A_{n+1}$ ($n \geqslant 1$) and that $\bigcap_n A_n = A$ in Ω ($A_n \subset A_{n+1}$ ($n \geqslant 1$) and $\bigcup_n A_n = A$ in Ω).

LEMMA I.3.1. *Monotone sequential continuity.*

$$A_n \downarrow A(n \to \infty) \quad \text{in } \mathscr{A} \Rightarrow P(A_n) \downarrow P(A);$$
$$A_n \uparrow A(n \to \infty) \quad \text{in } \mathscr{A} \Rightarrow P(A_n) \uparrow P(A).$$

PROOF. The lemma follows from axioms (b) and (c) and the relations

$$A_n = (A_n - A) + A \quad \text{and} \quad (A_n - A) \downarrow \varnothing \quad \text{in } \mathscr{A},$$

if $A_n \downarrow A$ in $\mathscr{A}$;

$$A_n = (A - A_n) + A_n \quad \text{and} \quad (A - A_n) \downarrow \varnothing \quad \text{in } \mathscr{A},$$

if $A_n \uparrow A$ in $\mathscr{A}$. ∎

LEMMA I.3.2. (σ-*additivity*). *In order that a mapping P of $\mathscr{A}$ into* [0, 1] *be a probability, it is necessary and sufficient that:*

(a) $0 \leqslant P(A) \leqslant 1$ $(A \in \mathscr{A})$; $P(\Omega) = 1$;
(b′) $P(\sum_I A_i) = \sum_I P(A_i)$

for every countable family (finite or infinite) $\{A_i, i \in I\}$ of pairwise disjoint events such that $\sum_I A_i \in \mathscr{A}$.

PROOF. In fact, if P is a probability on $(\Omega, \mathscr{A})$ and if $\{A_n, n \geqslant 1\}$ is a countably infinite family of pairwise disjoint events such that $\sum_{n \geqslant 1} A_n \in \mathscr{A}$, it follows from the convergence $\sum_1^n A_m \uparrow \sum_{m \geqslant 1} A_m$ in $\mathscr{A}$, when $n \uparrow \infty$, that by virtue of axiom (b) and the preceding lemma we have

$$P\Big(\sum_{m \geqslant 1} A_m\Big) = \lim_{n \uparrow \infty} \uparrow P\Big(\sum_1^n A_m\Big) = \lim_{n \uparrow \infty} \uparrow \sum_1^n P(A_m)$$
$$= \sum_{m \geqslant 1} P(A_m).$$

Conversely, to show that axioms (a) and (b′) imply (c), let us consider a sequence $\{A_n, n \geqslant 1\}$ of events which decreases to $\varnothing$; it then follows from the identity $A_n = \sum_{m \geqslant n} (A_m - A_{m+1})$ that

$$1 \geqslant P(A_n) = \sum_{m \geqslant n} P(A_m - A_{m+1}) \downarrow 0 \qquad (n \uparrow \infty). \quad \blacksquare$$

LEMMA I.3.3. (*σ-subadditivity*). *For every countable family $\{A_i, i \in I\}$ of events such that $\bigcup_I A_i \in \mathscr{A}$ one has*

$$P\left(\bigcup_I A_i\right) \leqslant \sum_I P(A_i).$$

More generally, if the countable families $\{A_i, i \in I\}$ and $\{B_i, i \in I\}$ of events are such that $A_i \supset B_i$ $(i \in I)$ and $\bigcup_I A_i \in \mathscr{A}$, $\bigcup_I B_i \in \mathscr{A}$, then

$$P\left(\bigcup_I A_i\right) - P\left(\bigcup_I B_i\right) \leqslant \sum_I [P(A_i) - P(B_i)].$$

(We leave the proof to the reader.)

Complements and problems

I.3.1. **Metric Boolean algebra.** If $\mathscr{A}$ is a Boolean algebra and if P is a set function defined on $\mathscr{A}$, satisfying axioms (a), (b) of this section, the formula $d(A_1, A_2) = P(A_1 \triangle A_2)$ $(A_1, A_2 \in \mathscr{A})$ defines a function d from $\mathscr{A} \times \mathscr{A}$ into [0, 1] which satisfies the triangle inequality. On the other hand, the relation between events defined by $A_1 \underset{P}{=} A_2$ if $P(A_1 \triangle A_2) = 0$ is an equivalence relation [$A_1 \underset{P}{=} A_1$ for every A_1; $A_1 \underset{P}{=} A_2$ is equivalent to $A_2 \underset{P}{=} A_1$; $A_1 \underset{P}{=} A_2$ and $A_2 \underset{P}{=} A_3$ implies $A_1 \underset{P}{=} A_3$]; moreover, the Boolean algebra structure of $\mathscr{A}$ induces on the quotient $\mathscr{A}/P$, or the ensemble of classes $\mathring{A}_1 = \{A: A \underset{P}{=} A_1\}$ of P-equivalent events, a Boolean algebra structure. [For the operation c, for example, it follows from

$$A_1 \underset{P}{=} A_2 \Leftrightarrow A_1^c \underset{P}{=} A_2^c$$

that $\mathring{A}_1^c = \{A: A^c \in \mathring{A}_1\}$; one therefore sets $\left(\mathring{A}_1\right)^c = \mathring{A}_1^c$ upon observing that this definition depends upon A_1 only through $\mathring{A}_1$.] Since $A_1 \underset{P}{=} A_2$ implies $P(A_1) = P(A_2)$, we can define an additive set function $\mathring{P}$ on $\mathscr{A}/P$ by setting $\mathring{P}(\mathring{A}) = P(A_1)$ $(A_1 \in \mathring{A})$. The Boolean algebra $\mathscr{A}/P$ of classes of P-equivalent events is endowed with a metric $\mathring{d}$ by means of $\mathring{P}$; one calls it the metric Boolean algebra associated with $\mathscr{A}$ and P. Many notions introduced into probability theory relate not so much to events as to P-equivalence classes of events. In general we do not distinguish between the notations $\mathscr{A}$ and $\mathscr{A}/P$, P and $\mathring{P}$.

Show that the set function $P(\cdot)$ is uniformly continuous on $\mathscr{A}$ [in fact: $|P(A_1) - P(A_2)| \leqslant P(A_1 \triangle A_2)$]. Finally, in order that P satisfy axiom (c) of a probability measure, it is necessary and sufficient that $A_n \downarrow \varnothing$ in $\mathscr{A}$ imply $A_n \to \varnothing$ in the sense of the metric d. Then: $A_n \uparrow A$ or $A_n \downarrow A$ in $\mathscr{A}$ $(n \to \infty)$ implies $A_n \underset{d}{\longrightarrow} A$.

I.4. PROBABILITY SPACES

One of the essential results of this chapter is that every probability defined on a Boolean algebra $\mathscr{A}$ of subsets of a set Ω has a unique extension to a probability on the σ-algebra generated by $\mathscr{A}$. In the present section, we shall introduce various fundamental notions necessary for the proof of this result.

Definition I.4.1. A BOOLEAN σ-ALGEBRA $\mathscr{A}$ (OR BOREL FIELD) OF SUBSETS OF A SET Ω IS A CLASS OF SUBSETS OF Ω WHICH CONTAINS $\varnothing$ AND Ω AND IS CLOSED UNDER THE OPERATIONS OF COMPLEMENTATION, COUNTABLE UNION AND COUNTABLE INTERSECTION. THE PAIR $(\Omega, \mathscr{A})$ CONSISTING OF A SET Ω AND A (BOOLEAN) σ-ALGEBRA $\mathscr{A}$ OF SUBSETS OF Ω IS CALLED A MEASURABLE SPACE.

We remark that every class $\mathscr{A}$ of subsets of Ω which contains $\varnothing$ and Ω and is closed under complementation and countable union is already a σ-algebra.

Given a monotone increasing (decreasing) sequence $\{A_n, n \geqslant 1\}$ of subsets of Ω, we set $\lim_n \uparrow A_n = \bigcup_n A_n$ $(\lim_n \downarrow A_n = \bigcap_n A_n)$.

Definition I.4.2. A CLASS $\mathscr{C}$ OF SUBSETS OF Ω IS SAID TO BE MONOTONE IF IT IS CLOSED UNDER THE OPERATIONS $\lim \uparrow$ AND $\lim \downarrow$ (SEQUENTIAL LIMITS).

PROPOSITION I.4.1. *In order that a Boolean algebra $\mathscr{A}$ be a σ-algebra, it is necessary and sufficient that it also be a monotone class.*

PROOF. Clearly, a Boolean σ-algebra is closed under the operations of monotone limits. Conversely, consider a class $\mathscr{C}$ of subsets of Ω which is closed under finite union; we shall show that $\mathscr{C}$ is closed under countable union if and only if $\mathscr{C}$ is closed under the operation $\lim \uparrow$. To this end, we observe simply that for every sequence $\{A_n, n \geqslant 1\}$ of subsets of Ω we have

$$\bigcup_n A_n = \lim_m \uparrow \left(\bigcup_{n \leqslant m} A_n \right). \quad \blacksquare$$

Given a class $\mathscr{C}$ of subsets of Ω, the smallest σ-algebra (= the intersection of all σ-algebras) containing $\mathscr{C}$ is called the σ-algebra generated by $\mathscr{C}$. Similarly, the smallest monotone class containing $\mathscr{C}$ is called the monotone class generated by $\mathscr{C}$.

PROPOSITION I.4.2. *The Boolean σ-algebra generated by a Boolean algebra $\mathscr{A}$ is identical with the monotone class generated by $\mathscr{A}$.*

PROOF. Let $\mathscr{B}$ be the Boolean σ-algebra generated by $\mathscr{A}$ and let $\mathscr{M}$ be the monotone class generated by $\mathscr{A}$. By Proposition I.4.1, $\mathscr{B}$ is a monotone class; hence $\mathscr{M} \subset \mathscr{B}$. It therefore suffices to prove that $\mathscr{M}$ is a Boolean algebra in order to show (Proposition I.4.1) that $\mathscr{M}$ is a Boolean σ-algebra and hence that $\mathscr{B} \subset \mathscr{M}$.

To show first that $\mathscr{M}$ is closed under complementation, we must prove that the class $\mathscr{M}' = \{B\colon B \text{ and } B^c \in \mathscr{M}\}$ coincides with $\mathscr{M}$. But this follows from $\mathscr{A} \subset \mathscr{M}' \subset \mathscr{M}$ and the fact that $\mathscr{M}'$ is a monotone class by virtue of the formulas

$$(\lim \uparrow B_n)^c = \lim \downarrow B_n^c, \qquad (\lim \downarrow B_n)^c = \lim \uparrow B_n^c.$$

We next introduce, for each $A \in \mathscr{M}$, the subclass

$$\mathscr{M}_A = \{B\colon B \in \mathscr{M}, AB \in \mathscr{M}\} \quad \text{of} \quad \mathscr{M}.$$

The identity $\lim AB_n = A \lim B_n$ which holds for every monotone sequence $\{B_n, n \geqslant 1\}$ shows, to begin with, that the $\mathscr{M}_A$ are monotone classes. When $A \in \mathscr{A}$, we verify at once that $\mathscr{A} \subset \mathscr{M}_A \subset \mathscr{M}$; this is possible only if $\mathscr{M}_A = \mathscr{M}$. This implies, by virtue of the equivalence

$$A \in \mathscr{M}_B \Leftrightarrow B \in \mathscr{M}_A,$$

that $A \in \mathscr{M}_B$ for every $A \in \mathscr{A}$ and $B \in \mathscr{M}$. Consequently $\mathscr{A} \subset \mathscr{M}_B \subset \mathscr{M}$ for every $B \in \mathscr{M}$, from which we conclude that $\mathscr{M}_B = \mathscr{M}$ for every $B \in \mathscr{M}$. This shows that $\mathscr{M}$ is closed under intersection, and is therefore a Boolean algebra. $\blacksquare$

Definition I.4.3. A BOOLEAN σ-ALGEBRA $\mathscr{A}$ OF SUBSETS OF A SET Ω IS SAID TO BE OF COUNTABLE TYPE (OR SEPARABLE) IF THERE EXISTS A COUNTABLE FAMILY OF SUBSETS OF Ω WHICH GENERATES $\mathscr{A}$.

Most of the σ-algebras which are considered in the applications are of countable type. This is the case for the σ-algebra generated by a countable partition $\{A_i, i \in I\}$, which consists of the unions of all subfamilies of the partition. One should be cautioned against supposing that every σ-algebra of countable type can be generated by a countable partition of the space.

Given an arbitrary sequence $\{A_n, n \geqslant 1\}$ of subsets of Ω, we define the subsets $\limsup_{n\to\infty} A_n$ and $\liminf_{n\to\infty} A_n$ by the formulas

$$\limsup_{n\to\infty} A_n = \lim_n \downarrow (\sup_{m\geqslant n} A_m) = \bigcap_n \bigcup_{m\geqslant n} A_m,$$

$$\liminf_{n\to\infty} A_n = \lim_n \uparrow (\inf_{m\geqslant n} A_m) = \bigcup_n \bigcap_{m\geqslant n} A_m.$$

The subset $\limsup_n A_n$ ($\liminf_n A_n$) *of* Ω *consists of those* $\omega \in \Omega$ *which are contained in infinitely many* (*all but a finite number*) *of the* A_n ($n \geqslant 1$). Clearly one always has $\liminf_n A_n \subset \limsup_n A_n$. When these two sets are identical, they are denoted by $\lim_n A_n$; in particular, when the sequence $\{A_n\}$ is monotone increasing (decreasing), then $\lim_n \uparrow A_n = \lim_n A_n$ ($\lim_n \downarrow A_n = \lim_n A_n$).

Every Boolean σ-algebra is clearly closed under the (sequential) operations lim sup and lim inf. We also observe that *the event* $\limsup_n A_n$ ($\liminf_n A_n$) *occurs if and only if an infinite number of the events* A_n (*all of the events* A_n *with the exception of at most finitely many*) *occur.*

Definition I.4.4. A PROBABILITY SPACE $(\Omega, \mathscr{A}, P)$ IS DEFINED BY THE SPECIFICATION OF A NONEMPTY SET Ω (THE SPACE OF TRIALS), A BOOLEAN σ-ALGEBRA $\mathscr{A}$ OF SUBSETS OF Ω (EVENTS) AND A PROBABILITY P DEFINED ON $\mathscr{A}$.

PROPOSITION I.4.3. (*Sequential continuity of a probability.*) *For every sequence* $\{A_n, n \geqslant 1\}$ *of events defined in a probability space* $(\Omega, \mathscr{A}, P)$ *one has the inequalities*

$$P(\liminf_n A_n) \leqslant \liminf_n P(A_n) \leqslant \limsup_n P(A_n) \leqslant P(\limsup_n A_n).$$

In particular, if $\lim_n A_n$ *exists, then* $\lim_n P(A_n)$ *exists and equals* $P(\lim_n A_n)$.

PROOF. This proposition is a consequence of Lemma I.3.1, which it generalizes. In fact, by virtue of this lemma we have

$$P(\liminf_n A_n) = \lim_m P(\inf_{n\geqslant m} A_n) \leqslant \liminf_m P(A_m),$$

$$P(\limsup_n A_n) = \lim_m P(\sup_{n\geqslant m} A_n) \geqslant \limsup_m P(A_m). \quad \blacksquare$$

The following result is used very frequently in the calculus of probability:

PROPOSITION I.4.4. *If* $\{A_n, n \geqslant 1\}$ *is a sequence of events in* $(\Omega, \mathscr{A}, P)$ *such that* $\sum_n P(A_n) < \infty$, *then* $P(\limsup_n A_n) = 0$.

PROOF. It suffices to let $n \to \infty$ in the following inequality, which is deduced from Lemma I.3.3: $P(\sup_{m \geqslant n} A_m) \leqslant \sum_{m \geqslant n} P(A_m)$. ▮

Definition I.4.5. A SET N IN A PROBABILITY SPACE $(\Omega, \mathscr{A}, P)$ IS SAID TO BE NEGLIGIBLE (FOR THE PROBABILITY P) IF THERE EXISTS A SET $A \in \mathscr{A}$ SUCH THAT $N \subset A$, $P(A) = 0$. THE PROBABILITY SPACE $(\Omega, \mathscr{A}, P)$ IS SAID TO BE COMPLETE IF $\mathscr{A}$ CONTAINS EVERY P-NEGLIGIBLE SUBSET OF Ω.

It is clear that every subset of a negligible set is again negligible, and it follows from Lemma I.3.3 that the union of every countable family of negligible sets is again negligible.

PROPOSITION I.4.5. *If* $\mathscr{N}$ *denotes the class of negligible sets of a probability space* $(\Omega, \mathscr{A}, P)$, *the class* $\bar{\mathscr{A}}$ *of sets of the form* $A \cup N$, *where* $A \in \mathscr{A}$ *and* $N \in \mathscr{N}$, *is identical with the* σ*-algebra generated by* $\mathscr{A}$ *and* $\mathscr{N}$. *Moreover the formula* $\bar{P}(A \cup N) = P(A)$ *defines (unambiguously) the unique probability* $\bar{P}$ *on* $\bar{\mathscr{A}}$ *which extends* P, *and the probability space* $(\Omega, \bar{\mathscr{A}}, \bar{P})$ *is complete.*

The space $(\Omega, \bar{\mathscr{A}}, \bar{P})$ is called the completion of $(\Omega, \mathscr{A}, P)$. (This operation of completion has nothing in common with the operation of completion in the theory of metric spaces and uniform spaces.)

PROOF. The class $\bar{\mathscr{A}}$ is (as are the classes $\mathscr{A}$ and $\mathscr{N}$) closed under the operation of countable union. It is closed under complementation as well, for if $N \subset B$ where $P(B) = 0$, then

$$(A \cup N)^c = (A \cup B)^c + B \cap (A \cup N)^c.$$

The class $\bar{\mathscr{A}}$ is thus identical with the σ-algebra generated by $\mathscr{A}$ and $\mathscr{N}$.

Since $A_1 \cup N_1 = A_2 \cup N_2$ implies that $A_1 \triangle A_2 \subset N_1 \cup N_2$ and consequently that $P(A_1 \triangle A_2) = 0$ and thus that $P(A_1) = P(A_2)$, the formula in the proposition defines $\bar{P}$ on $\bar{\mathscr{A}}$ unambiguously. One can then verify immediately that $\bar{P}$ is a probability and that the space $(\Omega, \bar{\mathscr{A}}, \bar{P})$ is complete. ▮

It is interesting to connect this simple result with the properties of the outer and inner probabilities defined on a probability space $(\Omega, \mathscr{A}, P)$.

Definition I.4.6. THE OUTER PROBABILITY P^* AND INNER PROBABILITY P_* ON A PROBABILITY SPACE $(\Omega, \mathscr{A}, P)$ ARE DEFINED AS THE SET FUNCTIONS ON $\mathscr{P}(\Omega)$:

$$P^*(\Omega_0) = \inf\{P(A); \Omega_0 \subset A \in \mathscr{A}\},$$
$$P_*(\Omega_0) = \sup\{P(A); \Omega_0 \supset A \in \mathscr{A}\}.$$

These functions have the following obvious properties:

$$P_*(\Omega_0) \leqslant P^*(\Omega_0) \qquad \text{for every } \Omega_0,$$
$$P_*(A) = P(A) = P^*(A) \qquad \text{if } A \in \mathscr{A},$$
$$P_*(\Omega_0) = 1 - P^*(\Omega_0^c) \qquad \text{for every } \Omega_0.$$

PROPOSITION I.4.6. *Given a probability space $(\Omega, \mathscr{A}, P)$, the σ-algebra $\overline{\mathscr{A}}$, the completion of $\mathscr{A}$ for P introduced in Proposition* I.4.5, *is identical with the class of subsets of Ω on which P_* and P^* coincide, therefore also with the class $\{\Omega_0 : P^*(\Omega_0) + P^*(\Omega_0^c) = 1\}$ of subsets of Ω. Moreover, $\bar{P} = P^* = P_*$ on $\overline{\mathscr{A}}$.*

PROOF. We shall begin by proving the following lemma, which makes essential use of the closure of $\mathscr{A}$ under the operations of countable union and intersection.

LEMMA. *The infimum and supremum in the formulas defining P_* and P^* are attained.*

To see this in the case of P^*, for example, it suffices to note that if Ω_0 is a subset of Ω and if $\{A_n\}$ is a sequence in $\mathscr{A}$ such that $\Omega_0 \subset A_n$, $P(A_n) \to P^*(\Omega_0)$, the set $A = \bigcap A_n$ belongs to $\mathscr{A}$, contains Ω_0, and is such that $P(A) = P^*(\Omega_0)$.

The preceding lemma thus shows the existence, for each subset Ω_0 of Ω, of two sets A and $A' \in \mathscr{A}$ such that $A \subset \Omega_0 \subset A'$ and

$$P(A) = P_*(\Omega_0), \qquad P(A') = P^*(\Omega_0).$$

Hence if $P_*(\Omega_0) = P^*(\Omega_0)$, the set $A' - A$ is negligible and $\Omega_0 \in \overline{A}$; moreover $\bar{P}(\Omega_0) = P_*(\Omega_0) = P^*(\Omega_0)$.

Conversely, for every set $\overline{A} = A \cup N$ in $\overline{\mathscr{A}}$ we can write $P(A) \leqslant P_*(\overline{A}) \leqslant P^*(\overline{A}) \leqslant P(A \cup B)$ where $B \in \mathscr{A}$ is chosen so that $N \subset B$ and $P(B) = 0$; the preceding inequalities are thus equalities, and the proposition is proved. ▮

The preceding argument also shows that the outer (inner) probabilities defined starting from $(\Omega, \mathscr{A}, P)$ and from $(\Omega, \overline{\mathscr{A}}, \overline{P})$, respectively, are identical.

Given a measurable space $(\Omega, \mathscr{A})$, those subsets of Ω which, for every probability P on $(\Omega, \mathscr{A})$, belong to the completion of $\mathscr{A}$ for P, are called *universally measurable*. Clearly these sets form a σ-algebra to which every probability on $(\Omega, \mathscr{A})$ can be extended.

Complements and problems

I.4.1. If Ω is the real line and A_n is the interval $(-\infty, a_n)$ $(n \geqslant 1)$, what are $\limsup_n A_n$, $\liminf_n A_n$?

I.4.2. Demonstrate and interpret the following identities in terms of events:

$$(\liminf_n A_n)^c = \limsup_n (A_n^c)$$

$$\limsup_n (A_n \cup B_n) = \limsup_n A_n \cup \limsup_n B_n$$

$$\liminf_n A_n \cap \limsup_n B_n \subset \limsup_n (A_n \cap B_n) \subset \limsup_n A_n \cap \limsup_n B_n.$$

I.4.3. An *atom* in a probability space $(\Omega, \mathscr{A}, P)$ is defined as (the P-equivalence class of) a set $A \in \mathscr{A}$ such that $P(A) > 0$ and $A \supset B \in \mathscr{A} \Rightarrow P(B)$ or $P(A - B) = 0$ [compare with the notion of an atom of a Boolean algebra (Proposition I.2.1) and observe that the notion of an atom is a notion in the metric Boolean algebra $\mathscr{A}/P$ (Problem I.3.2)]. Since two distinct (i.e., non P-equivalent) atoms have as intersection (the P-equivalence class of) the empty set, a probability space contains at most n atoms with probabilities $\geqslant n^{-1}$ and therefore at most countably many atoms. Every probability space can be decomposed into a countable union of atoms and a "non-atomic" part; if the latter has probability zero, the space is said to be atomic.

If $(\Omega, \mathscr{A}, P)$ is a probability space without atoms, then for every $a \in [0, 1]$ there exists at least one set $A \in \mathscr{A}$ of probability $P(A) = a$. [Let $\mathring{B}_0$ be a maximal element of the subclass $\mathscr{B}$ of $\mathscr{A}/P$ consisting of those $\mathring{B}$ such that $P(\mathring{B}) \leqslant a$, which subclass is inductive under inclusion. Show that $P(\mathring{B}_0) < a$ would imply that the subclass $\mathscr{C}$ of $\mathscr{A}/P$ of those $\mathring{C}$ such that $P(\mathring{C}) > 0$ and $\mathring{C} \cap \mathring{B} = \varnothing$ is inductive for $\supset$; but every maximal element of $\mathscr{C}$ can only be an atom.]

Show that for every probability space $(\Omega, \mathscr{A}, P)$ and for every $\epsilon > 0$ there exists a finite partition of Ω in $\mathscr{A}$, each of whose elements either has probability $\leqslant \epsilon$ or is an atom with probability $> \epsilon$.

I.4.4. **The trace probability and conditional probability relative to a set.** If $(\Omega, \mathscr{A})$ is a measurable space and Ω_1 is a nonempty subset of Ω, show that $\Omega_1 \cap \mathscr{A} \doteq \{\Omega_1 A; A \in \mathscr{A}\}$ is a σ-algebra of subsets of Ω_1 (called the *trace* of $\mathscr{A}$ on Ω_1). Show that if $\mathscr{F}$ is a class of subsets of Ω which generates the σ-algebra $\mathscr{A}$, then $\Omega_1 \cap \mathscr{F}$ generates $\Omega_1 \cap \mathscr{A}$.

If $P^*(\Omega_1) = 1$, show that the formula $P_1(\Omega_1 A) = P^*(\Omega_1 A)$ unambiguously defines a probability P_1 on $(\Omega_1, \Omega_1 \cap \mathscr{A})$, called the *trace* of P on Ω_1. Show also that the metric Boolean algebras $\mathscr{A}/P$ and $\Omega_1 \cap \mathscr{A}/P_1$ are isomorphic (use the lemma of Proposition I.4.6).

For any $B \in \mathscr{A}$ with probability $P(B) > 0$, the formula $P_B(A) = P(AB)/P(B)$ defines a probability on both $(\Omega, \mathscr{A})$ and $(B, B \cap \mathscr{A})$. Show that this result remains valid for a set B not belonging to $\mathscr{A}$, if one sets $P_B(A) = P^*(AB)/P^*(B)$.

I.4.5. **σ-additive class of sets.** We apply this name to a class $\mathscr{F}$ of subsets of Ω such that: (a) $\Omega \in \mathscr{F}$; (b) $F_1, F_2 \in \mathscr{F}$ implies $F_1 + F_2 \in \mathscr{F}$ if $F_1 F_2 = \varnothing$, and $F_1 - F_2 \in \mathscr{F}$ if $F_1 \supset F_2$; (c) $\mathscr{F} \ni F_n \uparrow$ implies $\lim_n F_n \in \mathscr{F}$.

Every class $\mathscr{C}$ of subsets of Ω is contained in a smallest σ-additive class, which is said to be "generated by $\mathscr{C}$." Show that if $\mathscr{C}$ is a class of subsets of Ω which is closed under intersection, the σ-additive class $\mathscr{F}$ generated by $\mathscr{C}$ is identical with the Boolean σ-algebra generated by $\mathscr{C}$. [One shows that $\mathscr{F}$ is closed under intersection by observing that $\{A: AB \in \mathscr{F}$ for every $B \in \mathscr{C}\}$ is a σ-additive class containing $\mathscr{C}$, contained in $\mathscr{F}$ and thus identical with $\mathscr{F}$, and then deducing from this by a similar argument that $\{A: AB \in \mathscr{F}$ for every $B \in \mathscr{F}\}$ is identical with $\mathscr{F}$.]

If P_1 and P_2 are two probabilities on the Boolean σ-algebra $(\Omega, \mathscr{A})$, the class $\{F: P_1(F) = P_2(F)\}$ is a σ-additive class of subsets of Ω in $\mathscr{A}$. Deduce from this that if P_1 and P_2 coincide on a subclass $\mathscr{C}$ of $\mathscr{A}$ which is closed under intersection, then they coincide on the σ-algebra generated by $\mathscr{C}$.

I.5. EXTENSION OF A PROBABILITY

The aim of this section is to prove the fundamental theorem on the extension of a probability on a Boolean algebra to the generated σ-algebra, while elucidating as much as possible the various arguments which the proof of this result requires.

If $\mathscr{A}$ is a Boolean algebra of subsets of a set Ω, we define $\mathscr{G}$ as the class of all unions of countable families of subsets of Ω in $\mathscr{A}$ or, what is equivalent, as the class of unions of increasing sequences contained in $\mathscr{A}$. If P is a probability on $(\Omega, \mathscr{A})$, it is possible, taking account of the lemma below, to define a set function Π on $\mathscr{G}$ by

$$\Pi(G) = \lim_n \uparrow P(A_n) \quad \text{if} \quad A_n \uparrow G (n \to \infty) \quad \text{with} \quad A_n \in \mathscr{A};$$

the lemma shows in fact that the second member does not depend on the sequence $\{A_n\}$, but only on G.

LEMMA I.5.1. *If* $\{A_m, m \geqslant 1\}$ *and* $\{A'_n, n \geqslant 1\}$ *are two increasing sequences in* $\mathscr{A}$ *such that* $\bigcup_m A_m \subset \bigcup_n A'_n$, *then* $\lim_m \uparrow P(A_m) \leqslant \lim_n \uparrow P(A'_n)$. *If, moreover,* $\bigcup_m A_m = \bigcup_n A'_n$, *then*

$$\lim_m \uparrow P(A_m) = \lim_n \uparrow P(A'_n).$$

PROOF. Since for every fixed m, $\{A_m A'_n, n \geqslant 1\}$ is an increasing sequence in $\mathscr{A}$ such that $\bigcup_n A_m A'_n = A_m$, we have

$$\lim_n \uparrow P(A'_n) \geqslant \lim_n \uparrow P(A_m A'_n) = P(A_m),$$

using the sequential continuity of P. The assertion of the lemma follows from this by letting $m \to \infty$. ▮

The following proposition establishes the properties of $\mathscr{G}$ and Π, defined above; it states, in particular, that $\mathscr{G}$ is the smallest class of subsets of Ω containing $\mathscr{A}$ and closed under the operations of finite intersection and countable union.

PROPOSITION I.5.1. *The class* $\mathscr{G}$ *and the set function* Π *defined above have the following properties:*

(a) $\varnothing \in \mathscr{G}$ *and* $\Pi(\varnothing) = 0$; $\Omega \in \mathscr{G}$ *and* $\Pi(\Omega) = 1$;
$0 \leqslant \Pi(G) \leqslant 1 (G \in \mathscr{G})$;

(b) $G_1, G_2 \in \mathscr{G} \Rightarrow \begin{cases} G_1 \cup G_2, G_1 \cap G_2 \in \mathscr{G}; \\ \Pi(G_1 \cup G_2) + \Pi(G_1 \cap G_2) = \Pi(G_1) + \Pi(G_2); \end{cases}$

(c) $G_1 \subset G_2$, $G_1, G_2 \in \mathscr{G} \Rightarrow \Pi(G_1) \leqslant \Pi(G_2)$;

(d) $G_n \uparrow G\ (n \to \infty)$ *with* $G_n \in \mathscr{G} \Rightarrow G \in \mathscr{G}$, $\Pi(G) = \lim_n \Pi(G_n)$.

Moreover $\mathscr{G}$ *is the smallest class of sets in* Ω *containing* $\mathscr{A}$ *and enjoying the preceding properties (relative to* $\mathscr{G}$*); finally,* $\Pi(A) = P(A)$ *if* $A \in \mathscr{A}$.

PROOF. The verification of (a) is immediate. Next, let us consider two increasing sequences $\{A_{n,1}; n \geqslant 1\}$ and $\{A_{n,2}; n \geqslant 1\}$ in $\mathscr{A}$ with limits G_1 and G_2 respectively; to show (b), it suffices to let $n \to \infty$ in

$$P(A_{n,1}) + P(A_{n,2}) = P(A_{n,1} \cup A_{n,2}) + P(A_{n,1} \cap A_{n,2})$$

upon observing that $A_{n,1} \overset{\cap}{\cup} A_{n,2} \uparrow G_1 \overset{\cap}{\cup} G_2\ (n \to \infty)$. Property (c) follows from the lemma above. To prove property (d), suppose that

$$A_{m,n} \uparrow G_n \quad (m \uparrow \infty, n \geqslant 1) \qquad \text{with} \qquad A_{m,n} \in \mathscr{A} \quad (m, n \geqslant 1)$$

and that $G_n \uparrow G$ $(n \uparrow \infty)$. We then set $D_m = \sup_{n \leqslant m} A_{m,n} \in \mathscr{A}$; the sequence $\{D_m, m \geqslant 1\}$ is increasing since

$$D_m = \sup_{n \leqslant m} A_{m,n} \subset \sup_{n \leqslant m} A_{m+1,n} \subset D_{m+1}.$$

We have $A_{m,n} \subset D_m \subset G_m$ and thus $P(A_{m,n}) \leqslant P(D_m) \leqslant \Pi(G_m)$ for $n \leqslant m$. It suffices to let m and then n tend to $+\infty$ in these relations, to obtain

$$D_m \uparrow G \in \mathscr{G}, \qquad \Pi(G) = \lim_m \uparrow \Pi(D_m) = \lim_m \uparrow \Pi(G_m).$$

The last part of the proposition is clear. ▮

PROPOSITION I.5.2. *Let $\mathscr{G}$ be a class of subsets of a set Ω and Π a set function defined on $\mathscr{G}$, with $\mathscr{G}$ and Π having properties* (a)–(d) *of Proposition* I.5.1. *Under these conditions, the set function Π^* defined on $\mathscr{P}(\Omega)$ by*

$$\Pi^*(\Omega_1) = \inf\{\Pi(G); \Omega_1 \subset G \in \mathscr{G}\}$$

has the following properties (the Ω_1 vary in $\mathscr{P}(\Omega)$):

(a) $\Pi^*(G) = \Pi(G)$ *if* $G \in \mathscr{G}$; $0 \leqslant \Pi^*(\Omega_1) \leqslant 1$;
(b) $\Pi^*(\Omega_1 \cup \Omega_2) + \Pi^*(\Omega_1 \cap \Omega_2) \leqslant \Pi^*(\Omega_1) + \Pi^*(\Omega_2)$, *in particular* $\Pi^*(\Omega_1) + \Pi^*(\Omega_1^c) \geqslant 1$;
(c) $\Omega_1 \subset \Omega_2 \Rightarrow \Pi^*(\Omega_1) \leqslant \Pi^*(\Omega_2)$;
(d) $\Omega_n \uparrow \Omega_\infty (n \uparrow \infty) \Rightarrow \Pi^*(\Omega_n) \uparrow \Pi^*(\Omega_\infty)$.

PROOF. Properties (a) are an easy consequence of the hypotheses. To prove (b), we fix $\epsilon > 0$ and choose $G_1, G_2 \in \mathscr{G}$ such that $\Omega_i \subset G_i$, $\Pi^*(\Omega_i) + \epsilon/2 \geqslant \Pi(G_i)$ for $i = 1, 2$; then

$$\begin{aligned}\Pi^*(\Omega_1) + \Pi^*(\Omega_2) + \epsilon &\geqslant \Pi(G_1) + \Pi(G_2)\\ &= \Pi(G_1 \cup G_2) + \Pi(G_1 \cap G_2)\\ &\geqslant \Pi^*(\Omega_1 \cup \Omega_2) + \Pi^*(\Omega_1 \cap \Omega_2).\end{aligned}$$

Property (c) follows from the monotonicity of Π. To prove (d), we fix $\epsilon > 0$ and choose a sequence of $\epsilon_n > 0$ $(n \geqslant 1)$ such that $\sum_n \epsilon_n = \epsilon$ and a sequence of $G_n \in \mathscr{G}$ such that $\Omega_n \subset G_n$, $\Pi^*(\Omega_n) + \epsilon_n \geqslant \Pi(G_n)$. We then set $G'_n = \bigcup_{m \leqslant n} G_m$, so that $\Omega_n \subset G'_n$ $(n \geqslant 1)$ and $\{G'_n, n \geqslant 1\}$ is an increasing sequence in $\mathscr{G}$. We shall next show by induction on n that

$$\Pi^*(\Omega_n) + \sum_{m \leqslant n} \epsilon_m \geqslant \Pi(G'_n) \qquad (n \geqslant 1).$$

This relation is by hypothesis satisfied for $n = 1$; suppose that it holds for n. Then by virtue of $\Omega_n \subset G'_n \cap G_{n+1} \in \mathscr{G}$, we have

$$\begin{aligned}\Pi(G'_{n+1}) &= \Pi(G'_n \cup G_{n+1}) = \Pi(G'_n) + \Pi(G_{n+1}) - \Pi(G'_n \cap G_{n+1}) \\ &\leqslant [\Pi^*(\Omega_n) + \sum_{m \leqslant n} \epsilon_m] + [\Pi^*(\Omega_{n+1}) + \epsilon_{n+1}] - \Pi^*(\Omega_n) \\ &= \Pi^*(\Omega_{n+1}) + \sum_{m \leqslant n+1} \epsilon_m.\end{aligned}$$

The preceding relation is thus proved; letting $n \to \infty$ and taking into account that $\Omega_\infty \subset \lim_n \uparrow G'_n \in \mathscr{G}$, we obtain

$$\lim_n \uparrow \Pi^*(\Omega_n) + \epsilon \geqslant \Pi(\lim_n \uparrow G'_n) \geqslant \Pi^*(\Omega_\infty).$$

Since ϵ is arbitrary and since, conversely, $\Pi^*(\Omega_n) \leqslant \Pi^*(\Omega_\infty)$ $(n \geqslant 1)$ by virtue of (c), property (d) is proved. ▮

COROLLARY. *Under the conditions of the preceding proposition, the class $\mathscr{D}$ of sets D in Ω such that $\Pi^*(D) + \Pi^*(D^c) = 1$ is a Boolean σ-algebra. The restriction of Π^* to $\mathscr{D}$ is a complete probability on $(\Omega, \mathscr{D})$.*

PROOF. It follows from the definition of $\mathscr{D}$ that

$$D \in \mathscr{D} \Rightarrow D^c \in \mathscr{D},$$

and from property (a) that $\Pi^*(\varnothing) + \Pi^*(\Omega) = 1$, and therefore that $\varnothing, \Omega \in \mathscr{D}$.

If $D_1, D_2 \in \mathscr{D}$, the sum of the right sides of the inequalities

$$\begin{gathered}\Pi^*(D_1 \cup D_2) + \Pi^*(D_1 \cap D_2) \leqslant \Pi^*(D_1) + \Pi^*(D_2), \\ \Pi^*[(D_1 \cup D_2)^c] + \Pi^*[(D_1 \cap D_2)^c] \leqslant \Pi^*(D_1^c) + \Pi^*(D_2^c),\end{gathered}$$

equals 2. Since property (b) of the proposition implies, on the other hand, that

$$\begin{gathered}\Pi^*(D_1 \cup D_2) + \Pi^*[(D_1 \cup D_2)^c] \geqslant 1, \\ \Pi^*(D_1 \cap D_2) + \Pi^*[(D_1 \cap D_2)^c] \geqslant 1,\end{gathered}$$

we see that the four preceding inequalities are compatible only if they are all equalities. It follows that $D_1 \overset{\cap}{\cup} D_2 \in \mathscr{D}$. The class $\mathscr{D}$ is thus closed under finite union and intersection; the function Π^* is additive (in the strong sense) on $\mathscr{D}$.

If $\{D_n, n \geqslant 1\}$ is an increasing sequence in $\mathscr{D}$, it follows from properties (c) and (d) that

$$\Pi^*\left[\bigcup_n D_n\right] = \lim_n \uparrow \Pi^*(D_n),$$

$$\Pi^*\left[\left(\bigcup_n D_n\right)^c\right] \leqslant \Pi^*(D_m^c) \qquad \text{if} \qquad m \geqslant 1.$$

This implies that $\Pi^*[\bigcup_n D_n] + \Pi^*[(\bigcup_n D_n)^c] \leqslant 1$ and consequently (by property (b)) that $\bigcup_n D_n \in \mathscr{D}$. The preceding suffices to prove that $\mathscr{D}$ is a σ-algebra of subsets of Ω and that the restriction of Π^* to $\mathscr{D}$ is a probability. The corollary is proved upon noting that

$$\Omega_1 \subset D \in \mathscr{D}, \qquad \Pi^*(D) = 0$$

implies that

$$\Pi^*(\Omega_1) + \Pi^*(\Omega_1^c) \leqslant 0 + 1 = 1$$

and therefore that $\Omega_1 \in \mathscr{D}$. ▮

The extension theorem for a probability defined on a Boolean algebra follows immediately from the two preceding propositions and from the corollary.

THEOREM (EXTENSION OF A PROBABILITY). *Every probability P defined on a Boolean algebra $\mathscr{A}$ of subsets of Ω has a unique extension to a probability on the Boolean σ-algebra generated by $\mathscr{A}$.*

PROOF. If P is a probability on $(\Omega, \mathscr{A})$, we apply the results of the corollary of Proposition I.5.2 to the class $\mathscr{G}$ and the set function Π defined at the beginning of this section. We note moreover that Π and Π^* coincide with P on $\mathscr{A}$ and hence that $\mathscr{A} \subset \mathscr{D}$; consequently the restriction P' of Π^* to the σ-algebra $\mathscr{A}'$ generated by $\mathscr{A}$, which is again contained in $\mathscr{D}$, is an extension of P to a probability on this σ-algebra.

To show the uniqueness of the extension of P to $\mathscr{A}'$, we consider a probability Q on $\mathscr{A}'$ whose restriction to $\mathscr{A}$ is equal to P; it is easy to see that $Q = \Pi$ on $\mathscr{G}$ and hence that $Q \leqslant P'$ on $\mathscr{A}'$. This implies that $Q = P'$, for: $Q(A) < P'(A)$ for some $A \in \mathscr{A}$ would imply the contradiction $Q(\Omega) = Q(A) + Q(A^c) < P'(A) + P'(A^c) = 1$. The theorem is thus proved. ▮

Since the class $\mathscr{G}$ is clearly contained in $\mathscr{A}'$, the outer probability P'^* associated with P' coincides on $\mathscr{P}(\Omega)$ with the set function Π^*. Proposition I.4.4 then shows that $[\Omega, \mathscr{D}, (\Pi^*)_{\mathscr{D}}]$ is simply the completion of $(\Omega, \mathscr{A}', P')$.

Complements and problems

I.5.1. Let $(\Omega, \mathscr{A}, P)$ be a probability space. Show that the metric space $\mathscr{A}/P$ (defined in Problem I.3.1) is complete. If $\mathscr{B}$ is a Boolean algebra of subsets of Ω which generates the σ-algebra $\mathscr{A}$, show that $\mathscr{B}/P$ is isometric to a dense subspace of $\mathscr{A}/P$; hence $\mathscr{A}/P$ is isometric to the metric completion of $\mathscr{B}/P$. [Prove that

$$\sum_n P(A_n \triangle A_{n+1}) < \infty \Rightarrow \overline{\lim_n} A_n \underset{P}{=} \underline{\lim_n} A_n \Rightarrow \lim_{m,n\to\infty} P(A_m \triangle A_n) = 0$$

for every sequence $\{A_n, n \geqslant 1\}$ in $\mathscr{A}$ and observe that one can extract from every Cauchy sequence $\{A_n, n \geqslant 1\}$ in $\mathscr{A}/P$ a subsequence $\{A_{n_j}, j \geqslant 1\}$ such that $\sum_j P(A_{n_j} \triangle A_{n_{j+1}}) < \infty$.] Show how one can derive the extension theorem for a probability from the theorem on metric completion.

I.5.2. Let $(\Omega, \mathscr{A}, P)$ be a probability space. If $\mathscr{B}$ is a Boolean algebra of subsets of Ω which generates the σ-algebra $\mathscr{A}$ (possibly up to negligible sets), show that the classes $\mathscr{B}_{\sigma\delta}$ and $\mathscr{B}_{\delta\sigma}$ differ from $\mathscr{A}$ only by negligible sets. (The notation is that of Problem I.2.1.)

I.5.3. Let $(\Omega, \mathscr{A}, P)$ be a probability space and let $\mathscr{F}$ be a σ-filter of subsets F of Ω [Definition: if $F_n \in \mathscr{F}$ $(n \geqslant 1)$, then $\bigcap_n F_n \in \mathscr{F}$] having outer probability $P^*(F) = 1$. Show that there exists a probability P' on the σ-algebra generated by $\mathscr{A}$ and $\mathscr{F}$, equal to P on $\mathscr{A}$ and identically 1 on $\mathscr{F}$ [apply Proposition I.5.2 to the set function $\Pi(\Omega_0) = \inf\{P(A); A \in \mathscr{A}, \Omega_0 \subset A \cup F^c$ for some $F \in \mathscr{F}\}$].

*I.5.4. **Theorem on capacities.** Let $\mathscr{F}$ be a class of subsets of Ω containing $\varnothing$ which is closed under finite union and countable intersection. A capacity ψ is then a mapping of $\mathscr{P}(\Omega)$ into $\bar{R}$ such that

(a) $\Omega_1 \subset \Omega_2 \Rightarrow \psi(\Omega_1) \leqslant \psi(\Omega_2)$;
(b) $\Omega_n \uparrow \Omega_\infty \Rightarrow \psi(\Omega_n) \uparrow \psi(\Omega_\infty)$;
(c) $F_n \downarrow F$ in $\mathscr{F} \Rightarrow \psi(F_n) \downarrow \psi(F)$.

Show that for every set A in the Souslin class $\mathscr{F}_S$ one has:

$$\psi(A) = \sup\{\psi(F); F \in \mathscr{F}, F \subset A\}.$$

To prove this, write A in the form

$$A = \bigcup_\nu F_\nu, \quad \text{where} \quad F_\nu = \lim_p \downarrow F_{(\nu_1,\ldots,\nu_p)}$$

and determine a sequence of positive integers $n_1, n_2, \ldots$ in such a way that

$$\psi(G_p) > \psi(A) - \epsilon \qquad \text{where} \qquad G_p = \bigcup_{\nu:\nu_1\leqslant n_1,\ldots,\nu_p\leqslant n_p} F_\nu.$$

Then set $H_p = \bigcup_{\nu_1\leqslant n_1}\cdots\bigcup_{\nu_p\leqslant n_p} F_{(\nu_1,\ldots,\nu_p)}$; observe that $G_p \subset H_p$ and that H_p decreases in $\mathscr{F}$ with the result that $\psi(\lim_p \downarrow H_p) \geqslant \psi(A) - \epsilon$. Finally, show that $\lim_p \downarrow H_p \subset A$ by observing that for every $\omega \in \lim_p \downarrow H_p$ the nonempty sets

$$\{\nu: \nu_i \leqslant n_i \quad \text{for every } i, \quad \omega \in F_{(\nu_1,\ldots,\nu_p)}\}$$

form a decreasing sequence of closed sets in the compact space $\prod_i [1, n_i]$.

If $(\Omega, \mathscr{A}, P)$ is a probability space, one can apply the preceding result to $\mathscr{F} = \mathscr{A}$ and $\psi = P^*$. Deduce from this that the Souslin class $\mathscr{A}_S$ is contained in the σ-algebra of universally measurable sets of $(\Omega, \mathscr{A})$; in particular, if $(\Omega, \mathscr{A}, P)$ is complete, $\mathscr{A} = \mathscr{A}_S$.

I.6. BOOLEAN SEMIALGEBRAS, COMPACT CLASSES, AND DISTRIBUTION FUNCTIONS ON THE REAL LINE

The notion of a Boolean semialgebra which is introduced below is an auxiliary notion which is useful particularly in the study of probabilities on the real line (this section) and in product spaces (Chapter III).

Definition I.6.1. A CLASS $\mathscr{S}$ OF SUBSETS OF A SET Ω IS CALLED A BOOLEAN SEMIALGEBRA IF IT SATISFIES THE FOLLOWING CONDITIONS:

(a) $\varnothing, \Omega \in \mathscr{S}$;

(b) $\mathscr{S}$ IS CLOSED UNDER FINITE INTERSECTION;

(c) IF $S \in \mathscr{S}$, THEN S^c IS THE UNION OF A FINITE FAMILY OF PAIRWISE DISJOINT SUBSETS OF Ω IN $\mathscr{S}$.

PROPOSITION I.6.1. *The Boolean algebra $\mathscr{A}$ generated by a Boolean semialgebra $\mathscr{S}$ of subsets of Ω consists of the sums $A = \sum_I S_i$ of finite families $\{S_i, i \in I\}$ of pairwise disjoint subsets of Ω in $\mathscr{S}$.*

For every additive set function P mapping $\mathscr{S}$ into $[0, 1]$ *such that $P(\Omega) = 1$, the formula $P'(A) = \sum_I P(S_i)$ defines (unambiguously) the unique extension P' of P which is additive on $\mathscr{A}$. If the function P is σ-additive on $\mathscr{S}$, then P' is a probability on $\mathscr{A}$; in this case there exists a unique probability on the σ-algebra generated by $\mathscr{S}$ (= that generated by $\mathscr{A}$) which extends P.*

PROOF. The class $\mathscr{A}$ of sums $\sum_I S_i$ is a Boolean algebra of subsets of Ω, for (1) it contains $\varnothing$ and Ω; (2) it is closed under finite intersection since $(\sum_I S_i) \cap (\sum_J S'_j) = \sum_{I \times J} S_i S'_j$; (3) it is closed under complementation because $(\sum_I S_i)^c = \bigcap_I S_i^c$, and $S_i^c \in \mathscr{A}$ by axiom (c) of the definition of a semialgebra. It is clear that $\mathscr{S}$ generates $\mathscr{A}$.

The function P' will be defined unambiguously on $\mathscr{A}$ if we show that $\sum_I S_i = \sum_J S'_j$ implies $\sum_I P(S_i) = \sum_J P(S'_j)$; but this follows from

$$\sum_{i \in I} P(S_i) = \sum_{I \times J} P(S_i \cap S'_j) = \sum_{j \in J} P(S'_j)$$

by using the additivity of P on $\mathscr{S}$ and the formulas

$$S_i = \sum_J S_i \cap S'_j, \qquad S'_j = \sum_I S_i \cap S'_j.$$

The additivity (σ-additivity) of P' on $\mathscr{A}$ is proved in a similar way. In fact, if the finite (countable) family of sets $A^j = \sum_{i\in I_j} S_i^j$ in $\mathscr{A}$ ($S_i^j \in \mathscr{S}$, I_j finite) indexed by $j \in J$ is a partition of the set $A = \sum_{k\in K} S_k$ in $\mathscr{A}$, it follows from the decompositions

$$S_k = \sum_{j\in J}\sum_{i\in I_j} S_i^j \cap S_k \qquad \text{where} \qquad k \in K,$$

and

$$S_i^j = \sum_{k\in K} S_i^j \cap S_k \qquad \text{where} \qquad i \in I_j \qquad \text{and} \qquad j \in J,$$

using the additivity (σ-additivity) of P on $\mathscr{S}$, that

$$P'(A) = \sum_{k\in K} P(S_k) = \sum_{k\in K}\sum_{j\in J}\sum_{i\in I_j} P(S_i^j \cap S_k)$$

$$= \sum_{j\in J}\sum_{i\in I_j}\sum_{k\in K} P(S_i^j \cap S_k) = \sum_{j\in J}\sum_{i\in I_j} P(S_i^j) = \sum_{j\in J} P'(A_j).$$

Finally, the uniqueness of the extension P' is evident and the last assertion of the theorem is a consequence of the extension theorem of Section I.5. ▮

It is often difficult, indeed sometimes impossible, to show in probability theory that a set function which one has constructed possesses the property of σ-additivity, even when it is by construction additive. Still, one can generally arrive at a proof of σ-additivity by introducing an additional compactness hypothesis into the spaces one is considering. In the rest of this section we intend to introduce this hypothesis in the simplest possible form.

Definition I.6.2. A CLASS $\mathscr{C}$ OF SUBSETS OF A SET Ω IS SAID TO BE COMPACT IF FOR EVERY SEQUENCE $\{C_n, n \geqslant 1\}$ IN $\mathscr{C}$ WITH INTERSECTION $\bigcap C_n = \varnothing$ THERE EXISTS AN INTEGER N SUCH THAT $\bigcap_{n\leqslant N} C_n = \varnothing$.

We are concerned here with compactness in the sequential sense. Every class of compact subsets of a topological space Ω is clearly compact in the sense of the preceding definition; further on we shall encounter other important compact classes.

LEMMA I.6.1. *If the class $\mathscr{C}$ of subsets of Ω is compact, the same is true of the class $\mathscr{C}'$, closed under the operations of finite union and countable intersection, which is generated by $\mathscr{C}$.*

PROOF. To prove first that the class $\mathscr{C}_s$ of unions of finite families of sets from $\mathscr{C}$ is compact, let us consider a sequence $D_n = \bigcup_{m=1}^{M_n} C_n^m$ in $\mathscr{C}_s$ such that $\bigcap_{n \leqslant p} D_n \neq \varnothing$ for every $p > 0$ and show that $\bigcap_n D_n \neq \varnothing$. We form the subsets J_p, in the space $J = \prod_n \{1, 2, \ldots, M_n\}$ of all sequences $\{m_n, n \geqslant 1\}$ of integers such that $1 \leqslant m_n \leqslant M_n$, of sequences $\{m_n\}$ such that $\bigcap_{n \leqslant p} C_n^{m_n} \neq \varnothing$. The distributivity formula

$$\bigcap_{n \leqslant p} D_n = \bigcup_J \left(\bigcap_{n \leqslant p} C_n^{m_n} \right)$$

then shows that $J_p \neq \varnothing$ for every $p > 0$. It is easily seen that the J_p are decreasing; hence it suffices to prove the existence of a sequence $\{m_n^*\}$ in $\lim \downarrow J_p$ in order to show that $\bigcap_n D_n \supset \bigcap_n C_n^{m_n^*} \neq \varnothing$, since $\bigcap_{n \leqslant p} C_n^{m_n^*} \neq \varnothing$ and $\mathscr{C}$ is compact.

But, after having chosen a sequence $\{m_n^{(q)}\}$ in each of the sets J_q, it is possible to determine, by induction on p, a sequence $\{m_p^*\}$ such that for each p there is an infinity of q such that $m_n^{(q)} = m_n^*$ $(1 \leqslant n \leqslant p)$. For a given p, we choose such a q which is at least as large as p; then the sequence $\{m_n^{(q)}\}$ belongs to J_p, as does $\{m_n^*\}$, because the definition of J_p enters only in the first p terms of the sequences. We have thus shown that $\{m_n^*\}$ belongs to J_p for every p. (The preceding argument can be replaced by Tychonov's theorem: In the space J with the topology the product of the discrete topologies on the factors, the J_p form a decreasing sequence of nonempty closed sets; as J is compact by the theorem cited, we have $\lim \downarrow J_p \neq \varnothing$.)

Since the class $\mathscr{C}_s$ is compact from the foregoing, so is the class $\mathscr{C}_{s\delta}$ of intersections of countable families in $\mathscr{C}_s$, as is immediately seen. But $\mathscr{C}' = \mathscr{C}_{s\delta}$, hence the lemma is proved. ▮

PROPOSITION I.6.2. *Let $\mathscr{A}$ be a Boolean algebra or semialgebra of subsets of a set Ω and let $\mathscr{C}$ be a compact subclass of $\mathscr{A}$. Every additive set function P mapping $\mathscr{A}$ into* $[0, 1]$, *such that $P(\Omega) = 1$ and having the approximation property*

$$P(A) = \sup \{P(C); C \subset A, C \in \mathscr{C}\}$$

for every $A \in \mathscr{A}$, is necessarily σ-additive.

PROOF. We shall first prove the proposition for the case of a Boolean algebra by showing that the function P has the property of monotone continuity: if $A_n \downarrow \varnothing$ in $\mathscr{A}$, then $P(A_n) \downarrow 0$. To this end, given $\epsilon > 0$

we choose C_n in $\mathscr{C}$ so that $C_n \subset A_n$ and $P(A_n) \leqslant P(C_n) + \epsilon 2^{-n}$. As $\bigcap_n C_n \subset \bigcap_n A_n = \varnothing$, there exists an integer N such that $\bigcap_{n \leqslant N} C_n = \varnothing$. The formula $A_N = \bigcap_{n \leqslant N} A_n \subset \bigcap_{n \leqslant N} (A_n - C_n)$ and the finite additivity and subadditivity of P now show that

$$P(A_N) \leqslant \sum_{n \leqslant N} P(A_n - C_n) \leqslant \sum_n [P(A_n) - P(C_n)] \leqslant \epsilon.$$

Letting $\epsilon \downarrow 0$, we obtain $\lim \downarrow P(A_n) = 0$.

To show that the validity of the proposition for an algebra $\mathscr{A}$ implies its validity for the case of a semialgebra $\mathscr{S}$, we shall use Lemma I.6.1 and Proposition I.6.1. By the lemma, the class $\mathscr{C}_s$, which is obviously contained in the Boolean algebra $\mathscr{A}$ generated by $\mathscr{S}$, is again compact. On the other hand, let $A = \sum_1^n S_i$ be a set in $\mathscr{A}$; if the sets C_i in $\mathscr{C}$ are so chosen that $C_i \subset S_i$, $P(S_i) \leqslant P(C_i) + \epsilon/N$ $(i = 1, \ldots, N)$, then we have

$$\sum_1^n C_i \subset A \qquad \text{and} \qquad P'(A) \leqslant P'\left(\sum_1^n C_i\right) + \epsilon.$$

Since $\sum C_i \in \mathscr{C}_s$, this shows that the algebra $\mathscr{A}$, the class $\mathscr{C}_s$ and the function P' satisfy the hypotheses of the proposition; consequently P' is σ-additive on $\mathscr{A}$. ∎

Probabilities are generally introduced on the real line by means of distribution functions [real functions F of a real variable which are non-decreasing, continuous from the left and such that $\lim_{x \to -\infty} F(x) = 0$, $\lim_{x \to +\infty} F(x) = 1$]. These functions, which are in fact of very little practical use (except in certain questions where the order structure of the real line plays a predominant role), should have disappeared a long time ago to the benefit of the ensemble definition of the notion of probability. We shall show here the one-to-one correspondence which exists between distribution functions and probabilities defined on the real line.

The class $\mathscr{S}$ of all intervals (open, semi-open and closed) of the real line clearly constitutes a Boolean semialgebra; it generates the Boolean algebra of finite sums of disjoint intervals. We denote by $\mathscr{R}$ the Boolean σ-algebra generated by $\mathscr{S}$. Since every interval of R and every open set of R is a countable union or intersection of open intervals, we see that $\mathscr{R}$ is also the smallest σ-algebra of subsets of R which contains all the open sets. The subsets of R in $\mathscr{R}$ are called *Borel sets*.

PROPOSITION I.6.3. *The formula $P(I_x) = F(x)$, where $x \in R$ and I_x is the open interval $(-\infty, x)$ of R, establishes a one-to-one correspondence between probabilities P on $(R, \mathscr{R})$ and distribution functions F on R.*

Proof. Let P be a probability on $(R, \mathscr{R})$. The required properties of the function F defined by $F(x) = P(I_x)$ follow from:

$$I_x \subset I_y \quad \text{if} \quad x < y; \qquad I_{x_n} \uparrow I_x \quad \text{if} \quad x_n \uparrow x;$$
$$I_{x_n} \downarrow \varnothing \quad \text{if} \quad x_n \downarrow -\infty; \qquad I_{x_n} \uparrow R \quad \text{if} \quad x_n \uparrow +\infty.$$

Conversely if F is a distribution function, we define P on $\mathscr{S}$ by:

$$P\{[a, b)\} = F(b) - F(a); \qquad P\{(a, b)\} = F(b) - F(a + 0);$$
$$P\{[a, b]\} = F(b + 0) - F(a); \qquad P\{(a, b]\} = F(b + 0) - F(a + 0).$$

The reader can verify that P is an additive set function mapping $\mathscr{S}$ into $[0, 1]$ and such that $P(R) = 1$. Let us denote the class of compact intervals of R by $\mathscr{C}$; the class $\mathscr{C}$ is compact, and by virtue of the continuity properties of F, the hypothesis of Proposition I.6.2 is satisfied. It follows that P is σ-additive and hence has a unique extension which is a probability on $(R, \mathscr{R})$. ∎

Complements and problems

I.6.1. Show that Proposition I.6.2 remains valid if it is no longer assumed that $\mathscr{C}$ is contained in $\mathscr{A}$ and if $P(C)$ is replaced by $P^*(C)$ in the formula in the statement. Show next that under this weakened hypothesis, and if P' is the probability on the σ-algebra $\mathscr{A}'$ generated by $\mathscr{A}$ which extends P, the subclass $\mathscr{C}' = \mathscr{C}_\delta \cap \mathscr{A}'$ of $\mathscr{A}'$ is compact and such that

$$P'(A') = \sup \{P'(C'); C' \subset A', C' \in \mathscr{C}'\}$$

for every $A' \in \mathscr{A}'$.

I.6.2. If $\mathscr{A}_1$ and $\mathscr{A}_2$ are two Boolean semialgebras of subsets of Ω, show that the class $\mathscr{B} = \{A_1A_2; A_1 \in \mathscr{A}_1, A_2 \in \mathscr{A}_2\}$ is again a Boolean semialgebra of subsets of Ω. The Boolean algebra (Boolean σ-algebra) generated by $\mathscr{B}$ is identical with that generated by $\mathscr{A}_1 \cup \mathscr{A}_2$.

I.6.3. Extend Proposition I.6.3 to the spaces R^n by replacing the intervals I_x by the "rectangles" $I_x = \{\bar{y}: y_i < x_i \ (i = 1, \ldots, n)\}$.

CHAPTER II

INTEGRATION OF RANDOM VARIABLES

II.1. MEASURABLE MAPPINGS

To every mapping X of a set Ω into a set Ω' there corresponds the *inverse mapping*, denoted by X^{-1}, of $\mathscr{P}(\Omega')$ into $\mathscr{P}(\Omega)$ and defined by $X^{-1}(A') = \{\omega: X(\omega) \in A'\}$. This mapping is a homomorphism for the operations of complementation, union and intersection (infinite), that is, it has the following properties:

$$X^{-1}(\varnothing) = \varnothing, \qquad X^{-1}(\Omega') = \Omega;$$
$$X^{-1}(A'^c) = (X^{-1}(A'))^c;$$
$$X^{-1}\left(\bigcup_I A'_i\right) = \bigcup_I X^{-1}(A'_i), \qquad X^{-1}\left(\bigcap_I A'_i\right) = \bigcap_I X^{-1}(A'_i);$$

where $\{A'_i, i \in I\}$ is an arbitrary family of subsets of Ω'.

We denote by $X^{-1}(\mathscr{C}')$ the class of subsets $X^{-1}(C')$ (of Ω) obtained when C' varies in the class $\mathscr{C}'$ of subsets of Ω'. It follows immediately from the formulas above that $X^{-1}(\mathscr{A}')$ is a σ-algebra (algebra) of subsets of Ω whenever $\mathscr{A}'$ is a σ-algebra (algebra) of subsets of Ω'. Similarly we have the following result:

LEMMA II.1.1. *For every class $\mathscr{C}'$ of subsets of Ω', the inverse image $X^{-1}(\mathscr{A}')$ of the σ-algebra $\mathscr{A}'$ (of subsets of Ω') generated by $\mathscr{C}'$ is identical with the σ-algebra $\mathscr{A}$ (of subsets of Ω) generated by $X^{-1}(\mathscr{C}')$.*

PROOF. Since $X^{-1}(\mathscr{A}')$ is a σ-algebra containing $X^{-1}(\mathscr{C}')$, we have $X^{-1}(\mathscr{A}') \supset \mathscr{A}$. On the other hand, the class $\mathscr{B}' = \{B': X^{-1}(B') \in \mathscr{A}\}$ is, as one verifies directly, a σ-algebra of subsets of Ω' which contains $\mathscr{C}'$; consequently this class contains $\mathscr{A}'$ and we now have

$$X^{-1}(\mathscr{A}') \subset X^{-1}(\mathscr{B}') \subset \mathscr{A}. \quad \blacksquare$$

Given a mapping X of Ω into Ω' and a σ-algebra $\mathscr{A}$ of subsets of Ω, the class $\mathscr{A}' = \{A' : X^{-1}(A') \in \mathscr{A}\}$ is a σ-algebra of subsets of Ω' which is said to be *induced* by X from $\mathscr{A}$. If P is a probability on $(\Omega, \mathscr{A})$, the formula $P'(A') = P[X^{-1}(A')]$ defines a probability on $(\Omega', \mathscr{A}')$ and one says of the probability space $(\Omega', \mathscr{A}', P')$ that it is *induced* by X from $(\Omega, \mathscr{A}, P)$.

Given two measurable spaces $(\Omega_1, \mathscr{A}_1)$ and $(\Omega_2, \mathscr{A}_2)$, a *mapping* X of Ω_1 into Ω_2 is said to be *measurable* if $X^{-1}(\mathscr{A}_2) \subset \mathscr{A}_1$; this is the same as saying that the σ-algebra of subsets of Ω_2 induced by X from $\mathscr{A}_1$ contains $\mathscr{A}_2$. From the lemma above we immediately deduce the following important result:

PROPOSITION II.1.1. *In order that a mapping X of a measurable space $(\Omega_1, \mathscr{A}_1)$ into a measurable space $(\Omega_2, \mathscr{A}_2)$ be measurable, it is sufficient that there exists a class $\mathscr{C}$ of subsets of $\mathscr{A}_2$ which generates $\mathscr{A}_2$ and is such that $X^{-1}(\mathscr{C}) \subset \mathscr{A}_1$.*

If $\{X_i, i \in I\}$ is an arbitrary family of measurable mappings of $(\Omega, \mathscr{A})$ into measurable spaces $(\Omega_i, \mathscr{A}_i)$ which need not be distinct, we denote by $\mathscr{B}(X_i, i \in I)$ the σ-subalgebra of $\mathscr{A}$ generated by the $X_i^{-1}(\mathscr{A}_i)$. In particular, $\mathscr{B}(X_1) = X_1^{-1}(\mathscr{A}_1)$. The σ-algebra $\mathscr{B}(X_i, i \in I)$ is, as is easily seen, the smallest σ-subalgebra $\mathscr{B}$ of $\mathscr{A}$ such that the X_i $(i \in I)$ are measurable mappings of $(\Omega, \mathscr{B})$ into the respective spaces $(\Omega_i, \mathscr{A}_i)$.

Complements and problems

II.1.1. If the mappings X of $(\Omega, \mathscr{B})$ into $(\Omega', \mathscr{B}')$ and X' of $(\Omega', \mathscr{B}')$ into $(\Omega'', \mathscr{B}'')$ are measurable, the same is true of the composite mapping $X' \circ X$ of $(\Omega, \mathscr{B})$ into $(\Omega'', \mathscr{B}'')$.

II.1.2. A mapping X of Ω into Ω' is said to be *injective* if $X(\omega_1) \neq X(\omega_2)$ whenever $\omega_1 \neq \omega_2$ in Ω, *surjective* if $X(\Omega) = \Omega'$, and *bijective* if it is both injective and surjective. We shall use the same notation X for the mapping of $\mathscr{P}(\Omega)$ into $\mathscr{P}(\Omega')$ defined by $X(A) = \{X(\omega); \omega \in A\}$. Show (a) that

$$X\Big(\bigcup_I A_i\Big) = \bigcup_I X(A_i)$$

for every family $\{A_i, i \in I\}$; (b) that

$$X\left(\bigcap_I A_i\right) = \bigcap_I X(A_i)$$

for every family $\{A_i, i \in I\}$ if and only if X is injective; (c) that $X[X^{-1}(A)] = A$ for every A if and only if X is surjective; (d) that $[X(A)]^c = X(A^c)$ for every A if and only if X is bijective.

*II.1.3. **(Souslin operation**; continuation of Problem I.2.2.) If X is a mapping of the set Ω into the set Ω' and $\mathscr{F}$ is an arbitrary class of subsets of Ω', show that $X^{-1}(\mathscr{F}_S) = [X^{-1}(\mathscr{F})]_S$.

II.2. REAL RANDOM VARIABLES

Let $(\Omega, \mathscr{A})$ be a measurable space which we shall suppose fixed throughout this section. (The first results of this section only make use of the Boolean algebra structure of $\mathscr{A}$.)

Definition II.2.1. A REAL STEP RANDOM VARIABLE (STEP r.r.v.) ON $(\Omega, \mathscr{A})$ IS A MAPPING X OF Ω INTO THE REAL LINE R OF THE FORM

$$X(\omega) = x_i \quad \text{IF} \quad \omega \in A_i \quad (i \in I),$$

WHERE $\{A_i, i \in I\}$ IS A FINITE PARTITION OF $(\Omega, \mathscr{A})$ AND THE REAL NUMBERS x_i $(i \in I)$ ARE PAIRWISE DISTINCT.

PROPOSITION II.2.1. *In order that a mapping X of Ω into R be a step* r.r.v., *it is necessary and sufficient that $X^{-1}(\mathscr{R})$ be a finite σ-subalgebra of $\mathscr{A}$ ($\mathscr{R}$ is the σ-algebra of Borel sets in R).*

PROOF. The condition is necessary since $X^{-1}(\mathscr{R})$ is clearly identical with the Boolean σ-algebra generated by the A_i $(i \in I)$. To show that the condition is sufficient, using Proposition I.2.1 we form the finite partition $\{A_i, i \in I\}$ of Ω in $\mathscr{A}$ which generates $X^{-1}(\mathscr{R})$. The mapping X is then constant on each set A_i; in fact, were there two points ω and ω' in some A_i such that $X(\omega) \neq X(\omega')$, one could choose a Borel set S in $\mathscr{R}$ containing $X(\omega)$ but not $X(\omega')$; hence $X^{-1}(S) \cap A_i$ would be a nonempty set belonging to $X^{-1}(\mathscr{R})$, strictly contained in A_i, which is impossible. Finally the values of X on the sets A_i must be pairwise distinct, as otherwise the A_i could not all belong to $X^{-1}(\mathscr{R})$. ∎

With every set $A \in \mathscr{A}$ we associate the step r.r.v. 1_A, called the *indicator of A*, defined by

$$1_A(\omega) = 1 \quad \text{if} \quad \omega \in A, \quad = 0 \quad \text{if} \quad \omega \notin A.$$

In particular we denote by 1 (instead of 1_Ω) the r.r.v. everywhere equal to unity. The following formulas are obvious:

$$1_{A^c} = 1 - 1_A; \qquad 1_{A+B} = 1_A + 1_B \text{ if } AB = \varnothing; \qquad 1_A \cdot 1_B = 1_{AB};$$
$$1_{\sup(A,B)} = \sup(1_A, 1_B); \qquad 1_{\inf(A,B)} = \inf(1_A, 1_B).$$

PROPOSITION II.2.2. *The set* $\mathscr{E}$ *of step* r.r.v.'s *on* $(\Omega, \mathscr{A})$ *has the structure of a lattice algebra (see below) which extends the Boolean algebra structure of* $\mathscr{A}$.

PROOF. The preceding assertion means the following:

(1) *$\mathscr{E}$ is a vector space.* More precisely, $\mathscr{E}$ is, in the vector space of all real functions defined on Ω, the subspace generated by the indicator r.r.v.'s 1_A ($A \in \mathscr{A}$). Indeed, it is obvious that $1_A \in \mathscr{E}$ for every $A \in \mathscr{A}$ and that every $X \in \mathscr{E}$ can be written in the form of a linear combination of indicator functions: $X = \sum_i x_i 1_{A_i}$. As $X \in \mathscr{E}$ clearly implies $cX \in \mathscr{E}$ for every $c \in R$, it remains to show only that $X, Y \in \mathscr{E} \Rightarrow X + Y \in \mathscr{E}$. But if, in accordance with the definitions, $X = x_i$ on A_i ($i \in I$), and $Y = y_j$ on B_j ($j \in J$), we have

$$X + Y = \sum_I x_i 1_{A_i} + \sum_J y_j 1_{B_j} = \sum_{I \times J} (x_i + y_j) 1_{A_i} 1_{B_j}.$$

The sets $A_i B_j$ which are not empty form a finite partition of $(\Omega, \mathscr{A})$; it remains only to form the unions of those of them corresponding to the same value of $x_i + y_j$ in order to obtain a representation of $X + Y$ in the desired form: $X + Y = \sum_K z_k 1_{C_k}$ where the z_k are pairwise distinct and the $C_k \in \mathscr{A}$ form a finite partition of Ω.

(2) *$\mathscr{E}$ is an algebra.* More precisely, the product XY of two functions $X, Y \in \mathscr{E}$ belongs to $\mathscr{E}$. In fact, we have

$$XY = \Big(\sum_I x_i 1_{A_i}\Big)\Big(\sum_J y_j 1_{B_j}\Big) = \sum_{I \times J} x_i y_j 1_{A_i B_j}$$

and it suffices to take appropriate unions of the nonempty $A_i B_j$ as in (1) to see that $XY \in \mathscr{E}$.

(3) *$\mathscr{E}$ is a lattice* for the natural ordering defined in the space of all real functions on Ω: $X \leqslant Y$ if $X(\omega) \leqslant Y(\omega)$ for every $\omega \in \Omega$; in other words, if $X, Y \in \mathscr{E}$ then $\sup(X, Y)$ and $\inf(X, Y) \in \mathscr{E}$. Indeed,

$$\sup(X, Y) = \sup(x_i, y_j), \qquad \inf(X, Y) = \inf(x_i, y_j) \qquad \text{on } A_i B_j \quad (i \in I, j \in J).$$

(4) *The structure of* $\mathscr{E}$ *extends that of* $\mathscr{A}$; this is just what the formulas preceding the proposition show. ▮

The following formulas hold for all real functions defined on Ω and in particular for the step r.r.v.'s.

$$\sup(-X, -Y) = -\inf(X, Y);$$
$$\sup(X, Y) + \inf(X, Y) = X + Y.$$

If we write X^+ for $\sup(X, 0)$ and X^- for $\sup(-X, 0) = -\inf(X, 0)$, then the mappings X^+ and X^- of Ω into R are positive, and

$$X = X^+ - X^-.$$

Definition II.2.2. A REAL RANDOM VARIABLE (r.r.v.) ON $(\Omega, \mathscr{A})$ IS A MAPPING X OF Ω INTO THE EXTENDED REAL LINE $\bar{R} = [-\infty, +\infty]$ WHICH IS THE POINTWISE LIMIT OF A SEQUENCE OF STEP r.r.v.'s. THE r.r.v. X IS SAID TO BE FINITE IF $X(\Omega) \subset R$, AND POSITIVE IF $X(\Omega) \subset \bar{R}_+ \equiv [0, +\infty]$.

PROPOSITION II.2.3. *In order that a mapping X of Ω into $\bar{R}$ be a* r.r.v. *on $(\Omega, \mathscr{A})$, it is necessary and sufficient that it be measurable relative to $\mathscr{A}$ and to the σ-algebra $\bar{\mathscr{R}}$ of Borel sets in $\bar{R}$. For this it is sufficient that $\{\omega: X(\omega) < x\} \in \mathscr{A}$ for every $x \in \bar{R}$ (or for every x in a set which is dense in $\bar{R}$).*

The definition of the σ-algebra $\bar{\mathscr{R}}$ of Borel sets in $\bar{R}$ is analogous to that of the σ-algebra $\mathscr{R}$ (p. 28); note that $\mathscr{R}$ is then the trace of $\bar{\mathscr{R}}$ on R (Problem I.4.4).

PROOF. If X is a r.r.v., let $\{X_n, n \geqslant 1\}$ be a sequence of step r.r.v.'s such that $X_n(\omega) \to X(\omega)$ ($\omega \in \Omega, n \to \infty$) in $\bar{R}$. Then it follows from

$$\sup_{k>0} \liminf_{n\to\infty} \left\{\omega: X_n(\omega) < x - \frac{1}{k}\right\} = \{\omega: X(\omega) < x\} \qquad (x \in \bar{R})$$

that $\{\omega: X(\omega) < x\} \in \mathscr{A}$ and hence, since the class of intervals $[-\infty, x]$ generates $\bar{\mathscr{R}}$, that X is measurable (see Proposition II.1.1).

Conversely, let X be a measurable mapping of $(\Omega, \mathscr{A})$ into $(\bar{R}, \bar{\mathscr{R}})$. Since X is the difference $X^+ - X^-$ of two positive mappings which are measurable (the proof is simple), it suffices to show that every positive measurable mapping of $(\Omega, \mathscr{A})$ into $(\bar{R}, \bar{\mathscr{R}})$ is the pointwise limit of a sequence of step r.r.v.'s. But if we set, for such a mapping Y,

$$Y_n = \sum_{q=1}^{n2^n} \frac{q-1}{2^n} 1_{\{q-1 \leqslant Y \cdot 2^n < q\}} + n 1_{\{Y \geqslant n\}} \qquad (n \geqslant 1),$$

the Y_n ($n \geqslant 1$) form an increasing sequence of positive step r.r.v.'s, and moreover

$$Y_n \leqslant Y \quad \text{on} \quad \Omega; \qquad Y_n \geqslant Y - 2^{-n} \quad \text{on} \quad \{Y < n\};$$
$$Y_n = n \quad \text{on} \quad \{Y \geqslant n\}.$$

Letting $n \to \infty$, we obtain $Y(\omega) = \lim_{n\to\infty} \uparrow Y_n(\omega)$ for every $\omega \in \Omega$. ∎

We have thus proved Proposition II.2.3 and at the same time the following result.

PROPOSITION II.2.4. *Every positive* r.r.v. Y *defined on* $(\Omega, \mathscr{A})$ *is the limit of at least one increasing sequence of positive step* r.r.v.'s. *Moreover this sequence can be chosen in such a way that the limit is uniform on every subset of* Ω *on which* Y *is bounded from above.*

The definition of a r.r.v. and the criterion of Proposition II.2.3 enable us to show that the operations of arithmetic and of passage to the limit (for sequences) when applied to r.r.v.'s result in r.r.v.'s, as long as these operations do not introduce indeterminate expressions such as $\infty - \infty$, $0 \cdot \infty$, etc. More precisely, if X and Y are r.r.v.'s and if $c \in R$, the following expressions are again r.r.v.'s:

(a) cX;
(b) $X + Y$ as long as $X(\omega) + Y(\omega) \neq \infty - \infty$ for every ω;
(c) XY as long as $X(\omega)Y(\omega) \neq 0 \cdot \infty$ for every ω;
(d) X/Y as long as $X(\omega)/Y(\omega) \neq \infty/\infty$ for every ω.

In particular, therefore, the finite r.r.v.'s form an algebra. Furthermore if $\{X_i, i \in I\}$ is a countable family of r.r.v.'s, the mappings $\sup_I X_i$ and $\inf_I X_i$ are again r.r.v.'s. This property allows us to define, for every sequence $\{X_n, n \geqslant 1\}$ of r.r.v.'s, new r.r.v.'s $\limsup_{n\to\infty} X_n$ and $\liminf_{n\to\infty} X_n$. The *convergence set* of a sequence $\{X_n, n \geqslant 1\}$ is then defined as the measurable set $\{\limsup_n X_n = \liminf_n X_n\}$; in particular, when $\limsup_n X_n = \liminf_n X_n$ on Ω, one says that the sequence $\{X_n, n \geqslant 1\}$ converges everywhere and writes $\lim X_n$ for the preceding common limit: thus *the limit of every convergent sequence of* r.r.v.'s *is again a* r.r.v.

In accordance with the definitions of Section II.1, a r.r.v. Y defined on $(\Omega, \mathscr{A}, P)$ is said to be measurable relative to a σ-subalgebra $\mathscr{B}$ of $\mathscr{A}$ (for brevity: $\mathscr{B}$-measurable) if the σ-algebra $\mathscr{B}(Y) = \{Y^{-1}(S), S \in \overline{\mathscr{R}}\}$ is contained in $\mathscr{B}$. In particular, if $\mathscr{B}$ is generated by a r.r.v. X (that is, $\mathscr{B} = \mathscr{B}(X)$), the following proposition characterizes all the r.r.v.'s which are $\mathscr{B}(X)$-measurable.

PROPOSITION II.2.5. *Let $\mathscr{B}(X)$ be the σ-subalgebra of $(\Omega, \mathscr{A})$ generated by a given* r.r.v. *X. In order that a* r.r.v. *Y on $(\Omega, \mathscr{A})$ be $\mathscr{B}(X)$-measurable, it is necessary and sufficient that Y have the form $Y = f(X)$, where f is a measurable mapping of $(\bar{R}, \bar{\mathscr{R}})$ into itself.*

PROOF. The condition is clearly sufficient. To show that it is necessary, we first consider the case of a step r.r.v. Y which is $\mathscr{B}(X)$-measurable. By hypothesis, then, there exists a finite partition

$$\{B_i, 1 \leqslant i \leqslant n\}$$

of Ω in $\mathscr{B}(X)$ and pairwise distinct real numbers y_i $(1 \leqslant i \leqslant n)$ such that $Y = y_i$ on B_i; since $B_i \in \mathscr{B}(X)$ there exists a family of Borel sets S_i $(1 \leqslant i \leqslant n)$ in $\bar{R}$ such that $B_i = \{X \in S_i\}$. The Borel sets

$$S_i' = S_i - \bigcup_{j<i} S_j \quad (1 \leqslant i \leqslant n) \qquad \text{and} \qquad \left(\bigcup S_i\right)^c = \left(\sum S_i'\right)^c$$

form a finite partition of $\bar{R}$; it follows from $\{X \in S_i S_j\} = B_i B_j = \varnothing$ $(i \neq j)$ that we still have $B_i = \{X \in S_i'\}$. Consequently if f is the measurable (step) mapping of $(\bar{R}, \bar{\mathscr{R}})$ into itself defined by $f = y_i$ on S_i' and $f = 0$ on $(\sum S_i')^c$, we see that $Y = f(X)$.

If the r.r.v. Y which is assumed $\mathscr{B}(X)$-measurable is not a step r.r.v., let $\{Y_n, n \geqslant 1\}$ be a sequence of step r.r.v.'s which are $\mathscr{B}(X)$-measurable and such that $Y = \lim Y_n$. Furthermore, let $Y_n = f_n(X)$ be a representation of Y_n as obtained above. It remains only to define the measurable mapping f of $(\bar{R}, \bar{\mathscr{R}})$ into itself by $f = \limsup_{n\to\infty} f_n$ in order to have $Y(\omega) = \lim_n f_n\,[X(\omega)] = f[X(\omega)]$ for every $\omega \in \Omega$. ∎

Complements and problems

II.2.1. Let E be a vector space of bounded measurable functions defined on the measurable space $(\Omega, \mathscr{A})$ such that: (a) $1 \in E$; (b) $f, g \in E \Rightarrow \sup(f, g) \in E$; (c) $\{f_n, n \geqslant 1\}$ an increasing sequence of functions in E bounded by a constant $\Rightarrow \lim f_n \in E$. Then there exists a σ-subalgebra $\mathscr{B}$ of $\mathscr{A}$ such that E is the space of all bounded $\mathscr{B}$-measurable functions. [Set $\mathscr{B} = \{B: 1_B \in E\}$. To show that

$$\{f > a\} \in \mathscr{B} \qquad \text{if} \qquad f \in E,$$

observe that

$$1_{\{f>a\}} = \lim_n \uparrow \inf\,[1, n(f-a)^+].]$$

II.2.2. **Random variables with values in a metric space.** Given a measurable space $(\Omega, \mathscr{A})$ and a metric space E with a metric d, to define step random variables and random variables in E we replace the line R or $\bar{R}$ in Definitions II.2.1 and II.2.2 by the space E. Show that if the X_i $(i = 1, \ldots, n)$ are r.v's defined on $(\Omega, \mathscr{A})$ with values in the metric spaces E_i $(i = 1, \ldots, n)$ respectively and if u is a continuous mapping of ΠE_i into a metric space E, then $u(X_1, \ldots, X_n)$ is a r.v. on $(\Omega, \mathscr{A})$ into E; in particular, if X_1 and X_2 are two r.v.'s into E, then $d(X_1, X_2)$ is a positive r.r.v. Show that a mapping X of $(\Omega, \mathscr{A})$ into a metric space E is a r.v. if and only if

(a) $X(\Omega)$ contains a dense sequence;

(b) $X^{-1}(B) \in \mathscr{A}$ for every open ball B in E.

II.3. THE EXPECTATION OF REAL RANDOM VARIABLES

If P is a probability on a Boolean algebra $\mathscr{A}$ of subsets of Ω, in particular if $(\Omega, \mathscr{A}, P)$ is a probability space, we associate with every step r.r.v. X defined on $(\Omega, \mathscr{A})$ the real number $\sum_I x_i P(A_i)$ (using the notation of Definition II.2.1). This number is called the *expectation* or the *integral* of X and is denoted by $E(X)$, EX, $\int X(\omega)P(d\omega)$, $\int X\,dP$ or even $\int X$.

PROPOSITION II.3.1. *The expectation $E(\cdot)$ defined on the vector lattice $\mathscr{E}$ of step* r.r.v.'s *on $(\Omega, \mathscr{A})$ by means of the probability P is the unique positive linear functional on $\mathscr{E}$ such that $E(1_A) = P(A)$. It furthermore has the property of sequential monotone continuity: $X_n \uparrow X$ (respectively $\downarrow$) in $\mathscr{E} \Rightarrow E(X_n) \uparrow E(X)$ (respectively $\downarrow$).*

Conversely, if E is a positive linear functional on $\mathscr{E}$ such that $E(1) = 1$ and $X_n \downarrow 0$ in $\mathscr{E} \Rightarrow E(X_n) \downarrow 0$, then it is the expectation associated with the probability P defined by $P(A) = E(1_A)$ $(A \in \mathscr{A})$.

PROOF. The definition of $E(\cdot)$ implies immediately that:

(1) $E(1_A) = P(A)$, $E(1) = 1$;

(2) $E(X) \geqslant 0$ if $X \geqslant 0$;

(3) $E(cX) = cE(X)$ for every real constant c. The additivity of E follows (using the notation of Proposition II.2.2, Part (1)) from

$$E(X + Y) = \sum_k z_k P(C_k) = \sum_I \sum_J (x_i + y_j) P(A_i B_j)$$

$$= \sum_I x_i P(A_i) + \sum_J y_j P(B_j) = E(X) + E(Y).$$

We note that the additivity of $E(\cdot)$ renders the properties of positivity and monotonicity of $E(\cdot)$ equivalent; in fact, if $X \leqslant Y$ in $\mathscr{E}$, then

$$E(Y) = E(X) + E(Y - X) \geqslant E(X) \qquad \text{since } Y - X \geqslant 0.$$

If $\{X_n, n \geqslant 1\}$ is a decreasing sequence in $\mathscr{E}$ with limit 0 and if k is the largest value taken by X_1, and therefore by the sequence $\{X_n\}$, it follows from $0 \leqslant X_n \leqslant k1_{\{X_n > \epsilon\}} + \epsilon$ $(n \geqslant 1, \epsilon > 0)$ that

$$0 \leqslant E(X_n) \leqslant kP(\{X_n > \epsilon\}) + \epsilon.$$

As $\{X_n > \epsilon\} \downarrow \varnothing$, the preceding inequality and axiom (c) of the definition of a probability imply that $\lim_n \downarrow E(X_n) = 0$, by letting $n \to \infty$ and then $\epsilon \downarrow 0$. The monotone sequential continuity of $E(\cdot)$ follows from this, since

$$X_n \downarrow X \Rightarrow (X_n - X) \downarrow 0 \quad \text{and}$$
$$E(X_n) = E(X) + E(X_n - X) \downarrow E(X),$$

while

$$X_n \uparrow X \Rightarrow (X - X_n) \downarrow 0 \quad \text{and}$$
$$E(X_n) = E(X) - E(X - X_n) \uparrow E(X)$$

as $n \uparrow \infty$.

The proof of the converse is immediate. ▮

Given a probability space $(\Omega, \mathscr{A}, P)$ and the associated expectation $E(\cdot)$ on the space $\mathscr{E}$ of step r.r.v.'s, it is possible, using in particular the result of Proposition II.2.4, to extend the expectation to the set of all positive r.r.v.'s on $(\Omega, \mathscr{A}, P)$ while preserving its properties of linearity, monotonicity and monotone continuity. To this end, if X is a positive r.r.v., we choose an increasing sequence $\{X_n, n \geqslant 1\}$ in $\mathscr{E}$ which converges to X and set $E(X) = \lim_n \uparrow E(X_n)$, after showing that the right side does not depend upon the sequence $\{X_n\}$ chosen; we then establish the properties of the extension of the expectation thus obtained. We shall carry out this program in a slightly more general context which is suggested by the preceding proposition; the reader will observe that the argument of the following proof is the generalization to functions of the argument which in Lemma I.5.1 and Proposition I.5.1 was applied to sets.

PROPOSITION II.3.2. *Let $\mathscr{E}$ be a vector space of real functions, defined on a set Ω, which is closed under the lattice operations (a Reisz space).*

Let $E(\cdot)$ be a positive linear functional on $\mathscr{E}$ such that $X_n \downarrow 0$ in $\mathscr{E} \Rightarrow E(X_n) \downarrow 0$. We assume in addition that $1 \in \mathscr{E}$ and that $E(1) = 1$.

If $\mathscr{J}_+$ denotes the set of limits $X = \lim_n \uparrow X_n$ of increasing sequences $\{X_n, n \geqslant 1\}$ of positive functions in $\mathscr{E}$, then the formula $E(X) = \lim_n \uparrow E(X_n)$ unambiguously defines an extension of $E(\cdot)$ from $\mathscr{E}_+$ to $\mathscr{J}_+$ having the following properties:

(a) $0 \leqslant E(X) \leqslant \infty$ $(X \in \mathscr{J}_+)$;

(b) $X \in \mathscr{J}_+, c \geqslant 0 \Rightarrow cX \in \mathscr{J}_+$ and $E(cX) = cE(X)$;
$X_1, X_2 \in \mathscr{J}_+ \Rightarrow \sup(X_1, X_2), \inf(X_1, X_2) \in \mathscr{J}_+$ *and*
$E(X_1) + E(X_2) = E[\sup(X_1, X_2)] + E[\inf(X_1, X_2)]$;

(c) $X_1 \leqslant X_2$ *in* $\mathscr{J}_+ \Rightarrow E(X_1) \leqslant E(X_2)$;

(d) $X_n \uparrow$ *in* $\mathscr{J}_+ \Rightarrow \lim \uparrow X_n \in \mathscr{J}_+$ *and* $E(\lim \uparrow X_n) = \lim \uparrow E(X_n)$.

Remark. Let us strengthen the continuity hypothesis concerning E in the preceding assertion by assuming that $\lim \downarrow E(X_\alpha) = 0$ for every generalized sequence $\{X_\alpha\}$ decreasing to 0, with X_α in $\mathscr{E}_+$; then the class $\mathscr{J}_+^*$ of limits of increasing generalized sequence of positive functions from $\mathscr{E}$ and the extension of E to $\mathscr{J}_+^*$ defined (unambiguously) by the formula

$$E(\lim \uparrow X_\alpha) = \lim \uparrow E(X_\alpha)$$

again have the properties (a)–(d) above (property (d) being valid for an increasing generalized sequence in $\mathscr{J}_+^*$). To prove this one has only to replace every sequence in the following proof by a generalized sequence.

Proof. We start by extending Lemma I.5.1 to functions:

Lemma. *If $\{X'_m, m \geqslant 1\}$ and $\{X''_n, n \geqslant 1\}$ are two increasing sequences in $\mathscr{E}_+$ and if $\lim_m \uparrow X'_m \leqslant \lim_n \uparrow X''_n$, then $\lim_m \uparrow E(X'_m) \leqslant \lim_n \uparrow E(X''_n)$.*

Since, by the hypothesis of the theorem, the linear functional E has the property of monotone sequential continuity, i.e. $X_n \downarrow 0 \Rightarrow E(X_n) \downarrow 0$, we deduce from the hypothesis of the lemma that

$$\lim_n \uparrow \inf(X'_m, X''_n) = X'_m \qquad (m \geqslant 1)$$

in $\mathscr{E}$, and thus that

$$\lim_n \uparrow E(X''_n) \geqslant \lim_n \uparrow E[\inf(X'_m, X''_n)] = E(X'_m) \qquad (m \geqslant 1).$$

Letting $m \to \infty$ proves the lemma.

It follows from the lemma that if $X = \lim_n \uparrow X_n$ $(X_n \in \mathscr{E}_+, X \in \mathscr{J}_+)$, the expression $\lim_n \uparrow E(X_n)$ depends only on X and not on the sequence

$\{X_n, n \geqslant 1\}$. This justifies the definition of $E(X)$ when $X \in \mathscr{J}_+$, and it clearly follows from the positivity of E that we have thus obtained a positive extension of E from $\mathscr{E}_+$ to $\mathscr{J}_+$. Furthermore, the lemma proves property (c) above.

To prove properties (b), it is sufficient to observe that if

$$X_1 = \lim_n \uparrow X_{n,1} \quad \text{and} \quad X_2 = \lim_n \uparrow X_{n,2} \quad (X_{n,i} \in \mathscr{E}_+, X_i \in \mathscr{J}_+),$$

then

$$\begin{aligned} cX_1 &= \lim_n \uparrow cX_{n,1} \quad \text{if} \quad c \geqslant 0, \\ X_1 + X_2 &= \lim_n \uparrow (X_{n,1} + X_{n,2}), \\ \sup(X_1, X_2) &= \lim_n \uparrow \sup(X_{n,1}, X_{n,2}) \end{aligned}$$

and

$$\inf(X_1, X_2) = \lim_n \uparrow \inf(X_{n,1}, X_{n,2}),$$

and then to apply the definition of $E(\cdot)$. To prove property (d), we observe that if $X_n = \lim_m \uparrow Y_{m,n}$ $(Y_{m,n} \in \mathscr{E}_+; n \geqslant 1)$ increases in $\mathscr{J}_+$ with n, then, setting

$$Z_m = \sup_{n \leqslant m} Y_{m,n} \in \mathscr{E}_+ \qquad (m \geqslant 1),$$

we have

$$\begin{aligned} Y_{m,n} \leqslant Z_m \leqslant X_m \ (m \geqslant n), &\qquad Z_m \leqslant Z_{m+1}; \\ E(Y_{m,n}) \leqslant E(Z_m) \leqslant E(X_m) \ (m \geqslant n), &\qquad EZ_m \leqslant EZ_{m+1}; \end{aligned}$$

hence, letting $m \to \infty$ and then $n \to \infty$, we obtain

$$\lim \uparrow X_m = \lim \uparrow Z_m \in \mathscr{J}_+$$

and

$$\lim_m \uparrow EX_m = \lim_m \uparrow EZ_m = E(\lim_m \uparrow Z_m). \quad \blacksquare$$

In the case where the space $\mathscr{E}$ of the preceding proposition is the space of step r.r.v.'s on a probability space $(\Omega, \mathscr{A}, P)$, Proposition II.2.4 shows that the class $\mathscr{J}_+$ is identical with the class of all positive r.r.v.'s (finite or not) on $(\Omega, \mathscr{A}, P)$. The preceding proposition then establishes the properties of the expectation of positive r.r.v.'s.

A r.r.v. X is said to be *integrable* if $E(X^+) < \infty$ and $E(X^-) < \infty$; in particular, every bounded r.r.v. and every step r.r.v. is integrable; a positive r.r.v. X is integrable if and only if $E(X) < \infty$. For every integrable r.r.v. X, we set $E(X) = E(X^+) - E(X^-)$; we thus obtain an extension of $E(\cdot)$ to all integrable r.r.v.'s which still has the property of linearity, positivity and monotone continuity (see the following proposition).

More generally, a r.r.v. X is said to be *quasi-integrable* if at least one of the numbers $E(X^+)$ and $E(X^-)$ is finite; this condition is the most general which still permits us to define the expectation $E(X)$ as

$$E(X) = E(X^+) - E(X^-).$$

PROPOSITION II.3.3. *Given a probability space* $(\Omega, \mathscr{A}, P)$, *the expectation* $E(\cdot)$ *defined on the set of quasi-integrable* r.r.v.'s *has the following properties:*

(a) $E(X) \in \bar{R}$; $E(X) \in R$ *if and only if* X *is integrable, in which case* $P(\{X = \pm\infty\}) = 0$;
  $E(X) \geqslant 0$ *if* $X \geqslant 0$, *or, in fact, if* $P(\{X < 0\}) = 0$;

(b) $E(cX) = cE(X)$ *for every finite constant* c;
  $E(X + Y) = E(X) + E(Y)$ *if* $X + Y$ *is defined and if* X^- *and* Y^- (*or* X^+ *and* Y^+) *are integrable;*

(c) $X \leqslant Y \Rightarrow E(X) \leqslant E(Y)$;

(d) $X_n \uparrow X \Rightarrow E(X_n) \uparrow E(X)$ *if* X_n^- *is integrable for at least one* n;
  $X_n \downarrow X \Rightarrow E(X_n) \downarrow E(X)$ *if* X_n^+ *is integrable for at least one* n.

PROOF. Properties (a) and the first of properties (b) follow immediately from the definitions. To prove the additivity of $E(\cdot)$, we note first that if X_1 and X_2 are two positive r.r.v.'s of which one at least is integrable, and if $X_1 - X_2 \neq \infty - \infty$ at every point of Ω, then the r.r.v. $X = X_1 - X_2$ is quasi-integrable and $E(X) = E(X_1) - E(X_2)$. In fact, we have $X^+ \leqslant X_1$, $X^- \leqslant X_2$ (from which it follows that X is quasi-integrable), and $X^+ + X_2 = X^- + X_1$ (from which it follows that $E(X^+) - E(X^-) = E(X_1) - E(X_2)$). The additivity of $E(\cdot)$ under the conditions (b) above is then a simple consequence of the decomposition

$$X + Y = (X^+ + Y^+) - (X^- + Y^-).$$

The monotonicity of $E(\cdot)$ follows from its linearity and positivity.

Let $\{X_n, n \geqslant 1\}$ be an increasing sequence of r.r.v.'s such that $X_{n_0}^-$ is integrable for some fixed n_0 and let $X = \lim \uparrow X_n$. Then $X_n^- \leqslant X_{n_0}^-$ $(n \geqslant n_0)$, $X^- \leqslant X_{n_0}^-$ so that the r.r.v.'s X_n $(n \geqslant n_0)$ and X are quasi-integrable; moreover $0 \leqslant X_n + X_{n_0}^- \uparrow X + X_{n_0}^-$ when $n_0 \leqslant n \uparrow \infty$, so that $E(X_n) + E(X_{n_0}^-) \uparrow E(X) + E(X_{n_0}^-)$ by property (b) and Proposition II.3.2. We have thus proved that $E(X_n) \uparrow E(X)$. The case of a decreasing sequence is treated analogously by considering the r.r.v.'s $-X_n + X_{n_0}^+$ $(n \geqslant n_0)$. ∎

COROLLARY (FATOU–LEBESGUE LEMMA). *If* $\{X_n, n \geqslant 1\}$ *is a sequence of* r.r.v.'s *and if* Y, Z *are integrable* r.r.v.'s, *then:*

$$X_n \leqslant Y \Rightarrow E[\limsup_n X_n] \geqslant \limsup_n E(X_n),$$

$$X_n \geqslant Z \Rightarrow E[\liminf_n X_n] \leqslant \liminf_n E(X_n).$$

In particular, if the sequence $\{X_n, n \geqslant 1\}$ *is convergent and if there exists an integrable* r.r.v. U *such that* $|X_n| \leqslant U$ $(n \geqslant 1)$, *then*

$$E(\lim_n X_n) = \lim_n E(X_n).$$

PROOF. We note first that if Y is an integrable r.r.v. and if the r.r.v. X is such that $X \leqslant Y$, then X^+ is integrable and X is quasi-integrable. The first hypothesis of the corollary thus implies that $(\sup_n X_n)^+$ is integrable; since $\sup_{m \geqslant n} X_m \downarrow \limsup_n X_n$, we deduce from property (d) of the proposition that

$$\sup_{m \geqslant n} E(X_m) \leqslant E[\sup_{m \geqslant n} X_m] \downarrow E[\limsup_n X_n] \quad \text{as} \quad n \to \infty.$$

The second implication of the corollary is proved in a similar way. Hence if $-U \leqslant X_n \leqslant +U$ where U is integrable, then

$$E[\liminf_n X_n] \leqslant \liminf_n E(X_n) \leqslant \limsup_n E(X_n) \leqslant E[\limsup_n X_n];$$

if the sequence $\{X_n, n \geqslant 1\}$ is in addition convergent, this implies that $\lim_n E(X_n)$ exists and equals $E[\lim_n X_n]$. ∎

With every positive r.r.v. X we associate the set function defined on $\mathscr{A}$ by $\int_A X = E[X1_A]$; this set function (called the *indefinite integral* of X) obviously has the following properties:

(a) $0 \leqslant \int_A X \leqslant E(X)$; $\int_A X = 0 \Leftrightarrow P(A\{X > 0\}) = 0$;

(b) $\int_{\Sigma A_i} X = \sum \int_{A_i} X$ for every countable family $\{A_i, i \in I\}$ of pairwise disjoint sets;

(c) $A_1 \subset A_2 \Rightarrow \int_{A_1} X \leqslant \int_{A_2} X$;

(d) $A_n \uparrow A \Rightarrow \int_{A_n} X \uparrow \int_A X$,

$A_n \downarrow A \Rightarrow \int_{A_n} X \downarrow \int_A X$ except possibly if $\int_{A_n} X = \infty$ for every $n \geqslant 1$.

More generally, the set function $\int_A X$ can be defined for every quasi-integrable r.r.v. X; it again has properties analogous to (a)–(d).

Complements and problems

II.3.1. **Extension of a probability.** Let $(\Omega, \mathscr{A}, P)$ be a complete probability space, $\{B_i, i \in I\}$ a countable partition of Ω, and $\mathscr{B}$ the σ-algebra generated by $\mathscr{A}$ and $\{B_i, i \in I\}$. By the lemma of Proposition I.4.6, there exist sets B_i^* $(i \in I)$ in $\mathscr{A}$ such that $B_i \subset B_i^*$, $P^*(B_i) = P(B_i^*)$.

Show that every set B in $\mathscr{B}$ can be written in the form $B = \sum_I A_i B_i$ where the A_i are subsets of the B_i^* belonging to $\mathscr{A}$, and are determined by B up to equivalence. Give an analogous representation for the $\mathscr{B}$-measurable r.r.v.'s. Show that the most general probability $\bar{P}$ on $(\Omega, \mathscr{B})$ whose restriction to $\mathscr{A}$ is equal to P is given by

$$\bar{P}(B) = \sum_I \int_{A_i} X_i \, dP,$$

where the X_i are positive r.r.v.'s defined on $(\Omega, \mathscr{A}, P)$, vanishing off the respective B_i^*, with $\sum_I X_i = 1$; these r.r.v.'s are determined by $\bar{P}$ up to equivalence. Deduce from this that except for the trivial case where all the B_i belong to $\mathscr{A}$, there exists an infinity of probabilities $\bar{P}$ on $(\Omega, \mathscr{B})$ which extend P.

II.4. ALMOST SURE CONVERGENCE AND CONVERGENCE IN PROBABILITY

Two r.r.v.'s X and X' are said to be equal almost surely (or almost everywhere) if $P(X \neq X') = 0$. This relation, which is clearly an equivalence relation, is indicated by $X \underset{\text{a.s.}}{=} X'$. One can show without difficulty that $X \underset{\text{a.s.}}{=} X'$ and $Y \underset{\text{a.s.}}{=} Y'$ implies that $cX \underset{\text{a.s.}}{=} cX'$, that $X + Y \underset{\text{a.s.}}{=} X' + Y'$ and that $XY \underset{\text{a.s.}}{=} X'Y'$ as long as the sums and products are meaningful; in the same way, if $X_i \underset{\text{a.s.}}{=} X_i'$ for every $i \in I$, where I is a countable index set, then $\sup_I X_i \underset{\text{a.s.}}{=} \sup_I X_i'$ and $\inf_I X_i \underset{\text{a.s.}}{=} \inf X_i'$.

Moreover, if X has an expectation, every r.r.v. $X' \underset{\text{a.s.}}{=} X$ has an expectation $E(X')$ equal to $E(X)$; in particular X' is integrable if and only if X is.

Given a r.r.v. X, we denote its equivalence class by $\tilde{X}$, i.e. $\tilde{X} = \{X' : X' \underset{\text{a.s.}}{=} X\}$; obviously $\tilde{X}$ is determined by any one of its elements. As will be seen in the sequel, most problems of the theory of probability involve equivalence classes of r.r.v.'s rather than r.r.v.'s themselves; the importance of the foregoing elementary properties lies in that they allow one to operate on equivalence classes of r.r.v.'s in the same way as on r.r.v.'s themselves, provided however that one considers only a countable family of r.r.v.'s at one time. In general one identifies (by abuse of language) an equivalence class of r.r.v.'s with an arbitrary one of its representatives; the reader should be warned that this is valid only if one is considering *countable* families of r.r.v.'s.

If $\{X_i, i \in I\}$ is a countable family of r.r.v.'s and if $\tilde{X}_i$ $(i \in I)$ are their respective equivalence classes, we have already remarked that the equivalence class of $\sup_I X_i$ depends only on the $\tilde{X}_i$ $(i \in I)$ and is therefore the supremum of the $\tilde{X}_i$ $(i \in I)$. We shall show that every family, even uncountable, $\{\tilde{X}_i, i \in I\}$ of *equivalence classes* of r.r.v.'s has a supremum, denoted by $\operatorname{ess\,sup}_I \tilde{X}_i$; one should note that in the uncountable case the function of ω: $\sup_I X_i(\omega)$ (where $X_i \in \tilde{X}_i$) is not necessarily a r.r.v., and that even if it is measurable, its equivalence class is not necessarily equal to $\operatorname{ess\,sup}_I \tilde{X}_i$ (see the example below).

PROPOSITION II.4.1. *The ensemble of equivalence classes of* r.r.v.'s *defined on* $(\Omega, \mathscr{A}, P)$ *is a complete lattice. In other words, for every family (countable or not)* $\{X_i, i \in I\}$ *of* r.r.v.'s *defined on* $(\Omega, \mathscr{A}, P)$ *there exist two* r.r.v.'s *uniquely determined up to equivalence, denoted by* $\operatorname{ess\,sup}_I X_i$ *and* $\operatorname{ess\,inf}_I X_i$, *such that for every* r.r.v. *Y one has:*

$$X_i \leqslant Y \quad \text{a.s.} \quad (i \in I) \Leftrightarrow \operatorname*{ess\,sup}_I X_i \leqslant Y \quad \text{a.s.}$$

$$X_i \geqslant Y \quad \text{a.s.} \quad (i \in I) \Leftrightarrow \operatorname*{ess\,inf}_I X_i \geqslant Y \quad \text{a.s.}$$

In particular, for every family $\{A_i, i \in I\}$ *of events in* $\mathscr{A}$ *there exist two events, determined up to equivalence and denoted by* $\operatorname{ess\,inf}_I A_i$, $\operatorname{ess\,sup}_I A_i$, *such that for every* $A \in \mathscr{A}$

$$A_i \underset{\text{a.s.}}{\subset} A \quad (i \in I) \Leftrightarrow \operatorname*{ess\,inf}_I A_i \underset{\text{a.s.}}{\subset} A,$$

$$A \underset{\text{a.s.}}{\subset} A_i \quad (i \in I) \Leftrightarrow A \underset{\text{a.s.}}{\subset} \operatorname*{ess\,sup}_I A_i.$$

[In this notation, ess = essential refers to the equivalence a.s.]

PROOF. If the family $\{X_i, i \in I\}$ is countable, we set

$$\operatorname*{ess\,sup}_I X_i = \sup_I X_i \qquad \text{and} \qquad \operatorname*{ess\,inf}_I X_i = \inf_I X_i.$$

Let f be an arbitrary continuous strictly increasing mapping of $[-\infty, +\infty]$ into a bounded interval of $(-\infty, +\infty)$, for example *arc tan*. The necessarily finite supremum of $E[f(\sup_J X_j)]$ as J runs through all countable subsets of I, say σ, is achieved by some countable subset J_0. [To see this it suffices to set $J_0 = \bigcup_1^\infty J_n$ after choosing countable subsets J_n of I such that $E[f(\sup_{J_n} X_j)] + 1/n \geqslant \sigma$.] We then set $U = \sup_{J_0} X_j$.

For every r.r.v. Y such that $X_i \leqslant Y$ a.s. $(i \in I)$ we obviously have $U \leqslant Y$ a.s. To show the converse implication, it suffices to show that $X_i \leqslant U$ a.s. for every $i \in I$. But it follows from the maximality property of J_0 that for every $i \in I$ we have $E(f[\sup(X_i, U)]) = E[f(U)] = \sigma$; hence $f[\sup(X_i, U)] \underset{\text{a.s.}}{=} f(U)$, and so $\sup(X_i, U) \underset{\text{a.s.}}{=} U$ for every $i \in I$. We have proved the existence of ess $\sup_I X_i$; its uniqueness up to equivalence a.s. is immediate. The existence and uniqueness of ess $\inf_I X_i$ can be proved in the same way. ∎

EXAMPLE. Let $(\Omega, \mathscr{A}, P)$ be the complete probability space constructed from the Lebesgue measure defined on the interval $[0, 1]$; we denote by X_r $(r \in [0, 1])$ the r.r.v.: $X_r(\omega) = 1$ if $\omega = r$, $= 0$ if $\omega \neq r$. In this case $X_r = 0$ a.s. and ess $\sup_r X_r = 0$ a.s. In contrast the supremum of the set $\{X_r, r \in [0, 1]\}$ of functions from Ω into R is equal to 1. Note the role played by the subsets of Ω with probability zero in this example and in the proof of the preceding proposition.

If $A \in \mathscr{A}$ has probability zero, two r.r.v.'s X and X' which are equal on A^c are a.s. equal; in other words the restriction of X to A^c already determines the equivalence class $\tilde{X}$ of X. A measurable mapping of A^c into $\bar{R}$ (for example the restriction of X to A^c) is called a *r.r.v. defined almost everywhere*; it is always possible to extend a r.r.v. defined almost everywhere to a r.r.v. on $(\Omega, \mathscr{A})$ [for example by setting it equal to 0 where it is undefined].

The interest in complete probability spaces (Section I.4) is due to the fact that one can modify a r.r.v. X arbitrarily on a negligible set of such a space, without in the process disturbing the measurability of X (nor by the way its equivalence class). We remark that by completing a probability space one increases the number of r.r.v.'s but does not introduce any new equivalence classes.

Definition II.4.1. A SEQUENCE $\{X_n, n \geqslant 1\}$ OF r.r.v.'s IS SAID TO CONVERGE ALMOST SURELY (a.s.) IF $\limsup_n X_n \underset{\text{a.s.}}{=} \liminf_n X_n$.

The limit of $\{X_n, n \geqslant 1\}$ is then, by definition, any one of the r.r.v.'s in the (uniquely determined) equivalence class of $\limsup_n X_n$; we write $\lim \text{a.s.}_{n\to\infty} X_n$ for this equivalence class or any one of its elements.

CAUCHY CRITERION. *In order that a sequence* $\{X_n, n \geqslant 1\}$ *of* a.s. *finite* r.r.v.'s *converge* a.s. *to an* a.s. *finite* r.r.v., *it is necessary and sufficient that it be a Cauchy sequence for* a.s. *convergence, that is, that*

$$\{X_m - X_n; m, n \geqslant 1\}$$

converge a.s. *to* 0 *as* $m, n \to \infty$.

This criterion results immediately from the Cauchy criterion for sequences of real numbers, upon observing that the sequence $\{X_n\}$ ($\{X_m - X_n; m, n \geqslant 1\}$) converges a.s. only if the sequence $\{X_n(\omega)\}$ ($\{X_m(\omega) - X_n(\omega); m, n \geqslant 1\}$) converges in R for every ω outside of a set having probability zero.

PROPOSITION II.4.2. *In order that a sequence* $\{X_n, n \geqslant 1\}$ *of* a.s. *finite* r.r.v.'s *converge* a.s., *it is sufficient that there exist a summable sequence* $\{\epsilon_n, n \geqslant 1\}$ *of positive numbers such that*

$$\sum_{n=1}^{\infty} P(|X_{n+1} - X_n| > \epsilon_n) < \infty;$$

the limit is then a.s. *finite.*

PROOF. We set $A_n = \{|X_{n+1} - X_n| > \epsilon_n\}$ for every $n \geqslant 1$. The hypothesis and Proposition I.4.4 imply that $\limsup_n A_n \underset{\text{a.s.}}{=} \varnothing$. We can therefore define, outside of the negligible set $\limsup_n A_n$, a r.v. N with positive integer values by setting

$$N(\omega) = n \quad \text{on} \quad \bigcup_{m \geqslant n} A_m - \bigcup_{m > n} A_m, \qquad = 0 \quad \text{on} \quad \Big(\bigcup_{m \geqslant 1} A_m\Big)^c.$$

Under these conditions the sequence $\{X_{n+1}(\omega) - X_n(\omega)\}$ is majorized in absolute value, from the $N(\omega) + 1$st term on, by the sequence ϵ_n; this suffices to show the existence of

$$X(\omega) = \lim_{n\to\infty} X_n(\omega) = X_1(\omega) + \sum_n [X_{n+1}(\omega) - X_n(\omega)]$$

for every $\omega \notin \limsup_n A_n$. ∎

In fact, the preceding proof gives us information concerning the rate of convergence of X_n to X, since it shows that

$$|X(\omega) - X_m(\omega)| \leqslant \sum_{n \geqslant m} \epsilon_n$$

as long as $N(\omega) < m$ (note that $P(\{N < m\}) \uparrow 1$ as $m \uparrow \infty$).

Definition II.4.2. A SEQUENCE $\{X_n, n \geqslant 1\}$ OF a.s. FINITE r.r.v.'s CONVERGES IN PROBABILITY TO THE a.s. FINITE r.r.v. X IF

$$P(|X_n - X| > \epsilon) \to 0 \quad (n \to \infty)$$

FOR EVERY $\epsilon > 0$. WE THEN WRITE $X_n \underset{P}{\to} X$.

CAUCHY CRITERION. *A sequence* $\{X_n, n \geqslant 1\}$ *of* a.s. *finite* r.r.v.'s *converges in probability if and only if it is a Cauchy sequence for convergence in probability, that is if* $X_m - X_n \underset{P}{\to} 0$ $(m, n \to \infty)$.

We shall establish this criterion simultaneously with the following result, which gives the connection between a.s. convergence and convergence in probability.

PROPOSITION II.4.3. *Every sequence* $\{X_n, n \geqslant 1\}$ *of* a.s. *finite* r.r.v.'s *which converges* a.s. *to an* a.s. *finite* r.r.v. *converges in probability to the same limit. Conversely, from every sequence* $\{X_n, n \geqslant 1\}$ *of* a.s. *finite* r.r.v.'s *which converges in probability one can extract a subsequence which converges* a.s. *to the same limit.*

PROOF. Let $\{X_n, n \geqslant 1\}$ be a sequence of a.s. finite r.r.v.'s, and let X be an a.s. finite r.r.v. Then:

(1) $X_n \underset{\text{a.s.}}{\longrightarrow} X \Rightarrow X_n \underset{P}{\longrightarrow} X$, since for every $\epsilon > 0$

$$\begin{aligned}\limsup_n P(\{|X_n - X| > \epsilon\}) &\leqslant P[\limsup_n \{|X_n - X| > \epsilon\}] \\ &\leqslant P(\{-\epsilon + \limsup_n X_n < X < \epsilon + \liminf_n X_n\}^c) = 0.\end{aligned}$$

(2) $X_n \underset{P}{\longrightarrow} X \Rightarrow (X_m - X_n) \underset{P}{\longrightarrow} 0$ $(m, n \to \infty)$, since, for every $\epsilon > 0$,

$$\{|X_m - X_n| > \epsilon\} \subset \{|X_m - X| > \epsilon/2\} \cup \{|X_n - X| > \epsilon/2\}$$

and hence

$$P(|X_m - X_n| > \epsilon) \leqslant P(|X_m - X| > \epsilon/2) + P(|X_n - X| > \epsilon/2) \to 0$$

as $m, n \to \infty$.

(3) $X_m - X_n \xrightarrow[P]{} 0 \ (m, n \to \infty) \Rightarrow X_{n_j} \xrightarrow[\text{a.s.}]{} X$ and $X_n \xrightarrow[P]{} X$ for some r.r.v. X and some subsequence $\{n_j\}$. In fact, we determine the terms of this subsequence step by step by setting $n_1 = 1$ and taking for n_j the smallest integer $N > n_{j-1}$ such that

$$P\left(|X_r - X_s| > \frac{1}{2^j}\right) < \frac{1}{3^j} \qquad \text{if} \quad r, s \geqslant N.$$

It follows, then, from $\sum_j P(|X_{n_{j+1}} - X_{n_j}| > 1/2^j) < \sum_j 1/3^j < \infty$ that the sequence $\{X_{n_j}, j \geqslant 1\}$ is a.s. convergent (Proposition II.4.2); moreover if X denotes its limit, it follows from

$$P(|X_n - X| > \epsilon) \leqslant P(|X_n - X_{n_j}| > \epsilon/2) + P(|X_{n_j} - X| > \epsilon/2),$$

letting n and j go to ∞, and using the hypothesis and (1), that $X_n \xrightarrow[P]{} X$.

The proof of the Cauchy criterion and the proposition is thus complete. ▮

Complements and problems

II.4.1. In order that the notions of almost sure convergence and convergence in probability be equivalent on a probability space $(\Omega, \mathscr{A}, P)$, it is necessary and sufficient that the space be atomic.

II.4.2. If $(\Omega, \mathscr{A}, P)$ is the interval $[0, 1]$ of the real line, taken with the σ-algebra of the Borel sets and the Lebesgue measure, let $\{A_n, n \geqslant 1\}$ be the sequence of subintervals of $[0, 1]$ of the form

$$A_n = \left[\frac{q}{2^p}, \frac{q+1}{2^p}\right],$$

where $2^p + q = n$ is the (unique) decomposition of $n \geqslant 1$ such that p and q are integers satisfying $p \geqslant 0$, $0 \leqslant q < 2^p$. Show that $1_{A_n} \xrightarrow[P]{} 0$ but that $\limsup_n 1_{A_n} = 1$, $\liminf_n 1_{A_n} = 0$.

II.4.3. The functional

$$\epsilon(X) = E\left(\frac{|X|}{1 + |X|}\right)$$

on the set V (of equivalence classes) of a.s. finite r.r.v.'s is such that $\epsilon(X + Y) \leqslant \epsilon(X) + \epsilon(Y)$ and $\epsilon(cX) \leqslant [\max(1, c)]\epsilon(X)$. Show that $d(X, Y) = \epsilon(X - Y)$ defines a metric on V, that the topology of the metric space (V, d) is that of convergence in probability (i.e., that $d(X_n, X) \to 0 \Leftrightarrow X_n \xrightarrow[P]{} X$) and that the metric space (V, d) is complete.

Show that for a subset H of V to be relatively compact in this topology, it is necessary and sufficient that for every $\epsilon > 0$ there exist a real constant C and a finite family $\{A_i, i \in I\}$ of measurable sets such that (a) $P(\bigcup_I A_i) \geqslant 1 - \epsilon$; (b) $|X| \underset{\text{a.s.}}{\leqslant} C$ on $\bigcup_I A_i$ for every $X \in H$; (c) $\operatorname{ess\,sup}_{A_i} X - \operatorname{ess\,inf}_{A_i} X \leqslant \epsilon$ for every $X \in H$.

II.4.4. **(Egorov's theorem.)** If $X_n \to X$ a.s. on $(\Omega, \mathscr{A}, P)$ and X is a.s. finite, then for every $\epsilon > 0$ there exists a set A_ϵ with probability $P(A_\epsilon) \geqslant 1 - \epsilon$ such that $X_n \to X$ uniformly on A_ϵ. [Take

$$A_\epsilon^c = \sup_k \sup_{n \geqslant n_k} \{|X_n - X| > 1/k\}$$

with a suitable choice of $\{n_k\}$.]

II.4.5. Let $(\Omega, \mathscr{A}, P)$ be a probability space and let $(\Omega, \overline{\mathscr{A}}, \bar{P})$ be its completion. Show that there is an identity between:

(1) the r.r.v.'s defined on $(\Omega, \overline{\mathscr{A}}, \bar{P})$;

(2) the mappings of Ω into $\bar{R}$ which are equal, except on a negligible set, to a r.r.v. defined on $(\Omega, \mathscr{A}, P)$.

II.4.6. Let $\{X_n, n \geqslant 1\}$ be a sequence of real random variables. Show that there exists a smallest (largest) equivalence class Y' (Y'') of r.r.v.'s such that for every $\epsilon > 0$ one has

$$\lim_n P(Y' - X_n \leqslant -\epsilon) = 0 \qquad (\lim_n P(Y'' - X_n \geqslant \epsilon) = 0).$$

Show next that $Y'' \leqslant Y'$ a.s. and that in order that $Y'' = Y'$ a.s., it is necessary and sufficient that the sequence $\{X_n\}$ converge in probability.

II.4.7. Let X and X_n $(n \geqslant 1)$ be finite r.r.v.'s and let $\{\epsilon_n, n \geqslant 1\}$ be a decreasing sequence of positive numbers tending to zero. Show that $X = \lim \text{a.s.}_{n\to\infty} X_n$ as long as

$$\sum_n P[|X_n - X| > \epsilon_n] < \infty.$$

II.5. UNIFORM INTEGRABILITY AND MEAN CONVERGENCE

Definition II.5.1. A FAMILY $\{X_i, i \in I\}$ OF INTEGRABLE r.r.v.'s DEFINED ON $(\Omega, \mathscr{A}, P)$ IS SAID TO BE UNIFORMLY INTEGRABLE IF

$$\sup_I \int_{|X_i| > a} |X_i| \downarrow 0,$$

AS $a \uparrow \infty$.

PROPOSITION II.5.1. *Every family* $\{X_i, i \in I\}$ *of* r.r.v.'s *which is majorized in absolute value by an integrable* r.r.v. X, *that is,*

$$|X_i| \underset{\text{a.s.}}{\leqslant} X \qquad (i \in I),$$

is uniformly integrable. In particular, every finite family of integrable r.r.v.'s *is uniformly integrable.*

PROOF. The monotone continuity properties of the expectation imply that for every positive integrable r.r.v. X we have

$$\lim_{a \uparrow \infty} \downarrow \int_{\{X > a\}} X = \int_{\{X = \infty\}} X = 0.$$

The first part of the proposition now follows from the fact that the inequality $|X_i| \leqslant X$ implies

$$\int_{\{|X_i| > a\}} |X_i| \leqslant \int_{\{X > a\}} X.$$

Every finite family $\{X_i, i \in I\}$ of integrable r.r.v.'s is majorized by the integrable r.r.v. $X = \sum_I |X_i|$, from which follows the second part of the proposition. ▮

PROPOSITION II.5.2. *A family* $\{X_i, i \in I\}$ *of integrable* r.r.v.'s *is uniformly integrable if and only if it satisfies the following two conditions:*

(a) (*uniform absolute continuity*) *for every* $\epsilon > 0$ *there exists an* $\eta_\epsilon > 0$ *such that*

$$\sup_I \int_A |X_i| \leqslant \epsilon \qquad \textit{whenever} \qquad P(A) \leqslant \eta_\epsilon \quad (A \in \mathscr{A});$$

(b) $\sup_I \int_\Omega |X_i| < \infty$.

PROOF. The inequality

$$\int_A X = \int_{A\{X \leqslant a\}} X + \int_{A\{X > a\}} X \leqslant aP(A) + \int_{\{X > a\}} X,$$

which is valid for every positive r.r.v. X when $a \geqslant 0$ and $A \in \mathscr{A}$, implies that for any family $\{X_i, i \in I\}$ of r.r.v.'s we have

$$\sup_I \int_A |X_i| \leqslant aP(A) + \sup_I \int_{\{|X_i| > a\}} |X_i|.$$

The necessity of the conditions of the proposition follows, on the one hand, by letting $P(A) \to 0$ and $a \uparrow \infty$, and on the other hand by taking $A = \Omega$.

Conversely, the elementary inequality

$$\int_\Omega X \geqslant \int_{\{X \geqslant a\}} X \geqslant aP(X \geqslant a),$$

which holds for every positive r.r.v. X, shows that for every family $\{X_i, i \in I\}$ of r.r.v.'s satisfying condition (b) of the proposition, we have

$$\sup_I P(|X_i| \geqslant a) \leqslant \frac{1}{a} \sup_I \int_\Omega |X_i| \downarrow 0$$

when $a \uparrow \infty$. If the family $\{X_i, i \in I\}$ is moreover uniformly absolutely continuous, we can choose $a < \infty$ so that $P(|X_i| \geqslant a) \leqslant \eta_\epsilon$ $(i \in I)$. We then have the inequality $\int_{\{|X_i| \geqslant a\}} |X_i| \leqslant \epsilon$ for every $i \in I$; the family $\{X_i, i \in I\}$ is thus uniformly integrable. ∎

Corollary. *Every family* $\{X_i, i \in I\}$ *of* r.r.v.'s *which is majorized in absolute value by an integrable* r.r.v. *is uniformly absolutely continuous. In particular, every finite family of integrable* r.r.v.'s *is uniformly absolutely continuous.*

Definition II.5.2. A SEQUENCE $\{X_n, n \geqslant 1\}$ OF (EQUIVALENCE CLASSES OF) INTEGRABLE r.r.v.'s IS SAID TO CONVERGE IN THE MEAN (OF ORDER 1) TO THE (EQUIVALENCE CLASS OF THE) INTEGRABLE r.r.v. X IF

$$\int |X_n - X| \to 0 \qquad \text{AS } n \to \infty.$$

WE WRITE $X_n \xrightarrow{L_1} X$.

The importance of mean convergence stems from the fact that it permits passage to the limit inside the integral, by the following result.

Proposition II.5.3. *In order that a sequence* $\{X_n, n \geqslant 1\}$ *of integrable* r.r.v.'s *converge in the mean to the integrable* r.r.v. X, *it is necessary and sufficient that* $\int_A X_n \to \int_A X$ *uniformly in* $A \in \mathscr{A}$ *as* $n \to \infty$. *In particular, if* $X_n \xrightarrow{L_1} X$ *and if* $P(A_n \triangle A) \to 0$, *then* $\int_{A_n} X_n \to \int_A X$ *as* $n \to \infty$.

PROOF. The necessity of the condition follows from

$$\left|\int_A X_n - \int_A X\right| \leqslant \int_A |X_n - X| \leqslant \int |X_n - X| \qquad (A \in \mathscr{A})$$

and the sufficiency from

$$\int |X_n - X| = \left(\int_{A_n} X_n - \int_{A_n} X\right) - \left(\int_{A_n^c} X_n - \int_{A_n^c} X\right)$$

where $A_n = \{X_n > X\}$. Finally, if $X_n \xrightarrow{L_1} X$ and if $P(A_n \triangle A) \to 0$, both terms on the right side of the inequality

$$\left|\int_{A_n} X_n - \int_A X\right| \leqslant \left|\int_{A_n} X_n - \int_{A_n} X\right| + \left|\int_{A_n} X - \int_A X\right|$$

tend to 0 as $n \to \infty$. ∎

We shall prove the following two results together.

CAUCHY CRITERION. *For every sequence* $\{X_n, n \geqslant 1\}$ *of integrable* r.r.v.'s *the following two conditions are equivalent:*

(a) $\{X_n\}$ *converges in the mean of order* 1 *as* $n \to \infty$;

(b) $\{X_n\}$ *is a Cauchy sequence for convergence in the mean, that is, a sequence such that* $E|X_n - X_m| \to 0$ *as* $m, n \to \infty$.

PROPOSITION II.5.4. *For every sequence* $\{X_n, n \geqslant 1\}$ *of integrable* r.r.v.'s *and for every* r.r.v. X, *the following two conditions are equivalent:*

(c) $\{X_n, n \geqslant 1\}$ *is uniformly integrable and* $X_n \xrightarrow[P]{} X$ *as* $n \to \infty$;

(d) X *is integrable and* $X_n \xrightarrow{L_1} X$ *as* $n \to \infty$.

PROOF. We shall prove that

$$(a) \Rightarrow (b) \Rightarrow (c) \Rightarrow (d) \Rightarrow (a).$$

The necessity of the Cauchy criterion follows from the fact that every sequence $\{X_n, n \geqslant 1\}$ of integrable r.r.v.'s which converges in the mean to the integrable r.r.v. X is such that

$$E|X_n - X_m| \leqslant E|X_n - X| + E|X_m - X| \to 0 \qquad \text{as} \quad m \text{ and } n \to \infty.$$

Next, we use the criterion of Proposition II.5.2 to show that every sequence $\{X_n, n \geqslant 1\}$ of integrable r.r.v.'s which is a Cauchy sequence for convergence in the mean is necessarily uniformly integrable. Let us first choose, for every $\epsilon > 0$, an index N_ϵ such that $\int |X_m - X_n| \leqslant \epsilon$ if $m, n \geqslant N_\epsilon$. The inequality $\int_A |X_n| \leqslant \int_A |X_m| + \int |X_n - X_m|$ now implies that

$$\sup_n \int_A |X_n| \leqslant \sup_{m \leqslant N_\epsilon} \int_A |X_m| + \epsilon$$

for every $A \in \mathscr{A}$. As the finite family $\{X_m, m \leqslant N_\epsilon\}$ is uniformly integrable (Proposition II.5.1), it follows that $\sup_n \int |X_n| < \infty$ and that $\sup_n \int_A |X_n| \leqslant 2\epsilon$ as long as $P(A)$ is sufficiently small. We complete the proof of (b) $\Rightarrow$ (c) upon observing that $E|X_m - X_n| \to 0$ implies that

$$P[|X_m - X_n| \geqslant \epsilon] \leqslant \frac{1}{\epsilon} E|X_m - X_n| \to 0 \qquad \text{as} \quad m, n \to \infty,$$

and that the sequence $\{X_n\}$ therefore converges in probability to a finite r.r.v. by virtue of the Cauchy criterion for convergence in probability.

Under the hypothesis (c), the r.r.v. X is necessarily integrable. In fact, if $\{n_j\}$ is an increasing sequence of integers such that $X_{n_j} \xrightarrow[\text{a.s.}]{} X$ (Proposition II.4.3), and therefore such that $|X_{n_j}| \xrightarrow[\text{a.s.}]{} |X|$, the Fatou-Lebesgue lemma shows that $E|X| \leqslant \liminf_j E|X_{n_j}| \leqslant \sup E|X_n| < \infty$ (Proposition II.5.2). Next, under the same hypothesis

$$\int |X_n - X| \leqslant \int_{\{|X_n - X| \leqslant \epsilon\}} |X_n - X| + \int_{\{|X_n - X| > \epsilon\}} |X_n - X|$$

$$\leqslant \epsilon + \int_{\{|X_n - X| > \epsilon\}} |X_n| + \int_{\{|X_n - X| > \epsilon\}} |X| \to 0$$

as $n \to \infty$ and then $\epsilon \to 0$, since $P[|X_n - X| > \epsilon] \to 0$ as $n \to \infty$ and since the sequence $\{X_n\}$ is uniformly absolutely continuous.

The proposition is proved, because (d) is equivalent to (a). ∎

Complements and problems

II.5.1. If X, Y are two positive integrable r.r.v.'s and if $Z = \sup(X, Y)$, then

$$\int_{\{Z > a\}} Z \leqslant \int_{\{X > a\}} X + \int_{\{Y > a\}} Y \qquad (a \geqslant 0).$$

Deduce from this that if the sequence $\{X_n, n \geqslant 1\}$ of r.r.v.'s is uniformly integrable, then

$$E\left[\frac{1}{n} \sup_{1 \leqslant m \leqslant n} |X_m|\right] \to 0 \qquad (n \to \infty).$$

II.5.2. In order that the family $\{X_i, i \in I\}$ of r.r.v.'s be uniformly integrable, it suffices that there exist a function f defined on $[0, \infty]$, which is real, positive, measurable and such that $\lim_{+\infty} (1/x)f(x) = \infty$ and

$$\sup_I E[f(|X_i|)] < \infty.$$

Examples: $f(x) = x^p$ for $p > 1$; $f(x) = x(\log x)^+$.

II.5.3. If the two families $\{X_i, i \in I\}$ and $\{Y_j, j \in J\}$ of integrable r.r.v.'s are uniformly absolutely continuous (uniformly integrable), the family $\{X_i + Y_j; i \in I, j \in J\}$ is again uniformly absolutely continuous (uniformly integrable).

II.5.4. For every integrable r.r.v. X, the set function $\int_A X$ is uniformly continuous on the Boolean metric algebra $\mathscr{A}$. In order that the family $\{X_i, i \in I\}$ of integrable r.r.v.'s be uniformly absolutely continuous, it is necessary and sufficient that the family $\left\{\int_A X_i, i \in I\right\}$ of set functions be equi-uniformly continuous on $\mathscr{A}$.

II.5.5. Show that for every atomless probability space $(\Omega, \mathscr{A}, P)$ the uniform integrability of a family of r.r.v.'s is equivalent to its uniform absolute continuity (use the existence for every $\epsilon > 0$ of a finite partition of the space consisting of sets with probability $< \epsilon$). Deduce from this that in the general case condition (b) in Proposition II.5.2 can be replaced by the following condition:

On every atom A the set of constant values taken by the X_i $(i \in I)$ is bounded. Consequently, one can always replace uniform integrability in condition (c) of Proposition II.5.4 by uniform absolute continuity.

II.5.6. Extend the definitions and the results of the last two sections to generalized sequences of r.r.v.'s.

A generalized sequence $\{X_\alpha\}$ of integrable r.r.v.'s is said to be *uniformly integrable at infinity* if for every $\epsilon > 0$ there exists an index α_ϵ and a real number a_ϵ such that

$$\int_{\{|X_\alpha| > a_\epsilon\}} |X_\alpha| \leqslant \epsilon \qquad \text{if} \qquad \alpha \geqslant \alpha_\epsilon.$$

Show that for a sequence of r.r.v.'s, this notion is equivalent to uniform integrability. Establish for uniform integrability at infinity a result analogous to Proposition II.5.2. Show that Proposition II.5.4 generalizes to generalized sequences of r.r.v.'s if we introduce uniform integrability at infinity in condition (c).

II.6. L_p SPACES

LEMMA II.6.1. *If φ is a real continuous and concave function defined on a convex domain D in R^n, then*

$$E[\varphi(X_1, \ldots, X_n)] \leqslant \varphi(EX_1, \ldots, EX_n)$$

for any integrable r.r.v.'s $X_1, \ldots, X_n$ *such that*

$$(X_1, \ldots, X_n) \in D \quad \text{a.s.}$$

It is not difficult to show that the condition $(X_1, \ldots, X_n) \in D$ a.s. implies $(EX_1, \ldots, EX_n) \in D$.

PROOF. Let $\lambda_1, \ldots, \lambda_n$ be the direction cosines of a hyperplane in R^{n+1} passing through the point $(EX_1, \ldots, EX_n, \varphi(EX_1, \ldots, EX_n))$ and lying above the surface φ; then

$$\varphi(x_1, \ldots, x_n) \leqslant \varphi(EX_1, \ldots, EX_n) + \sum_1^n \lambda_i[x_i - EX_i] \qquad \text{on} \quad D.$$

Replacing the x_i on the right side by the X_i, we obtain an integrable r.r.v. whose integral is equal to $\varphi(EX_1, \ldots, EX_n)$; it follows that

$$\varphi(X_1, \ldots, X_n)$$

is quasi-integrable and that $E[\varphi(X_1, \ldots, X_n)] \leqslant \varphi(EX_1, \ldots, EX_n)$. ∎

COROLLARY. *Let φ_α $(0 < \alpha < 1)$ and ψ_p $(1 \leqslant p < \infty)$ be real functions defined on $\{0 \leqslant u, v < \infty\}$ by:*

$$\varphi_\alpha(u, v) = u^\alpha v^{1-\alpha}; \qquad \psi_p(u, v) = (u^{1/p} + v^{1/p})^p.$$

Then for any positive integrable r.r.v.'s U, V *we have*

$$E[\varphi_\alpha(U, V)] \leqslant \varphi_\alpha(EU, EV); \qquad E[\psi_p(U, V)] \leqslant \psi_p(EU, EV).$$

PROOF. It suffices to show that φ_α and ψ_p are continuous and concave. Since

$$\varphi_\alpha(cu, cv) = c\varphi_\alpha(u, v), \qquad \psi_p(cu, cv) = c\psi_p(u, v) \quad (c \geqslant 0)$$

it is in fact enough to show that the functions

$$\varphi_\alpha(w, 1 - w) \qquad \text{and} \qquad \psi_p(w, 1 - w)$$

of the variable $w \in [0, 1]$ are continuous and concave. An elementary calculation shows that

$$\frac{d^2}{dw^2}\varphi_\alpha(w, 1 - w) = -\alpha(1 - \alpha)u^{\alpha-2}(1 - u)^{-\alpha-1} \leqslant 0,$$

$$\frac{d^2}{dw^2}\psi_p(w, 1 - w)$$

$$= -\frac{p-1}{p}[w^{1/p} + (1 - w)^{1/p}]^{p-2}[w(1 - w)]^{(1/p)-2} \leqslant 0. \quad \blacksquare$$

For every r.r.v. X let us introduce the real numbers

$$\|X\|_p = E(|X|^p)^{1/p} \qquad (1 \leqslant p < \infty)$$
$$\|X\|_\infty = \sup\{x\colon P(|X| > x) > 0\}$$

and show that they have the following properties:

(a) $0 \leqslant \|X\|_1 \leqslant \|X\|_p \leqslant \|X\|_q \leqslant \|X\|_\infty \leqslant \infty \quad (1 < p < q < \infty)$;
$P(|X| \neq 0) = 0 \Leftrightarrow \|X\|_p = 0 \quad (1 \leqslant p \leqslant \infty)$;

(b) $\|XY\|_r \leqslant \|X\|_p\|Y\|_q$ if $1 \leqslant p, q, r \leqslant \infty$ and $r^{-1} = p^{-1} + q^{-1}$;

(*Hölder's inequality*) in particular:

$$\int|XY| \leqslant \|X\|_p\|Y\|_q \quad \text{if} \quad 1 \leqslant p, q \leqslant \infty \quad \text{and} \quad 1 = p^{-1} + q^{-1}$$

(this is *Schwartz's inequality* if $p = q = 2$),

(c) $\|cX\|_p = c\|X\|_p \quad (c \in R, 1 \leqslant p \leqslant \infty)$;
$\|X + Y\|_p \leqslant \|X\|_p + \|Y\|_p \quad (1 \leqslant p \leqslant \infty)$

(*Minkowski's inequality*).

PROOF. To show (b), we assume that $\|X\|_p$ and $\|Y\|_q$ are finite. If $q = \infty$, we have $|XY| \leqslant |X|\,\|Y\|_\infty$ almost everywhere on Ω; the inequality follows immediately. The inequality with $p = \infty$ can be proved in the same way, hence we are led to consider only the case where $p, q < \infty$. In this case, the corollary above, applied to the function $\varphi_{r/p}$ and to the r.r.v.'s $U = |X|^p$, $V = |Y|^q$, gives the result at once.

The inequalities (a) follow from (b) by taking $Y = 1$ and noting that $\|1\|_q = 1$ for every $q \in [1, \infty]$.

The first inequality in (c) is immediate. The second inequality is trivial if $\|X\|_p$ or $\|Y\|_p$ equal ∞. Otherwise, for $p = \infty$ it follows from

$P(|X + Y| > x + y) \leqslant P(|X| > x) + P(|Y| > y)$. In the case where $p < \infty$; the corollary applied to the function ψ_p and to the r.r.v.'s $U = |X|^p$, $V = |Y|^p$ gives the result. ▮

Property (a) shows that the real number $\|X\|_p$ depends only on the equivalence class of the r.r.v. X. For every $p \in [1, \infty]$, we denote by $L_p(\Omega, \mathscr{A}, P)$ the set of equivalence classes of r.r.v.'s X such that $\|X\|_p < \infty$. By what was said in Section 2.5, it is important, in every question concerning more than a countable infinity of r.r.v.'s at one time, to distinguish between the space L_p of equivalence classes of r.r.v.'s whose p-th power is integrable (or which are essentially bounded, if $p = \infty$) and the space $\mathscr{L}_p$ of r.r.v.'s X whose p-th power is integrable (or which are essentially bounded, if $p = \infty$).

Property (c) and the equivalence $\|X\|_p = 0 \Leftrightarrow X \underset{\text{a.s.}}{=} 0$ imply that the space L_p is a normed vector space. We know that a notion of convergence is defined in these spaces by putting $X_n \xrightarrow{L_p} X$ if $\|X_n - X\|_p \to 0$ as $n \to \infty$, or, what is the same when $p < \infty$, if

$$\int |X_n - X|^p \to 0 \qquad (n \to \infty).$$

This convergence is called *convergence in the mean of order p* if $p < \infty$, and *essential uniform convergence* if $p = \infty$. It has, at least for $p < \infty$, properties analogous to those established in the previous section for the case where $p = 1$.

CAUCHY CRITERION. *Let $p \in [1, \infty]$. For every sequence of (equivalence classes of) r.r.v.'s $\{X_n\}$ in L_p, the following two conditions are equivalent:*

(a) *$\{X_n\}$ is a convergent sequence in L_p.*

(b) *$\{X_n\}$ is a Cauchy sequence in L_p, that is $\|X_m - X_n\|_p \to 0$ as $m, n \to \infty$.*

PROPOSITION II.6.1. *Let $p \in [1, \infty)$. For every sequence of (equivalence classes of) r.r.v.'s $\{X_n\}$ in L_p and for every (equivalence class of) r.r.v. X the following two conditions are equivalent:*

(c) *$\{|X_n|^p\}$ is uniformly integrable and $X_n \xrightarrow[P]{} X$ as $n \to \infty$.*

(d) *$X \in L_p$ and $X_n \xrightarrow{L_p} X$ as $n \to \infty$.*

PROOF. For $p < \infty$ the proof is completely analogous to that carried out in Section 2.5 in the special case $p = 1$. It suffices to replace, everywhere in that proof, the absolute values $|X|$ by $|X|^p$ and to use in place of the triangle inequality $|X + Y| \leqslant |X| + |Y|$ its generalization

$$|X + Y|^p \leqslant 2^{p-1}(|X|^p + |Y|^p)$$

which is valid for every $p \in [1, \infty)$.

The proof of the Cauchy criterion in the case $p = \infty$ goes through at once just as in the case of a.s. convergence. We observe also that the convergence $X_n \xrightarrow{L_\infty} X$ implies (a) that the sequence $\{X_n\}$ is essentially uniformly bounded, say $\sup_n |X_n(\omega)| \leqslant C$ for a constant C and for almost every ω; (b) $X_n \xrightarrow[\text{a.s.}]{} X$. ∎

COROLLARY. *Let $p \in [1, \infty)$ and let $\{X_n, n \geqslant 1\}$ be a sequence in L_p majorized in absolute value by $Y \in L_p$: $|X_n| \leqslant Y$. For every* r.r.v. *X the following two conditions are equivalent:*

(a) *$X_n \xrightarrow[P]{} X$ as $n \to \infty$.*

(b) *$X \in L_p$ and $X_n \xrightarrow{L_p} X$ as $n \to \infty$.*

A number of earlier results can be brought together in the following form:

PROPOSITION II.6.2. *For every $p \in [1, \infty]$, the space $L_p(\Omega, \mathscr{A}, P)$ is a complete normed vector space (a Banach space) and a complete lattice.*

PROOF. We have already shown that L_p is a normed vector space; the validity of the Cauchy criterion implies that it is a complete space, hence a Banach space.

A partially ordered vector space L is said to be a complete lattice if every finite family and every upper bounded (lower bounded) infinite family has a supremum (infimum). By virtue of Proposition II.4.1, it suffices to prove here: (a) that $\sup(X_1, X_2) \in L_p$ if $X_1, X_2 \in L_p$; (b) that if two positive r.r.v.'s X and Y are such that $X \leqslant Y$ and $Y \in L_p$, then $X \in L_p$. But (b) is immediate and (a) follows from it, since

$$|\sup(X_1, X_2)| \leqslant |X_1| + |X_2| \in L_p. \quad ∎$$

COROLLARY. *The space $L_2(\Omega, \mathscr{A}, P)$ is a Hilbert space for the scalar product*

$$\langle X, Y\rangle = E(XY)$$

and at the same time a complete lattice.

This corollary follows from the preceding theorem and from Hölder's inequality, which implies that $|\langle X, Y\rangle| \leqslant \|X\|_2 \|Y\|_2$ where by definition

$$\|X\|_2 = \sqrt{\langle X, X\rangle}.$$

Complements and problems

II.6.1. For every r.r.v. X the mapping of $[1, \infty]$ into $[0, \infty]$ defined by $p \to \|X\|_p$ is continuous except possibly at some one point p_0, at which it is then continuous from the left and such that $\|X\|_p < \infty$ if $p < p_0$, $\|X\|_p = \infty$ if $p > p_0$. Show that on the interval where $\|X\|_p < \infty$ the continuous function $\log \|X\|_p$ is convex in p.

II.6.2. If u is a continuous increasing mapping of $[0, \infty]$ onto itself and if v is its inverse, show that $xy \leqslant U(x) + V(y)$ for every $x, y \in [0, \infty]$, where $U(x) = \int_0^x u(z)\,dz$, $V(y) = \int_0^y v(z)\,dz$. It follows that if X, Y are two r.r.v.'s on $(\Omega, \mathscr{A}, P)$, the product XY is integrable whenever the r.r.v.'s $U[|X|]$ and $V[|Y|]$ are [example: $u(x) = x^{p-1}$ where $p > 1$].

II.6.3. Let E be the vector space of equivalence classes of step r.r.v.'s defined on a probability space $(\Omega, \mathscr{A}, P)$. Show that

$$E \subset L_\infty \subset L_q \subset L_p \subset L_1 \qquad (1 < p < q < \infty)$$

and that E and L_r are dense in L_s $(1 \leqslant s \leqslant r \leqslant \infty)$. In order that $X_n \xrightarrow{L_p} X$ it suffices that $X_n \xrightarrow{L_q} X$ if $q > p$; show that this condition is necessary only if $\mathscr{A}/P$ is finite.

II.6.4. Every positive linear mapping T of a space $L_p(\Omega, \mathscr{A}, P)$ into a space $L_{p'}(\Omega', \mathscr{A}', P')$ is necessarily continuous [arguing by contradiction, show that there exists a constant C such that $\|T(X)\|_{p'} \leqslant C\|X\|_p$ for every positive r.r.v. $X \in L_p$].

If T is a positive linear transformation of a space $L_1(\Omega, \mathscr{A}, P)$ into a space $L_1(\Omega', \mathscr{A}', P')$ such that $T(1) = 1'$, show that for every $p \in [1, \infty]$ the restriction of T to $L_p(\Omega, \mathscr{A}, P)$ is a positive linear mapping of $L_p(\Omega, \mathscr{A}, P)$ into $L_p(\Omega', \mathscr{A}', P')$ whose norm is equal to 1.

II.6.5. If the sequence $\{X_n, n \geqslant 1\}$ of *positive* integrable r.r.v.'s converges in probability to a positive r.r.v. X, show that the condition

$$\int X_n \to \int X \qquad (n \to \infty)$$

is enough to imply that $X_n \xrightarrow{L_1} X$.

[Show that $(X - X_n)^+ \xrightarrow{L_1} 0$ as $n \to \infty$.]

II.6.6. The space $L_\infty(\Omega, \mathscr{A}, P)$ is a Banach algebra. Show that the characters of this algebra (that is, the continuous linear functionals u on L_∞ such that $u(XY) = u(X)u(Y)$ for every $X, Y \in L_\infty$) are put in one-to-one correspondence with the maximal filters of $\mathscr{A}/P$ (Problem I.2.3) by the formula

$$\mathscr{E} = \{A: u(1_A) = 1\}.$$

II.6.7. **Integrability of r.v.'s in a Banach space.** Let $(\Omega, \mathscr{A}, P)$ be a probability space and let E be a Banach space. The random variables in E have been defined in Problem II.2.2; show that the norm $\|X(\cdot)\|$ in E of the random variable X is a positive r.r.v.

For every step r.v. X in E, $X = \sum_I x_i 1_{A_i}$, we define

$$\int X\,dP = \sum_I x_i P(A_i)$$

in E. Extend this integral by continuity to all the r.v.'s in E for which $\|X(\cdot)\|$ is in L_1, and show that $\|\int X\,dP\| \leqslant \int \|X\|\,dP$. Show that the space $L_1(E)$ of equivalence classes of r.v.'s in E whose norms are integrable is a Banach space for the norm $|||X||| = \int \|X\|\,dP$ and that the integral defines a continuous linear operator from $L_1(E)$ into E. Define the spaces $L_p(E)$.

II.6.8. Deduce from Proposition II.6.1 and from Problem II.4.3 a necessary and sufficient condition for a subset H in L_p to be relatively compact $(1 \leqslant p < \infty)$.

*II.7. INTEGRATION ON TOPOLOGICAL SPACES

In this section we intend to study the relations which can exist between the measurable structure and the topological structure of a given space Ω. Making use of the results of Sections I.5 and II.3, we start by proving the following fundamental result (Daniell).

PROPOSITION II.7.1. *Let $\mathscr{E}$ be a Riesz space (vector lattice) of real functions defined on a set Ω, containing the constant function* 1. *Let E be a positive linear functional defined on $\mathscr{E}$ such that $E(1) = 1$, and having the following sequential continuity property: $\lim_n \downarrow E(X_n) = 0$ for every sequence $\{X_n\}$ in $\mathscr{E}$ which decreases to* 0 *on Ω.*

If *$\mathscr{A}$ denotes the smallest σ-algebra of subsets of Ω with respect to which all the functions in $\mathscr{E}$ are measurable, there exists a unique probability P on $(\Omega, \mathscr{A})$ such that every function X in $\mathscr{E}$ is integrable and $E(X) = \int X\,dP$.*

PROOF. We shall adopt the notation of Proposition II.3.2; we denote by $\mathscr{G}$ the class $\{G: 1_G \in \mathscr{J}_+\}$ of subsets of Ω and set $\Pi(G) = E(1_G)$ on $\mathscr{G}$.

Then Proposition II.3.2 shows that the class $\mathscr{G}$ and the function Π satisfy the hypotheses of Proposition I.5.2; this latter proposition and its corollary show that if we introduce the set function

$$\Pi^*(\Omega_1) = \inf\{\Pi(G); G \in \mathscr{G}, G \supset \Omega_1\}$$

on $\mathscr{P}(\Omega)$, then the class $\mathscr{D} = \{D: \Pi^*(D) + \Pi^*(D^c) = 1\}$ is a σ-algebra and the restriction of Π^* to $\mathscr{D}$ is a probability.

For every $Z \in \mathscr{J}_+$ the sets $\{Z > a\}$ belong to $\mathscr{G}$ by virtue of the formula $1_{\{Z > a\}} = \lim_n \uparrow \min[1, n(Z - a)^+]$. This remark and the definition of $\mathscr{G}$ show that the σ-algebra generated by $\mathscr{G}$, and the smallest σ-algebra with respect to which the functions in $\mathscr{J}_+$ are measurable, are identical; moreover these σ-algebras also coincide with the σ-algebra $\mathscr{A}$ defined in the proposition, since every function in $\mathscr{J}_+$ is obviously $\mathscr{A}$-measurable.

We show next that $\mathscr{D}$ contains $\mathscr{G}$ and therefore also the σ-algebra $\mathscr{A}$ which $\mathscr{G}$ generates. To this end let us establish first that for every subset Ω_1 of Ω we have

$$\begin{aligned}\Pi^*(\Omega_1) &= \inf\{\Pi(G); G \in \mathscr{G}, G \supset \Omega_1\} \\ &= \inf\{E(Z); z \in \mathscr{E}_+, Z \geqslant 1_{\Omega_1}\}.\end{aligned}$$

The first equality being simply a definition and the second term being obviously larger than the third, it suffices to prove that $\Pi^*(\Omega_1) \leqslant E(Z)$ for every $Z \in \mathscr{J}_+$ such that $Z \geqslant 1_{\Omega_1}$. But for such a Z and every real $a \in (0, 1)$ the set $\{Z > a\}$ belongs to $\mathscr{G}$ and contains Ω_1; thus

$$E(Z) \geqslant \frac{1}{a}\,\Pi(\{Z > a\}) \geqslant \frac{1}{a}\,\Pi^*(\Omega_1),$$

and to obtain the desired inequality it remains only to let a tend to 1.

Now let G_0 be a set in $\mathscr{G}$. Since by definition there exists a sequence $\{X_n\}$ in $\mathscr{E}_+$ which increases to 1_{G_0}, we have:

$$\Pi(G_0) = \lim_n \uparrow E(X_n)$$

and

$$\Pi^*(G_0^c) = \inf\{E(Z); Z \in \mathscr{J}_+, Z \geqslant 1_{G_0^c}\} \leqslant \lim_n \downarrow E(1 - X_n).$$

It follows that $\Pi^*(G_0) + \Pi^*(G_0^c) \leqslant 1$; the strict inequality being impossible, G_0 belongs to $\mathscr{D}$. This shows that $\mathscr{G}$ and hence $\mathscr{A}$ is contained in the σ-algebra $\mathscr{D}$; we denote by P the restriction to $\mathscr{A}$ of the set function Π^* (P is a probability).

From the foregoing, every $Z \in \mathscr{J}_+$ is measurable with respect to the σ-algebra $\mathscr{A}$ generated by $\mathscr{G}$; we shall show that $E(Z) = \int Z\,dP$. It will then follow that every positive function Z in $\mathscr{E}$ has an integral with respect to P equal to $E(Z)$ and thus finite; by virtue of the decomposition $X = X^+ - X^-$, which is valid in $\mathscr{E}$ for every $X \in \mathscr{E}$, every element $X \in \mathscr{E}$ will be integrable and its integral will equal $E(X)$. For every element in $\mathscr{J}_+$ of the form $Z = \sum_I a_i 1_{G_i}$, where $G_i \in \mathscr{G}$ and $a_i \in R_+$ ($i \in I$, I finite), the additivity of E on $\mathscr{J}_+$ gives the result immediately. But every element Z in $\mathscr{J}_+$ is a limit of step functions of the preceding type by virtue of the formula

$$Z = \lim_n \uparrow \sum_{q=0}^{n2^n-1} \frac{q}{2^n} 1_{\left\{\frac{q}{2^n} < Z \leqslant \frac{q+1}{2^n}\right\}} + 1_{\{n<Z\}} = \lim_n \uparrow \frac{1}{2^n} \sum_{q=1}^{n2^n} 1_{\left\{Z > \frac{q}{2^n}\right\}};$$

the equality $E(Z) = \int Z\,dp$ then follows from the continuity of both sides on increasing sequences in $\mathscr{J}_+$.

Finally, to prove the uniqueness of P, let us consider two probabilities P and P' defined on $\mathscr{A}$, whose integrals coincide on $\mathscr{E}$. We consider these integrals on $\mathscr{J}_+$; P and P' are thus equal at least on $\mathscr{G}$. But the class $\{A: P(A) = P'(A)\}$, being σ-additive (Problem I.5.4), cannot contain $\mathscr{G}$, which is closed under intersection, without also containing the σ-algebra generated by $\mathscr{G}$. ∎

The preceding proof is based upon an explicit construction of the probability P; this construction in addition yields interesting properties of P, as we are going to show. We shall suppose below that the space $\mathscr{E}$ is closed in the topology of uniform convergence on Ω; this assumption is not, essentially, a restriction of generality, as it is always possible to complete $\mathscr{E}$ and to extend E to this completion by continuity.

Corollary. *Let us suppose that the hypotheses of the preceding proposition are satisfied and moreover that the space $\mathscr{E}$ is closed in the topology of uniform convergence on Ω. Let us denote by $\mathscr{G}$ the class of sets of the form $G = \{f > 0\}$ for $f \in \mathscr{E}_+$. Under these conditions the class $\mathscr{G}$ generates the σ-algebra $\mathscr{A}$; the probability P is defined on $\mathscr{G}$ by the formula*

$$P(G) = \sup\{E(X);\ X \leqslant 1_G,\ X \in \mathscr{E}_+\}$$

and has the "approximation property"

$$P(A) = \inf\{P(G);\ G \supset A,\ G \in \mathscr{G}\}.$$

PROOF. It suffices to prove that the class $\mathscr{G}$ introduced in the corollary coincides with that introduced in the preceding proof. But according to this proof the set $\{X > 0\}$ belongs to the class $\mathscr{G}$ of the proposition for all $X \in \mathscr{E}_+$; conversely, if G belongs to the class $\mathscr{G}$ of the proposition, let $\{X_n\}$ be a sequence in $\mathscr{E}_+$ which increases to 1_G; then $G = \{X > 0\}$ where the function X is defined in $\mathscr{E}_+$ as the sum of the uniformly convergent series $\sum_n 2^{-n} X_n$. ∎

We intend to apply the preceding results to the case where the space $\mathscr{E}$ is the space of bounded continuous functions defined on a topological space Ω.

Definition II.7.1. GIVEN A TOPOLOGICAL SPACE Ω, WE DEFINE A BAIRE SET AS ANY MEMBER OF THE SMALLEST σ-ALGEBRA OF SUBSETS OF Ω WITH RESPECT TO WHICH ALL THE CONTINUOUS (OR CONTINUOUS AND BOUNDED) FUNCTIONS ON Ω ARE MEASURABLE. THE BOREL SETS ARE DEFINED AS THOSE BELONGING TO THE σ-ALGEBRA GENERATED BY THE CLOSED SETS IN Ω.

Since every continuous function on Ω is the limit of at least one sequence of continuous and bounded functions, the two definitions concerning the Baire sets are obviously equivalent. Moreover every Baire set is a Borel set; in fact the sets $\{X \leqslant a\}$ are closed if X is continuous on Ω.

PROPOSITION II.7.2. *Let Ω be a normal topological space (in particular, metrizable or compact) and let $\mathscr{F}$ be the class of closed G_δ sets (that is, countable intersections of open sets) in Ω. Then the class $\mathscr{F}$ generates the σ-algebra $\mathscr{A}$ of Baire sets in Ω. The formula $E(X) = \int X\,dP$ establishes a one-to-one correspondence between probabilities P defined on $(\Omega, \mathscr{A})$, and positive linear functionals E defined on the space $C_\infty(\Omega)$ of bounded continuous functions, such that $E(1) = 1$, and having the continuity property*

$$\lim \downarrow E(X_n) = 0 \quad \text{if} \quad X_n \downarrow 0 \quad \text{on} \quad \Omega.$$

Every probability P on $(\Omega, \mathscr{A})$ has, as a consequence, the approximation property

$$P(A) = \sup\{P(F);\, F \subset A,\, F \in \mathscr{F}\}.$$

We remark that in the case where the space Ω is metrizable, every closed set is a G_δ set; hence in this case the σ-algebras of the Baire and Borel sets coincide.

PROOF. By the theory of integration developed in the previous sections, every probability on $(\Omega, \mathscr{A})$ defines on the space of $\mathscr{A}$-measurable integrable functions, and a fortiori on $C_\infty(\Omega)$, a functional E having the properties indicated.

Conversely, if E is a functional on $C_\infty(\Omega)$ of the preceding type, Proposition II.7.1 and its corollary are applicable. The class $\mathscr{G}$ turns out in the present case to be the class of open F_σ sets; in fact, on every topological space and for any $X \in C_\infty(\Omega)$, the set

$$\{X > 0\} = \bigcup_{n \geqslant 1} \{X \geqslant n^{-1}\}$$

is an open F_σ set. Conversely if $G = \bigcup_n F_n$ is an open countable union of closed sets F_n in a *normal* topological space, for every $n \geqslant 1$ there exists by Urysohn's theorem a continuous function X_n which vanishes on G^c, equals 1 on F_n and has values everywhere between 0 and 1; then

$$G = \{X > 0\} \qquad \text{where} \qquad X = \sum_n 2^{-n} X_n \in C_\infty(\Omega).$$

To complete the proof, it suffices to observe that the class $\mathscr{F}$ consists of the complements of the sets in $\mathscr{G}$ and that the stated approximation property is equivalent, passing to complements, to that in the corollary of Proposition II.7.1. ∎

PROPOSITION II.7.3. *Let $(\Omega, \mathscr{A})$ be a Polish space (complete separable metric space) considered with the σ-algebra of its Borel (=Baire) sets. Every probability on $(\Omega, \mathscr{A})$ has, relative to the class $\mathscr{K}$ of compact sets in Ω, the approximation property*

$$P(A) = \sup\{P(K); K \subset A, K \in \mathscr{K}\}.$$

PROOF. By the preceding proposition, this result is true when the class $\mathscr{K}$ is replaced by the larger class $\mathscr{F}$ of closed sets. It therefore suffices to show that for every $\epsilon > 0$ there exists a compact set K_ϵ with probability $P(K_\epsilon) \geqslant 1 - \epsilon$; this implies, in fact, that for any $F \in \mathscr{F}$ the compact subset FK_ϵ has probability $P(FK_\epsilon) \geqslant P(F) - \epsilon$ and consequently for every set A we have

$$\sup\{P(F); F \subset A, F \in \mathscr{F}\} = \sup\{P(K); K \subset A, K \in \mathscr{K}\}.$$

Let ω_i, $i \in I$ be a dense sequence in Ω. If $\bar{B}_{\omega,r}$ denotes the closed ball with center ω and radius r, we have $\bigcup_I \bar{B}_{\omega_i,r} = \Omega$ for every $r > 0$.

Given $\epsilon > 0$, there exists for every integer $n > 0$ a finite subset I_n of I such that $P(\bigcup_{I_n} \bar{B}_{\omega_i,1/n}) \geqslant 1 - \epsilon 2^{-n}$. The closed set

$$K_\epsilon = \bigcap_{n \geqslant 1} \bigcup_{I_n} \bar{B}_{\omega_i,1/n}$$

therefore has probability $P(K_\epsilon) \geqslant 1 - \epsilon$. Moreover this set is compact; in fact from any sequence of points in K_ϵ one can extract a subsequence such that, for each n, all of its terms, from some point on, lie in the same set $\bar{B}_{\omega_i,1/n}$ $(i \in I_n)$; this subsequence, being a Cauchy sequence in the complete space Ω, is convergent. ▮

We shall conclude this section by indicating briefly how the preceding results can be sharpened when one considers only positive linear functionals on the Riesz space having the stronger continuity property: for every generalized sequence $\{X_\alpha\}$ decreasing to 0 in $\mathscr{E}$, $\lim \downarrow E(X_\alpha) = 0$.

By the remark which follows the statement of Proposition II.3.2, such functionals E can be extended to the cone $\mathscr{J}_+^*$ of upper envelopes of functions in $\mathscr{E}_+$ while preserving the properties of linearity and of monotone continuity for increasing generalized sequence; to this end one sets $E(\lim \uparrow X_\alpha) = \lim \uparrow E(X_\alpha)$. By repeating the argument of the proof of Proposition II.7.1, we see that there exists a probability P defined, on the smallest σ-algebra $\mathscr{B}$ which renders all of the functions in $\mathscr{J}_+^*$ measurable, by the formulas

$$P(G) = E(1_G) \qquad (1_G \in J_+^*),$$
$$P(B) = \inf\{P(G); G \supset B, 1_G \in \mathscr{J}_+^*\} \qquad (B \in \mathscr{B})$$

and such that $E(X) = \int X \, dP$ for every $X \in \mathscr{J}_+^*$. Every element X in $\mathscr{E}_+$, hence also every element in $\mathscr{E}$, has an integral with respect to P which equals precisely $E(X)$. In general the σ-algebra $\mathscr{B}$ defined above strictly contains the σ-algebra $\mathscr{A}$ which renders the functions of $\mathscr{E}$ measurable (for in general there exist functions in $\mathscr{J}_+^*$ which are not $\mathscr{A}$-measurable). On the other hand the probability P is uniquely determined by the condition $E(X) = \int X \, dP \, (X \in \mathscr{J}_+^*)$. However, there can exist other probabilities P' on $(\Omega, \mathscr{B})$ such that $E(X) = \int X \, dP'$ for every $X \in \mathscr{E}$; this last condition implies only the equality of the restrictions of P and P' to $\mathscr{A}$.

Undoubtedly the most interesting case of the preceding results is that in which $\mathscr{E}$ is the space $C_\infty(\Omega)$ of bounded continuous functions defined on a completely regular (in particular, normal, metrizable or compact) topological space Ω. In such a space the class $\mathscr{G} = \{G: 1_G \in \mathscr{J}_+^*\}$ coincides with the class of open sets in Ω and the σ-algebra $\mathscr{B}$ is identical with that of the Borel sets. In fact *if* $X \in \mathscr{J}_+^*$, that is, if $X = \lim \uparrow X_\alpha$ where $X_\alpha \in C_\infty^+(\Omega)$, the sets $\{X > a\} = \bigcup_\alpha \{X_\alpha > a\}$ are open; hence every $X \in \mathscr{J}_+^*$ is measurable with respect to the σ-algebra of Borel sets, and every $G \in \mathscr{G}$ is open. Conversely if G is an open set in a completely regular space Ω, then for every $\omega \in G$ there exists a continuous function X_ω which equals zero on G^c, 1 at the point ω, and whose values lie between 0 and 1; the function $\sup_{\omega \in G} X_\omega$ is then equal to 1_G and belongs to $\mathscr{J}_+^*$ by construction, hence $G \in \mathscr{G}$.

PROPOSITION II.7.4. *Let $\mathscr{F}$ and $\mathscr{B}$ be respectively the class of closed sets and the σ-algebra of Borel sets of a completely regular topological space Ω. Then the formula $E(X) = \int X\,dP$ establishes a one-to-one correspondence between the probabilities P on $(\Omega, \mathscr{B})$ which are "regular" in the sense that* $\lim \downarrow P(F_\alpha) = P(\lim \downarrow F_\alpha)$ *for every decreasing generalized sequence $\{F_\alpha\}$ in $\mathscr{F}$, and the positive linear functionals defined on the space $C_\infty(\Omega)$ of bounded continuous functions, such that $E(1) = 1$ and with the continuity property*

$$\lim \downarrow E(X_\alpha) = 0$$

for every generalized sequence in $C_\infty^+(\Omega)$ which decreases to zero.

Every regular probability P on $(\Omega, \mathscr{B})$ has the approximation property

$$P(B) = \sup\{P(F); F \subset B, F \in \mathscr{F}\}.$$

PROOF. We have shown above how one can associate, with a functional E of the preceding type, a probability P on the σ-algebra $\mathscr{B}$ of Borel sets in Ω. The continuity properties of the extension of E to $\mathscr{J}_+^*$ imply that $P(\lim \uparrow G_\alpha) = \lim \uparrow P(G_\alpha)$ for every increasing generalized sequence of open sets G_α; the regularity of the probability P in the sense of the proposition is deduced from this by passing to the set of complements of the G_α. Similarly P has the approximation property since it is such that $P(B) = \inf\{P(G); G \supset B, G \text{ open}\}$ for every Borel set B.

Conversely let P' be a probability on $(\Omega, \mathscr{B})$ and let $E(X) = \int X\,dP'$ be the positive linear functional which P' defines on $C_\infty(\Omega)$. Let $\{X_\alpha\}$ be a generalized sequence decreasing to 0 in $C_\infty(\Omega)$; $\{X_\alpha\}$ can be supposed bounded by a constant C. Since for every $\epsilon > 0$ the sets $\{X_\alpha \geqslant \epsilon\}$ form a generalized sequence in $\mathscr{F}$ decreasing to $\varnothing$, the inequality

$$E(X_\alpha) \leqslant \epsilon + CP'(X_\alpha \geqslant \epsilon)$$

implies that $\lim \downarrow E(X_\alpha) = 0$ as long as the probability P' satisfies the condition

$$\lim \downarrow P'(F_\alpha) = 0$$

for every generalized sequence in $\mathscr{F}$ decreasing to $\varnothing$. Assuming that P' satisfies this condition, we denote by P the regular probability on $(\Omega, \mathscr{B})$ which we have associated with the functional E by the construction at the beginning; we will then have completed the proof of the proposition, upon showing that $P = P'$ on $\mathscr{B}$ if and only if P' is regular on $\mathscr{B}$.

To this end, it suffices to prove that if P' is regular, then

$$\int X\, dP' = \lim_\alpha \uparrow \int X_\alpha\, dP'$$

when $X = \lim_\alpha \uparrow X_\alpha$ ($X \in \mathscr{J}_+^*$, $X_\alpha \in C_\infty^+$); this implies, in fact, that the integrals of P and P' coincide on $\mathscr{J}_+^*$ and therefore that $P = P'$ on $\mathscr{B}$. But if $X = \lim_\alpha \uparrow X_\alpha$ in $\mathscr{J}_+^*$, then for every $a > 0$, $\{X > a\} = \lim_\alpha \uparrow \{X_\alpha > a\}$ in the class $\mathscr{G}$ of open sets and hence, if P' is regular,

$$P'(X > a) = \lim_\alpha \uparrow P'(X_\alpha > a).$$

By virtue of the formula

$$Y = \lim_{n \uparrow \infty} \uparrow \frac{1}{2^n} \sum_{q=1}^{n2^n} 1_{\{Y > q/2^n\}}$$

which holds for every positive function Y, the foregoing implies that

$$\lim_\alpha \uparrow \int X_\alpha\, dP' = \lim_{\alpha, n} \uparrow 2^{-n} \sum_{q=1}^{n2^n} P'\left(X_\alpha > \frac{q}{2^n}\right)$$

$$= \lim_n \uparrow 2^{-n} \sum_{q=1}^{n2^n} P'\left(X > \frac{q}{2^n}\right) = \int X\, dP'. \quad \blacksquare$$

When Ω is a compact topological space, every positive linear functional on $C(\Omega)$ such that $E(1) = 1$ has the continuity property introduced in the preceding proposition; in fact every generalized sequence of continuous functions on Ω which decreases to 0 decreases uniformly to 0 (Dini's lemma) and moreover we have $E(X) \leqslant \sup_\Omega |X|$. For such a space the results of this section assume the following simple form:

PROPOSITION II.7.5. *Let Ω be a compact topological space and let $\mathscr{F}$, $\mathscr{A}$ and $\mathscr{B}$ be the classes of closed sets, Baire sets and Borel sets, respectively, in Ω. Let us call a probability P on $(\Omega, \mathscr{B})$ regular if it satisfies one of the following equivalent conditions:*

(a) $P(B) = \sup\{P(F); F \in \mathscr{F}, F \subset B\}$ *for every* $B \in \mathscr{B}$;

(b) *for every* $F \in \mathscr{F}$ *and every* $\epsilon > 0$ *there exists an open set* G *containing* F *such that* $P(G) \leqslant P(F) + \epsilon$;

(c) *for every generalized sequence of closed sets* F_α *decreasing to* F,

$$\lim \downarrow P(F_\alpha) = P(F);$$

then the formula $E(X) = \int X\, dP$, *where* $X \in C(\Omega)$, *establishes a one-to-one correspondence between:*

(1) *the positive linear functionals* E *on* $C(\Omega)$ *such that* $E(1) = 1$;
(2) *the probabilities on* $(\Omega, \mathscr{A})$;
(3) *the regular probabilities on* $(\Omega, \mathscr{B})$.

PROOF. By virtue of the earlier results, it remains to show only that conditions (a)–(c) are equivalent for a probability P defined on $(\Omega, \mathscr{B})$. But property (a) is equivalent by passing to complements to the property $P(B) = \inf\{P(G); G \text{ open}, G \supset B\}$; restricting ourselves to closed sets B, we obtain property (b). If P satisfies condition (b) and $\{F_\alpha\}$ is a generalized sequence in $\mathscr{F}$ which decreases to F, we choose an open set $G \supset F$ such that $P(G) \leqslant P(F) + \epsilon$ for a given ϵ; since $\lim F_\alpha \cap G^c = \varnothing$, we have $F_{\alpha_0} \cap G^c = \varnothing$ for at least one α_0 by virtue of the compactness of Ω, and hence

$$\lim \downarrow P(F_\alpha) \leqslant P(F_{\alpha_0}) \leqslant P(G) \leqslant P(F) + \epsilon;$$

thus the probability P satisfies condition (c). Finally, by Proposition II.7.4, every probability P satisfying condition (c) also satisfies (a). ∎

Complements and problems

II.7.1. Show that every positive linear functional E defined on the Riesz space $C(\Omega)$ of continuous functions (bounded or not) defined on a topological space Ω, necessarily satisfies the following condition:

$$\lim \downarrow E(X_n) = 0$$

if $X_n \downarrow 0$ in $C(\Omega)$; deduce from this that $E(1) > 0$ if E is not to be identically zero. [If $X_n \downarrow 0$, show that $E[(X_n - \epsilon)^+] \downarrow 0$ for every $\epsilon > 0$, by noting that the series $\sum_n (X_n - \epsilon)^+$ defines a function which is continuous on each open set $\{X_m < \epsilon\}$ and therefore on Ω. Observe next that $E(1) = 0$ implies that $E(X) = E(X - a)^+$ for every $a > 0$ and every X.]

II.7.2. If a completely regular topological space Ω is the countable union of compact subsets (more generally, a Lindelöf space), every positive linear functional on $C_\infty(\Omega)$ such that $\lim_n \downarrow E(X_n) = 0$ for every sequence $\{X_n\}$ in $C_\infty(\Omega)$ which decreases to 0 necessarily has the stronger continuity property: $\lim_\alpha \downarrow E(X_\alpha) = 0$ for every generalized sequence $\{X_\alpha\}$ in $C_\infty(\Omega)$ which decreases to 0. Deduce from this that on such a space, every probability defined on the σ-algebra of Baire sets has a unique extension to the σ-algebra of Borel sets which is a regular probability. Carry over this result to the case of an arbitrary completely regular space and a probability whose support is a countable union of compact sets C_j.

II.7.3. **(Lusin's theorem.)** Let $(\Omega, \mathscr{A})$ be a Polish space taken with the σ-algebra of its Borel sets and let P be a probability on this space. Show that for every r.r.v. X defined on $(\Omega, \mathscr{A}, P)$ and for every $\epsilon > 0$ there exists a compact set K_ϵ of probability $P(K_\epsilon) \geqslant 1 - \epsilon$ such that the restriction of X to K_ϵ is a continuous mapping of K_ϵ into $\bar{R}$. [Use Proposition II.7.3 to prove this in the case of a step r.r.v. and Problem II.4.4 to pass to the case where X is a.s. finite.]

CHAPTER III

PRODUCT SPACES AND RANDOM FUNCTIONS

III.1. THE PRODUCT OF TWO MEASURABLE SPACES

Given two arbitrary sets Ω_1 and Ω_2, we denote by $\Omega_1 \times \Omega_2$ the product of Ω_1 and Ω_2, that is, by definition, the set of all pairs $\omega = (\omega_1, \omega_2)$ obtained when ω_1 runs through Ω_1 and ω_2 runs through Ω_2. The mapping of $\Omega_1 \times \Omega_2$ into Ω_i $(i = 1, 2)$ which takes $\omega = (\omega_1, \omega_2)$ into ω_i is called the i-th *coordinate.*

If A is an arbitrary subset of $\Omega_1 \times \Omega_2$, we denote by A_{ω_1} the *section* of A at ω_1, that is, the subset of Ω_2 defined by

$$A_{\omega_1} = \{\omega_2 : (\omega_1, \omega_2) \in A\}.$$

For every fixed ω_1 the mapping $A \to A_{\omega_1}$ of $\mathscr{P}(\Omega_1 \times \Omega_2)$ onto $\mathscr{P}(\Omega_2)$ is a homomorphism for the operations of union, intersection, and complementation; if $\{A^\alpha\}$ is a family in $\mathscr{P}(\Omega_1 \times \Omega_2)$, we in fact have

$$\left(\bigcap_\alpha A^\alpha\right)_{\omega_1} = \bigcap_\alpha A^\alpha_{\omega_1}, \qquad \left(\bigcup_\alpha A^\alpha\right)_{\omega_1} = \bigcup_\alpha A^\alpha_{\omega_1}, \qquad (A^c)_{\omega_1} = (A_{\omega_1})^c.$$

If X is an arbitrary mapping of $\Omega_1 \times \Omega_2$ into an arbitrary space, we denote by X_{ω_1} the *section* of X at ω_1, that is, the mapping defined on Ω_2 by $X_{\omega_1}(\omega_2) = X(\omega_1, \omega_2)$. We observe, to justify this terminology, that $(1_A)_{\omega_1} = 1_{A_{\omega_1}}$. The transformation $X \to X_{\omega_1}$ (ω_1 fixed) obviously preserves the usual operations on functions, including pointwise convergence.

A *rectangle* in $\Omega_1 \times \Omega_2$ is a subset of the form

$$A_1 \times A_2 = \{(\omega_1, \omega_2) : \omega_1 \in A_1, \omega_2 \in A_2\};$$

a rectangle is empty if and only if one of its sides A_1 or A_2 is empty. The section of a rectangle is given by: $(A_1 \times A_2)_{\omega_1} = A_2$ or $\varnothing$ according as $\omega_1 \in A_1$ or $\omega_1 \notin A_1$.

Let $\mathscr{A}_1$ and $\mathscr{A}_2$ be σ-algebras of subsets of Ω_1 and Ω_2 respectively. A rectangle $A_1 \times A_2$ is said to be measurable (with respect to $\mathscr{A}_1$ and $\mathscr{A}_2$) if $A_1 \in \mathscr{A}_1$, $A_2 \in \mathscr{A}_2$.

PROPOSITION III.1.1. *The measurable rectangles of* $(\Omega_1, \mathscr{A}_1) \times (\Omega_2, \mathscr{A}_2)$ *form a Boolean semialgebra of subsets of* $\Omega_1 \times \Omega_2$.

PROOF. It is obvious that $\varnothing$ and $\Omega_1 \times \Omega_2$ are measurable rectangles. The intersection of two measurable rectangles is again a measurable rectangle, since

$$(A_1 \times A_2) \cap (A_1' \times A_2') = (A_1 \cap A_1') \times (A_2 \cap A_2').$$

Lastly, the third axiom of the definition of a Boolean semialgebra is satisfied, since

$$(A_1 \times A_2)^c = A_1^c \times A_2 + \Omega_1 \times A_2^c. \quad \blacksquare$$

Thus (Proposition II.6.1) the Boolean algebra generated by the measurable rectangles consists of all finite sums of disjoint measurable rectangles. The σ-algebra generated by this algebra (or by the semialgebra of measurable rectangles) is denoted by $\mathscr{A}_1 \otimes \mathscr{A}_2$ and called the *product σ-algebra* of $\mathscr{A}_1$ and $\mathscr{A}_2$; the measurable space

$$(\Omega_1 \times \Omega_2, \mathscr{A}_1 \otimes \mathscr{A}_2)$$

is then called the product of the measurable spaces $(\Omega_1, \mathscr{A}_1)$ and $(\Omega_2, \mathscr{A}_2)$.

PROPOSITION III.1.2. *For every fixed* ω_1, *the section* A_{ω_1} *at* ω_1 *of every measurable set* A *in* $(\Omega_1 \times \Omega_2, \mathscr{A}_1 \otimes \mathscr{A}_2)$, *is a measurable set in* $(\Omega_2, \mathscr{A}_2)$. *Moreover, the section* X_{ω_1} *of every* r.r.v. X *on*

$$(\Omega_1 \times \Omega_2, \mathscr{A}_1 \otimes \mathscr{A}_2)$$

is a r.r.v. *on* $(\Omega_2, \mathscr{A}_2)$.

PROOF. Let $\mathscr{C}_{\omega_1}$ be the class of subsets A of $\Omega_1 \times \Omega_2$ such that $A_{\omega_1} \in \mathscr{A}_2$. It is easily seen that every measurable rectangle belongs to $\mathscr{C}_{\omega_1}$ and that $\mathscr{C}_{\omega_1}$ is closed under the operations of complementation and countable intersection. It follows that $\mathscr{C}_{\omega_1}$ contains $\mathscr{A}_1 \otimes \mathscr{A}_2$, which proves the first part of the proposition. The second part is then a simple consequence of the identity $(X_{\omega_1})^{-1}(B) = [X^{-1}(B)]_{\omega_1}$. $\blacksquare$

COROLLARY 1. *In order that the nonempty rectangle* $B_1 \times B_2$ *of* $\Omega_1 \times \Omega_2$ *belong to* $\mathscr{A}_1 \otimes \mathscr{A}_2$, *it is necessary and sufficient that* $B_1 \in \mathscr{A}_1$ *and* $B_2 \in \mathscr{A}_2$. *In order that the real, not identically zero, function* $X_1(\omega_1)X_2(\omega_2)$ *defined on* $\Omega_1 \times \Omega_2$ *be* $\mathscr{A}_1 \otimes \mathscr{A}_2$*-measurable, it is necessary and sufficient that* X_1 *and* X_2 *be* $\mathscr{A}_1$ *and* $\mathscr{A}_2$*-measurable, respectively.* (This corollary justifies the terminology "measurable rectangle" used above.)

PROOF. Indeed, if $B_1 \times B_2$ is nonempty, the set B_1 cannot be empty. Hence, if $\omega_1 \in B_1$, then $B_2 = (B_1 \times B_2)_{\omega_1}$ belongs to $\mathscr{A}_2$ by the preceding proposition. In the same way $B_1 \in \mathscr{A}_1$. A similar argument applies to functions. ▮

The family of subsets of $\Omega_1 \times \Omega_2$ of the form $\Omega_1 \times A_2$, where $A_2 \in \mathscr{A}_2$, is a σ-subalgebra of $\mathscr{A}_1 \otimes \mathscr{A}_2$ which is isomorphic to the σ-algebra $\mathscr{A}_2$ of measurable sets in Ω_2. By abuse of notation we agree to denote it again by $\mathscr{A}_2$. Proposition III.1.2 enables us to characterize this σ-algebra in another way.

COROLLARY 2. *The* σ*-subalgebra* $\mathscr{A}_2$ *of* $\mathscr{A}_1 \otimes \mathscr{A}_2$ *is identical with the* σ*-algebra of measurable sets* B *in* $(\Omega_1 \times \Omega_2, \mathscr{A}_1 \otimes \mathscr{A}_2)$ *which do not depend upon the coordinate* ω_1 *(that is, such that* B_{ω_1} *does not depend on* ω_1*).*

PROOF. We first note that for every subset B of $\Omega_1 \times \Omega_2$ it is the same to say that B_{ω_1} does not depend on ω_1 or that B is of the form $B = \Omega_1 \times C$; and then $B_{\omega_1} = C$. Such a set is $\mathscr{A}_1 \otimes \mathscr{A}_2$-measurable, by Corollary 1, if and only if $C \in \mathscr{A}_2$. ▮

Let us remark in conclusion that $\mathscr{A}_1 \otimes \mathscr{A}_2$ is the smallest σ-algebra of subsets of $\Omega_1 \times \Omega_2$ containing the σ-algebras $\mathscr{A}_1$ and $\mathscr{A}_2$ of subsets of $\Omega_1 \times \Omega_2$. This is the same as saying that $\mathscr{A}_1 \otimes \mathscr{A}_2$ is the smallest σ-algebra of subsets of $\Omega_1 \times \Omega_2$ which makes the coordinate mappings measurable.

Complements and problems

III.1.1. If Ω is a nondenumerably infinite set and if $\mathscr{A}$ is the smallest σ-algebra of subsets of Ω containing all one-point sets, the diagonal $\Delta = \{(\omega, \omega): \omega \in \Omega\}$ of $\Omega \times \Omega$ does not belong to $\mathscr{A} \otimes \mathscr{A}$, although all its sections belong to $\mathscr{A}$. The converse of Proposition III.1.2 is thus false.

*III.1.2. Given nonempty sets Ω and Ω', the mapping of $\mathscr{P}(\Omega \times \Omega')$ onto $\mathscr{P}(\Omega)$ defined by

$$\mathrm{proj}_\Omega(E) = \{\omega \in \Omega: E_\omega \neq \varnothing\}$$

is called the *projection on* Ω; this mapping extends the coordinate mapping to sets. Show that for any family $\{E_i, i \in I\}$ in $\mathscr{P}(\Omega \times \Omega')$,

$$\mathrm{proj}_\Omega \bigcup_I E_i = \bigcup_I \mathrm{proj}_\Omega (E_i),$$
$$\mathrm{proj}_\Omega \bigcap_I E_i \subset \bigcap_I \mathrm{proj}_\Omega (E_i)$$

and that in the second relation the inclusion is in general strict, even for a decreasing sequence of sets [nevertheless there is equality if the E_i $(i \in I)$ are rectangles in $\Omega \times \Omega'$ and if $\bigcap_I E_i \neq \varnothing$].

Let $\mathscr{A}$ be a subclass of $\mathscr{P}(\Omega)$ containing $\varnothing$ and let $\mathscr{F} \subset \mathscr{P}(\Omega')$. Show that in the notation of Problem I.3.2 one has $\mathrm{proj}_\Omega ((\mathscr{A} \times \mathscr{F})_\rho) \subset \mathscr{A}_\rho$ for the operations $\rho = s, d, \sigma, \delta, sd = ds, \delta s$ and $d\sigma$, as well as for the operations $s\delta$, $\sigma\delta$ and the Souslin operation when the class $\mathscr{F}$ is compact. [In the case of the Souslin operation, for example, if $B \in (\mathscr{A} \times \mathscr{F})_S$ is written in the form

$$B = \bigcup_\nu \bigcap_p (A_{\nu_1 \ldots \nu_p} \times F_{\nu_1 \ldots \nu_p}),$$

show that

$$\mathrm{proj}_\Omega (B) = \bigcup_\nu \bigcap_p A'_{\nu_1 \ldots \nu_p}$$

where $A'_{\nu_1 \ldots \nu_p} = A_{\nu_1 \ldots \nu_p}$ if $F_{\nu_1 \ldots \nu_p} \neq \varnothing$ and $= \varnothing$ otherwise.]

Let $(\Omega, \mathscr{A}, P)$ be a complete probability space. Let $\mathscr{A}'$ be the σ-algebra generated by a compact class $\mathscr{F}$ of subsets of a set Ω'; we suppose moreover that for every $F \in \mathscr{F}$ one can find a sequence of F_n in $\mathscr{F}$ such that $F^c = \bigcup_n F_n$. Show that under these hypotheses

$$\mathrm{proj}_\Omega (\mathscr{A} \otimes \mathscr{A}') \subset \mathscr{A}.$$

(Use Problem I.5.4.)

III.2. TRANSITION PROBABILITIES AND PRODUCT PROBABILITIES

Definition III.2.1. GIVEN TWO MEASURABLE SPACES $(\Omega_1, \mathscr{A}_1)$ AND $(\Omega_2, \mathscr{A}_2)$, A TRANSITION PROBABILITY P_2^1 IS A MAPPING OF $\Omega_1 \times \mathscr{A}_2$ INTO $[0, 1]$ SUCH THAT:

(a) FOR EVERY $\omega_1 \in \Omega_1$, $P_2^1(\omega_1, \cdot)$ IS A PROBABILITY ON $(\Omega_2, \mathscr{A}_2)$;
(b) FOR EVERY $A_2 \in \mathscr{A}_2$, $P_2^1(\cdot, A_2)$ IS MEASURABLE ON $(\Omega_1, \mathscr{A}_1)$.

We at once note two special cases:

(1) A transition probability which is independent of ω_1 reduces to a probability on $(\Omega_2, \mathscr{A}_2)$;

(2) if for every $\omega_1 \in \Omega_1$ we take a probability $P_2^1(\omega_1, \cdot)$ concentrated at one point, say $p(\omega_1)$, of Ω_2, then P_2^1 is a transition probability if and only if p is a measurable mapping of $(\Omega_1, \mathscr{A}_1)$ into $(\Omega_2, \mathscr{A}_2)$.

We remark also that when condition (a) is satisfied, condition (b) is satisfied for every $A_2 \in \mathscr{A}_2$ as long as it is satisfied for every set in a semialgebra generating $\mathscr{A}_2$.

PROPOSITION III.2.1. *Let $(\Omega_1, \mathscr{A}_1)$ and $(\Omega_2, \mathscr{A}_2)$ be two measurable spaces; let P_1 be a probability on $(\Omega_1, \mathscr{A}_1)$ and P_2^1 a transition probability on $\Omega_1 \times \mathscr{A}_2$. Then there exists a unique probability P on*

$$(\Omega_1 \times \Omega_2, \mathscr{A}_1 \otimes \mathscr{A}_2)$$

such that

$$P(A_1 \times A_2) = \int_{A_1} P_1(d\omega_1)P_2^1(\omega_1, A_2) \qquad (A_1 \in \mathscr{A}_1, A_2 \in \mathscr{A}_2).$$

For every positive (quasi-integrable) r.r.v. *X defined on*

$$(\Omega_1 \times \Omega_2, \mathscr{A}_1 \otimes \mathscr{A}_2)$$

the function

$$Y(\omega_1) = \int_{\Omega_2} P_2^1(\omega_1, d\omega_2)X_{\omega_1}(\omega_2)$$

is defined everywhere (P_1–a.e.), is $\mathscr{A}_1$-measurable on Ω_1 and positive (quasi-integrable with respect to P_1). Moreover

$$\int_{\Omega_1 \times \Omega_2} X\, dP = \int_{\Omega_1} P_1(d\omega_1) \int_{\Omega_2} P_2^1(\omega_1, d\omega_2)X_{\omega_1}(\omega_2).$$

PROOF. By Proposition I.6.1 and the extension theorem of Section I.5, in order to prove the existence and uniqueness of P on the product space $(\Omega_1 \times \Omega_2, \mathscr{A}_1 \otimes \mathscr{A}_2)$ it suffices to show that P is σ-additive on the Boolean semialgebra of measurable rectangles in $\Omega_1 \times \Omega_2$. But, on the one hand it is obvious that $P(A_1 \times A_2) \in [0, 1]$. On the other hand, if we have

$$A_1 \times A_2 = \sum_I A_1^i \times A_2^i \quad (I \text{ countable})$$

in $\Omega_1 \times \Omega_2$ or, what is the same, if

$$1_{A_1}(\omega_1)1_{A_2}(\omega_2) = \sum_I 1_{A_1^i}(\omega_1)1_{A_2^i}(\omega_2)$$

on $\Omega_1 \times \Omega_2$, then, upon integrating over Ω_2 with respect to $P_2^1(\omega_1, \cdot)$ and interchanging $\int$ and $\sum$, we obtain

$$1_{A_1}(\omega_1)P_2^1(\omega_1, A_2) = \sum_I 1_{A_1^i}(\omega_1)\cdot P_2^1(\omega_1, A_2^i).$$

Integrating next over Ω_1 with respect to P_1, we have

$$P(A_1 \times A_2) = \sum_I P(A_1^i \times A_2^i),$$

which proves the σ-additivity of P.

For every positive r.r.v. X on $(\Omega_1 \times \Omega_2, \mathscr{A}_1 \otimes \mathscr{A}_2)$ and for every $\omega_1 \in \Omega_1$, the section X_{ω_1} is a positive r.r.v. on $(\Omega_2, \mathscr{A}_2)$ [Proposition III.1.2]; the function Y is thus well defined on Ω_1. Moreover the correspondence $X \to Y$ is linear, monotone and continuous in the sense that

$$X_n \uparrow X \Rightarrow Y_n \uparrow Y \qquad (n \uparrow \infty).$$

Consequently, to show that Y is $\mathscr{A}_1$-measurable for every r.r.v. $X \geqslant 0$, we have to show that Y is $\mathscr{A}_1$-measurable when X is an indicator, say 1_A where $A \in \mathscr{A}_1 \otimes \mathscr{A}_2$. But the class of sets A in $\Omega_1 \times \Omega_2$ for which $P_2^1(\omega_1, A_{\omega_1})$ is $\mathscr{A}_1$-measurable contains all the measurable rectangles and hence the Boolean algebra generated by these rectangles; on the other hand it is closed under the operations of monotone limits and consequently [Proposition I.4.2] contains $\mathscr{A}_1 \otimes \mathscr{A}_2$.

The expression $\int P_1(d\omega_1) \int P_2^1(\omega_1, d\omega_2)X_{\omega_1}(\omega_2)$ is thus meaningful for every positive r.r.v. on $\Omega_1 \times \Omega_2$ and defines a linear functional which is monotone and continuous in the sense of monotone increasing convergence. On the other hand it coincides with $\int X\, dP$ for the r.r.v.'s of the form $1_{A_1 \times A_2}(A_1 \in \mathscr{A}_1, A_2 \in \mathscr{A}_2)$; by arguments analogous to those preceding, it is thus equal to $\int X\, dP$ for every r.r.v. $X \geqslant 0$. We now observe that if the r.r.v. $X \geqslant 0$ is integrable with respect to P, the r.r.v. $Y \geqslant 0$ is integrable with respect to P_1 and is therefore a.s. finite on Ω_1; thus X_{ω_1} is $P_2^1(\omega_1, \cdot)$-integrable for almost every ω_1.

In the case where the r.r.v. X is not of fixed sign but is quasi-integrable (say $EX^+ < \infty$ for definiteness), the foregoing shows that $(X^+)_{\omega_1} = (X_{\omega_1})^+$ is $P_2^1(\omega_1, \cdot)$-integrable for almost every ω_1, and therefore that X_{ω_1} is quasi-integrable for almost every ω_1. Thus Y is defined a.e.; moreover Y^+ is P_1-integrable and therefore Y is quasi-integrable with respect to P_1. The last formula of the proposition is meaningful and true because it is so for X^+ and X^- separately. ▮

In the course of this proof, we have also proved the following result:

COROLLARY 1. *Under the conditions of the preceding proposition, the following implications hold for every* r.r.v. $X \geqslant 0$:

$$\int X\,dP = 0 \Leftrightarrow \int X_{\omega_1}\,dP_2^1(\omega_1,\cdot) = 0 \qquad \text{a.s. } on \quad (\Omega_1, \mathscr{A}_2, P_1)$$

$$\int X\,dP < \infty \Rightarrow \int X_{\omega_1}\,dP_2^1(\omega_1,\cdot) < \infty \qquad \text{a.s. } on \quad (\Omega_1, \mathscr{A}_1, P_1).$$

COROLLARY 2. *Under the hypotheses of Proposition* III.2.1, *there exists a unique probability* P_2 *on* $(\Omega_2, \mathscr{A}_2)$ *such that*

$$P_2(A_2) = \int_{\Omega_1} P_1(d\omega_1)P_2^1(\omega_1, A_2) \qquad (A_2 \in \mathscr{A}_2).$$

For every positive (*quasi-integrable*) r.r.v. Z *defined on* $(\Omega_2, \mathscr{A}_2, P_2)$ *the function* $Y(\omega_1) = \int P_2^1(\omega_1, d\omega_2)Z(\omega_2)$ *is defined* a.e., *is* $\mathscr{A}_1$*-measurable on* Ω_1 *and is positive* (*quasi-integrable with respect to* P_1). *Moreover*

$$\int Z\,dP_2 = \int P_1(d\omega_1)\,Y(\omega_1).$$

The special case of the preceding proposition obtained by assuming that the transition probability does not depend on the variable ω_1 carries the name *Fubini's theorem.*

PROPOSITION III.2.2. *Let* $(\Omega_1, \mathscr{A}_1, P_1)$ *and* $(\Omega_2, \mathscr{A}_2, P_2)$ *be two probability spaces. There exists one and only one probability* P *on* $(\Omega_1 \times \Omega_2, \mathscr{A}_1 \otimes \mathscr{A}_2)$ *such that*

$$P(A_1 \times A_2) = P_1(A_1)P_2(A_2) \qquad (A_1 \in \mathscr{A}_1, A_2 \in \mathscr{A}_2).$$

This probability is also denoted by $P_1 \times P_2$. *For every positive or quasi-integrable* r.r.v. X *defined on* $(\Omega_1 \times \Omega_2, \mathscr{A}_1 \otimes \mathscr{A}_2, P_1 \times P_2)$ *the following formula is both meaningful and valid:*

$$\int_{\Omega_1 \times \Omega_2} X\,dP = \int_{\Omega_1} P_1(d\omega_1) \int_{\Omega_2} P_2(d\omega_2) X_{\omega_1}(\omega_2)$$

$$= \int_{\Omega_2} P_2(d\omega_2) \int_{\Omega_1} P_1(d\omega_1) X_{\omega_2}(\omega_1).$$

The probability space $(\Omega_1 \times \Omega_2, \mathscr{A}_1 \otimes \mathscr{A}_2, P_1 \times P_2)$ *is called the product of* $(\Omega_1, \mathscr{A}_1, P_1)$ *and* $(\Omega_2, \mathscr{A}_2, P_2)$*; it is also denoted by*

$$(\Omega_1, \mathscr{A}_1, P_1) \times (\Omega_2, \mathscr{A}_2, P_2).$$

PROOF. It suffices to apply Proposition III.2.1 to the probability P_1 and the transition probability $\{P_2^1(\omega_1, A_2) = P_2(A_2)\}$ on the one hand, and to the probability P_2 and the transition probability

$$\{P_1^2(\omega_2, A_1) = P_1(A_1)\}$$

on the other hand, and to observe that the two probabilities P thus constructed on $(\Omega_1 \times \Omega_2, \mathscr{A}_1 \otimes \mathscr{A}_2)$ are equal.

COROLLARY 1. *A* r.r.v. *X defined on* $(\Omega_1 \times \Omega_2, \mathscr{A}_1 \otimes \mathscr{A}_2, P_1 \times P_2)$ *is* a.s. *zero if and only if almost all of its sections* X_{ω_1} *are* a.s. *zero in* $(\Omega_2, \mathscr{A}_2, P_2)$. *If the* r.r.v. *X defined on the product space is integrable, almost all of its sections* X_{ω_1} *are integrable.*

COROLLARY 2. *Let X be a* r.r.v. *on* $(\Omega_1 \times \Omega_2)$, *measurable with respect to the σ-algebra* $\overline{\mathscr{A}_1 \otimes \mathscr{A}_2}$, *the completion of* $\mathscr{A}_1 \otimes \mathscr{A}_2$ *for* $P_1 \times P_2$. *Almost all of the sections* X_{ω_1} *are then measurable with respect to the σ-algebra* $\overline{\mathscr{A}_2}$, *the completion of* $\mathscr{A}_2$ *for* P_2*; moreover the formula of Proposition* III.2.2 *remains valid if X is quasi-integrable* (*in particular if X is positive*).

PROOF. Let X' be an $\mathscr{A}_1 \otimes \mathscr{A}_2$-measurable r.r.v. such that $\{X' \neq X\}$ is negligible; then X'_{ω_1} is $\mathscr{A}_2$-measurable for every ω_1 and $\{X'_{\omega_1} \neq X_{\omega_1}\}$ is negligible in $(\Omega_2, \mathscr{A}_2, P_2)$ for almost all ω_1, from which the corollary follows. ▮

Complements and problems

III.2.1. With every r.r.v. X defined on $(\Omega, \mathscr{A}, P)$ with values in $[0, 1]$, we associate the subset $G_X = \{(\omega, x): 0 \leqslant x \leqslant X(\omega)\}$ of the product space $\Omega \times [0, 1]$. Show that G_X is measurable. [To this end, study the properties of the correspondence $X \to G_X$.] If λ denotes Lebesgue measure on $[0, 1]$, show that $\int X\, dP = [P \times \lambda](G_X)$.

III.2.2. The last formula of Proposition III.2.2 is false if instead of assuming, a priori, the existence of $\int X\, dP$, we had assumed that of

$$\int dP_1 \int dP_2\, X.$$

To show this, consider for example a positive nonintegrable r.r.v. Z on a space $(\Omega_1, \mathscr{A}_1, P_1)$ and define, on the product of this space with the discrete space $\{0, 1\}$ with both points having equal probability, the variable

$$X: X(\omega, 0) = Z(\omega), \qquad X(\omega, 1) = -Z(\omega).$$

III.2.3. **Formalism of statistical decision theory.**

Let $(\Omega, \mathscr{A})$, $(\Theta, \mathscr{T})$ and $(\Delta, \mathscr{D})$ be three measurable spaces representing respectively the space of observations, the space of parameters and the space of decisions. Let $P = \{P(\theta, A)\}$ be a transition probability relative to $(\Theta, \mathscr{T})$ and $(\Omega, \mathscr{A})$; the probability $P(\theta, \cdot)$ governs the observation ω in Ω when θ is the value (unknown to the observer) of the parameter. Let $W = \{W(\theta, \delta)\}$ be a real measurable function defined on $(\Theta, \mathscr{T}) \times (\Delta, \mathscr{D})$ representing the *loss* following a decision δ when θ is the value of the parameter.

A *strategy* (or decision rule) is a measurable mapping s of $(\Omega, \mathscr{A})$ into $(\Delta, \mathscr{D})$; it consists of deciding on $s(\omega)$ after having observed ω. A *random strategy* (r.s.) is a transition probability on $(\Omega, \mathscr{A})$ and $(\Delta, \mathscr{D})$, say $S = \{S(\omega, D)\}$; it involves choosing a decision in Δ with probability $S(\omega, \cdot)$ after having observed ω [a strategy is a random strategy for which $S(\omega, \cdot)$ is concentrated on $s(\omega)$]. A r.s. S entails a *mean loss* $\int_\Delta W(\theta, \delta)S(\omega, d\delta)$ which is a measurable function of (θ, ω), and a *risk*

$$R_S(\theta) = \int_\Omega P(\theta, d\omega) \int_\Delta W(\theta, \delta)S(\omega, d\delta)$$

which is a measurable function of θ.

A *partial order* called *preference* (μ-*preference*) is defined on the r.s.'s by setting $S \subset S'$ if $R_S(\cdot) \leqslant R_{S'}(\cdot)$ on Θ [if $R_S(\cdot) \leqslant R_{S'}(\cdot)$ almost everywhere on Θ for the probability μ defined on $(\Theta, \mathscr{T})$]. A r.s. S is said to be *admissible* (μ-*admissible*) if no other r.s. is strictly preferable (strictly μ-preferable) to it (that is, if $S' \subset S$ implies $S \subset S'$) or, what is equivalent, if there does not exist S' such that $R_{S'} \leqslant R_S$ on Θ and such that $R_{S'} \not\equiv R_S$ [such that $R_{S'} \leqslant R_S$ μ-almost everywhere and such that $\mu\{R_{S'} \neq R_S\} \neq 0$]. A Bayes r.s. S (for the probability μ) is a strategy which minimizes $\int \mu(d\theta)R_S(\theta)$ over the ensemble of r.s.'s; show that such a strategy is necessarily μ-admissible. A class $\mathscr{S}$ of r.s.'s is said to be (μ-) *complete* if for every $S \notin \mathscr{S}$ there is a strategy $S' \in \mathscr{S}$ which is (μ-) preferable to S; the class of admissible r.s.'s is complete by Zorn's lemma if the relation of preference is inductive. [Show that this is the case if (a) for every sequence $\cdots S_{n+1} \subset S_n \subset \cdots \subset S_1$ of r.s.'s there exists a r.s. S which is preferable to all the S_n, (b) there exists a countable subset Θ_0 of Θ such that $R_S(\Theta) \subset \overline{R_S(\Theta_0)}$ for every S.] Under certain hypotheses, one can show that the class of Bayes strategies is a complete class.

SPECIAL CASE I. We are interested in *testing the hypothesis* $\theta \in T$ against $\theta \notin T$ (T is given in $\mathscr{T}$); the space Δ reduces to two decisions δ_a and δ_r, to accept or reject the hypothesis $\theta \in T$; the loss function W equals 0 if the decision is correct and is positive if not. Specifying a strategy s (a r.s. S) is equivalent to specifying the *critical region* $\{s = \delta_r\}$ of Ω [the *critical function* q, which is a measurable mapping of $(\Omega, \mathscr{A})$ into [0, 1] such that $S(\cdot, \delta_r) = q(\cdot)$].

SPECIAL CASE II. We are interested in *estimating* the value $f(\theta)$ of a real measurable function f of the parameter; the space Δ is R [or a Borel set containing $f(\Theta)$]. Frequently the quadratic loss function

$$W(\theta, \delta) = w(\theta)[f(\theta) - \delta]^2$$

is used. A strategy s, that is, a r.r.v. on $(\Omega, \mathscr{A})$, is here called an *estimator* [it consists of estimating $f(\theta)$ by $s(\omega)$]. In the case of a quadratic loss function, or more generally a loss function which is convex in δ, show that the class of nonrandom strategies is complete. [In fact $s(\omega) = \int \delta S(\omega, d\delta)$ is preferable to S.]

III.3. INFINITE PRODUCTS OF MEASURABLE SPACES AND CANONICAL PROBABILITY SPACES ASSOCIATED WITH RANDOM FUNCTIONS

Given an arbitrary family $\{\Omega_t, t \in T\}$ of nonempty sets, we denote by $\prod_T \Omega_t$ their product, that is, the collection of families

$$\omega = \{\omega_t, t \in T\}$$

obtained when ω_t runs through Ω_t for every $t \in T$. In particular, when the spaces Ω_t are identical, say $\Omega = \Omega_t$ for every $t \in T$, the product $\prod_T \Omega_t$ is denoted by Ω^T and can be identified with the space of all mappings of T into Ω. Product spaces play a fundamental role in the study of random functions: if a "function" is represented at each instant t ($t \in T$) by a point (or state) ω_t in a space Ω_t, then the space $\prod_T \Omega_t$ is identified with the space of all the possible trajectories in the course of time T. Let us make it clear that in the present section we shall not make any special hypothesis concerning the set T (such hypotheses will enter only in the study of the "regularity" of a function); the interpretation of t as a time variable is, however, convenient, for this is most often the case in the applications (but not in all of them!). Similarly, the space Ω_t is most often identified with a discrete space or a Euclidean space and very frequently does not depend explicitly on t; nevertheless in this last case it is generally clearer not to suppress the index t in Ω_t in order to thus mark the instant t being considered.

The mapping $\omega \to \omega_s$ of $\prod_T \Omega_t$ into Ω_s is called the s-th *coordinate* and is frequently denoted by X_s, that is, $\omega_s = X_s(\omega)$; thus $X_s(\omega)$ is the state of the trajectory ω at the instant s. For every subset S of T, the *section* at $\omega_S = \{\omega_s, s \in S\}$ of a subset A of $\prod_T \Omega_t$ (of a function Z defined on $\prod_T \Omega_t$) is defined as the set $A_{\omega_S} = \{\{\omega_u, u \in S^c\} : \{\omega_t, t \in T\} \in A\}$ in $\prod_{S^c} \Omega_u$ (the function Z_{ω_S} defined on $\prod_{S^c} \Omega_u$ by $Z_{\omega_S}[\omega_{S^c}] = Z[\omega_S, \omega_{S^c}]$). A subset A of $\prod_T \Omega_t$ is called a *cylinder* with base B in $\prod_S \Omega_s$ if it is of the form $A = B \times \prod_{S^c} \Omega_u$; in order that a set A be a cylinder with base in $\prod_S \Omega_s$, it is necessary and sufficient that its sections $A_{\omega_{S^c}}$ not depend on ω_{S^c}; then $B = A_{\omega_{S^c}}$. A *rectangle* in $\prod_T \Omega_t$ is a subset of the form

$$\prod_T A_t = \{\omega : \omega_t \in A_t \quad (t \in T)\}$$

where we assume that the subsets A_t of Ω_t are different from Ω_t for only *finitely many* $t \in T$. Every section of a rectangle is again a rectangle.

PROPOSITION III.3.1. *Given a family $\{(\Omega_t, \mathscr{A}_t); t \in T\}$ of measurable spaces, the family of measurable rectangles $\prod_T A_t$ ($A_t \in \mathscr{A}_t$, $A_t = \Omega_t$ except for a finite number at most of t) is a Boolean semialgebra.*

This proposition is proved in the same way as was Proposition III.1.1, which it generalizes; note that the restriction "$A_t = \Omega_t$ except for a finite number at most of t" in the definition of a measurable rectangle is essential in this proof. The finite sums of disjoint measurable rectangles form (Proposition I.6.1) a Boolean algebra. The σ-algebra generated by this Boolean algebra is denoted by $\bigotimes_T \mathscr{A}_t$ and called the product σ-algebra of the $\mathscr{A}_t$ ($t \in T$); it is also the smallest σ-algebra of subsets of $\prod_T \Omega_t$ with respect to which all the coordinate mappings are measurable. Finally the measurable space $(\prod_T \Omega_t, \bigotimes_T \mathscr{A}_t)$ is called the product of the measurable spaces $(\Omega_t, \mathscr{A}_t)$. It is easily seen that if $\{S_i, i \in I\}$ is a partition of $S \subset T$, the product of the measurable spaces $(\prod_{S_i} \Omega_s, \bigotimes_{S_i} \mathscr{A}_s)$ ($i \in I$) is identical with the space $(\prod_S \Omega_s, \bigotimes_S \mathscr{A}_s)$.

Proposition III.3.2, applied to the measurable spaces $(\prod_S \Omega_s, \bigotimes_S \mathscr{A}_s)$ and $(\prod_{S^c} \Omega_u, \bigotimes_{S^c} \mathscr{A}_u)$ whose product is $(\prod_T \Omega_t, \bigotimes_T \mathscr{A}_t)$, permits one to assert that every section A_{ω_S} of a set A in $\bigotimes_T \mathscr{A}_t$ (or every section Z_{ω_S} of a r.r.v. Z on $\prod_T \mathscr{A}_t$) is measurable in $(\prod_{S^c} \Omega_u, \bigotimes_{S^c} \mathscr{A}_u)$. In particular, if A is a cylinder set in $\prod_T \Omega_t$ with base B in $\prod_S \Omega_s$, then A is measurable, that is, belongs to $\bigotimes_T \mathscr{A}_t$, if and only if the base B is measurable, that is, belongs to $\bigotimes_S \mathscr{A}_s$. By an abuse of notation which identifies the cylinders whose bases are in $\prod_S \Omega_s$ with their bases, we shall denote by $\bigotimes_S \mathscr{A}_s$ the σ-subalgebra of $\bigotimes_T \mathscr{A}_t$ consisting of the measurable cylinders with bases in $\prod_S \Omega_s$, that is, of the measurable sets in $\prod_T \Omega_t$ which do not depend on the coordinates ω_u ($u \in S^c$).

PROPOSITION III.3.2. *Let $\{(\Omega_t, \mathscr{A}_t); t \in T\}$ be a family of measurable spaces. Then, on the one hand, the union $\mathscr{B}$ of the σ-algebras $\bigotimes_S \mathscr{A}_s$ obtained when S runs through all finite subsets of T is a Boolean algebra which generates $\bigotimes_T \mathscr{A}_t$. On the other hand, the union of the σ-algebras $\bigotimes_S \mathscr{A}_s$ obtained when S runs through all countable subsets of T is identical with $\bigotimes_T \mathscr{A}_t$. The qualification "all finite (countable) subsets of T" may be replaced by "a family $\mathscr{F}$ of finite (countable) subsets of T such that every finite (countable) subset of T is contained in some member of $\mathscr{F}$."*

PROOF. The class $\mathscr{B}$ is closed under complementation since each of the σ-algebras $\bigotimes_S \mathscr{A}_s$ is; it is closed under intersection as well, for if $A_i \in \bigotimes_{S_i} \mathscr{A}_s$ for every $i \in I$, I finite, then also $A_i \in \bigotimes_S \mathscr{A}_s$, where $S = \bigcup_I S_i$ is finite, and $\bigcap_I A_i \in \bigotimes_S \mathscr{A}_s \subset \mathscr{B}$. Thus $\mathscr{B}$ is a Boolean algebra; it is clear that it generates $\bigotimes_T \mathscr{A}_t$, since $\mathscr{A}_s \subset \mathscr{B} \subset \bigotimes_T \mathscr{A}_t$ for every $s \in T$. The second part is proved in an analogous way on taking account of the fact that every countable union of countable sets is again countable. ∎

COROLLARY. *Every σ-subalgebra $\mathscr{B}$ of $\bigotimes_T \mathscr{A}_t$ of countable type is contained in a σ-algebra $\bigotimes_S \mathscr{A}_s$ for a subset $S \subset T$ which is countable. In particular, every measurable subset of $\prod_T \Omega_t$ and every* r.r.v. *defined on $(\prod_T \Omega_t, \bigotimes_T \mathscr{A}_t)$ depends only on a countable family of coordinates.*

To make a "function" defined on a family $\{(\Omega_t, \mathscr{A}_t); t \in T\}$ of measurable state spaces random, the method most often used is the following. For every n-tuple $(t_1, \ldots, t_n)$ of instants one assumes some probability law, say $P_{(t_1, \ldots, t_n)}$ for

$$(\omega_{t_1}, \ldots, \omega_{t_n}) = (X_{t_1}(\omega), \ldots, X_{t_n}(\omega)).$$

One then seeks to define a probability P on the measurable space $(\prod_T \Omega_t, \bigotimes_T \mathscr{A}_t)$ of trajectories, whose restrictions to the σ-algebras $\bigotimes_1^n \mathscr{A}_{t_i}$ of events which depend only on the coordinates $t_1, \ldots, t_n$ shall be equal to the given probabilities $P_{(t_1, \ldots, t_n)}$. It is evidently indispensable to define such an extension P of the $P_{(t_1, \ldots, t_n)}$ if one is interested in properties of the process depending on an infinity of instants, for example if one is interested in the limit or continuity properties of the function.

In order for the problem to be well formulated mathematically, we state the following preliminary result, whose verification is left to the reader.

PROPOSITION III.3.3. *Given a family of probabilities $P_{(t_1,\ldots,t_n)}$ defined on the finite products $(\prod_1^n \Omega_{t_i}, \bigotimes_1^n \mathscr{A}_{t_i})$ of some family $\{(\Omega_t, \mathscr{A}_t); t \in T\}$ of measurable spaces, the following compatibility condition is necessary and sufficient for the existence of a set function P defined on $(\Omega, \mathscr{B})$, where $\mathscr{B} = \bigcup [\bigotimes_1^n \mathscr{A}_{t_i}]$, whose restrictions to the σ-algebras $\bigotimes_1^n \mathscr{A}_{t_i}$ are the probabilities $P_{(t_1,\ldots,t_n)}$:*

If $T_1 \subset T_2$ are two finite subsets of T, the restriction of P_{T_2} to $\bigotimes_{T_1} \mathscr{A}_t$ equals P_{T_1}.

(REMARK. Sometimes the following condition is added to the preceding condition: if $(t_1', \ldots, t_n')$ is a permutation of $(t_1, \ldots, t_n)$, then $P_{(t_1',\ldots,t_n')}$ is obtained from $P_{(t_1,\ldots,t_n)}$ by the same permutation of coordinates. This condition in fact comes in when one defines the probabilities $P_{(t_1,\ldots,t_n)}$ for every ordered n-tuple of instants rather than, as we have done, for every finite family $(t_1, \ldots, t_n)$ in T.)

It is important to see clearly that the above compatibility condition does not imply that P is σ-additive on $\mathscr{B}$ (see Problem III.3.1), but only that it is additive. Only by imposing further condition upon the given objects is one able to obtain the σ-additivity of P on $\mathscr{B}$ and consequently, by applying the extension theorem of Section I.6, to extend P to a probability on $(\Omega, \mathscr{A})$ [in a unique way].

THEOREM. *Let $\{P_{(t_1,\ldots,t_n)}\}$ be a family of probabilities, defined on the finite product spaces of the family $\{(\Omega_t, \mathscr{A}_t); t \in T\}$ of measurable spaces, which satisfies the compatibility condition of Proposition* III.3.3. *If for every $t \in T$ there exists a compact subclass $\mathscr{C}_t$ of $\mathscr{A}_t$ such that $P_{(t)}(A) = \sup \{P_{(t)}(C); C \in \mathscr{C}_t, C \subset A\}$ for every $A \in \mathscr{A}_t$, then there exists a unique probability P on the product space $(\prod_T \Omega_t, \bigotimes_T \mathscr{A}_t)$ which extends each of the probabilities $P_{(t_1,\ldots,t_n)}$.*

PROOF. Let P be the additive set function defined from the family $\{P_{(t_1,\ldots,t_n)}\}$ as in Proposition III.3.3. By Proposition I.6.2, in order that P be σ-additive on the semialgebra $\mathscr{S}$ of measurable rectangles and hence be extendable to a probability on the σ-algebra $\bigotimes_T \mathscr{A}_t$, it suffices that there exist a compact subclass $\mathscr{C}$ of $\mathscr{S}$ such that $P(A) = \sup\{P(C); C \subset A, C \in \mathscr{C}\}$ for every $A \in \mathscr{S}$.

But the class $\mathscr{D}$ of measurable rectangles of the form $C \times \prod_{s \neq t} \Omega_s$, where C runs through $\mathscr{C}_t$ and t runs through T, is a compact class. In fact, every intersection of a countable family $\{C_i \times \prod_{s \neq t_i} \Omega_s, i \in I\}$ of such sets is of the form $\prod_T B_t$, where $B_t = \bigcap_{\{i:t_i = t\}} C_i$. If this intersection is empty, one of the sets B_t, say B_u, is empty; the compactness of the class $\mathscr{C}_u$ now implies the existence of a finite subset J of $\{i: t_i = u\}$ such that $\bigcap_J C_i = \varnothing$, therefore such that $\bigcap_J [C_i \times \prod_{s \neq u} \Omega_s] = \varnothing$. We have thus proved that the class $\mathscr{D}$ is compact and it follows that the class $\mathscr{C}$ of countable intersections of sets in $\mathscr{D}$ is again compact.

On the other hand, if A is a measurable rectangle with base $\prod_1^n A_{t_i}$ in $\prod_1^n \Omega_{t_i}$ and if $\epsilon > 0$, we choose C_i in $\mathscr{C}_{t_i}$ such that

$$C_i \subset A_{t_i}, \qquad P_{t_i}(A_{t_i}) \leqslant P_{t_i}(C_i) + \epsilon/n.$$

The set $C = \bigcap_i [C_i \times \prod_{t \neq t_i} \Omega_t]$ belongs to $\mathscr{C}$ and is contained in A; moreover, the subadditivity of P and the formula

$$A - C \subset \bigcup_i \left\{(A_{t_i} - C_i) \times \prod_{s \neq t_i} \Omega_s\right\}$$

imply that

$$P(A) - P(C) \leqslant \sum_i [P_{t_i}(A_{t_i}) - P_{t_i}(C_i)] \leqslant \epsilon.$$

Letting $\epsilon \to 0$, we obtain $P(A) = \sup\{P(C); C \in \mathscr{C}, C \subset A\}$, which completes the proof of the theorem. ∎

Proposition II.7.3 and the preceding theorem imply the following result.

COROLLARY. *Let $\{(\Omega_t, \mathscr{A}_t); t \in T\}$ be a family of Polish spaces and the σ-algebras of their Borel sets. For any compatible family $\{P_{(t_1, \ldots, t_n)}\}$ of probabilities defined on the finite products of $\{(\Omega_t, \mathscr{A}_t); t \in T\}$, there exists a unique probability P on $(\prod_T \Omega_t, \bigotimes_T \mathscr{A}_t)$ which extends each of the probabilities $P_{(t_1, \ldots, t_n)}$.*

This result applies, in particular, when the spaces $(\Omega_t, \mathscr{A}_t)$ are isomorphic to the extended real line $(\overline{R}, \overline{\mathscr{R}})$. In this case, the space $(\prod_T \Omega_t, \bigotimes_T \mathscr{A}_t, P)$ is called the *canonical probability space* of the real random function $X = \{X_t, t \in T\}$ whose "*temporal law*" is given by the family $\{P_{(t_1, \ldots, t_n)}\}$.

Complements and problems

*III.3.1. Let $(\Omega_0, \mathscr{A}_0, P_0)$ be a probability space in which there exists a sequence $\{\Omega_n, n \geq 1\}$ of subsets of Ω_0 such that $\Omega_n \downarrow \varnothing$, $P_0^*(\Omega_n) = 1$; we assume in addition that the diagonal in $(\Omega_0)^n$ is measurable in $(\Omega_0, \mathscr{A}_0)^n$. Let P_n be the trace of P_0 on $(\Omega_n, \mathscr{A}_n = \mathscr{A}_0 \cap \Omega_n)$ (Problem I.4.4) and let

$$P_{(1,\ldots,n)} = P_n \circ \varphi_n^{-1}$$

be the probability induced on $(\prod_1^n \Omega_m, \bigotimes_1^n \mathscr{A}_m)$ by P_n and the mapping $\varphi_n(x) = (x, \ldots, x)$ of Ω_n into $\prod_1^n \Omega_m$. Show that the family

$$\{P_{(1,\ldots,n)}, n \geq 1\}$$

of probabilities is a compatible family relative to the sequence of measurable spaces (Ω_n, A_n); nevertheless the measurable sets $\Delta_n = \{\omega: \omega_1 = \cdots = \omega_n\}$ of $(\prod_{m \geq 1} \Omega_m, \bigotimes_{m \geq 1} \mathscr{A}_m)$ have probabilities equal to 1 and form a sequence which decreases to $\varnothing$. Thus there cannot exist a probability on the product space $(\prod_{m \geq 1} \Omega_m, \bigotimes_{m \geq 1} \mathscr{A}_m)$ extending the compatible probabilities $P_{(1,\ldots,n)}$; *the compactness hypotheses in the statement of the theorem of this section are thus essential for the validity of the theorem.*

III.3.2. **Gaussian families.**

(a) Let T be an arbitrary nonempty set and let $\Gamma = \{\Gamma(s, t); s, t \in T\}$ be a symmetric and positive semi-definite kernel on $T \times T$ (Definition: $\Gamma(s, t) = \Gamma(t, s)$ for every $s, t \in T$; $\sum c_i c_j \Gamma(t_i, t_j) \geq 0$ for every choice of n, of $t_1, \ldots, t_n$ in T and of $c_1, \ldots, c_n$ in R). Then there exists a unique probability P on $(\Omega, \mathscr{A}) = (R, \mathscr{R})^T$ such that the induced probability law of every vector $(X_{t_1}, \ldots, X_{t_n})$ is the centered Gaussian law with covariance $\{\Gamma(t_i, t_j)\}$.

If H denotes the vector space of functions on T generated by the functions $\Gamma(s, \cdot)$, where s runs through T, show that the scalar product defined by the formula

$$\langle \sum_i c_i \Gamma(s_i, \cdot), \sum_j c_j' \Gamma(s_j', \cdot) \rangle = \sum_i \sum_j c_i c_j' \Gamma(s_i, s_j')$$

endows the space H with the structure of a separated pre-Hilbert space; this scalar product is characterized by the *self-reproducing* property:

$$\langle \Gamma(s, \cdot), \Gamma(t, \cdot) \rangle = \Gamma(s, t).$$

Show that the completed Hilbert space $\overline{H}$ is again a space of functions on T by establishing the following formula, which is valid for every $h \in \overline{H}$ and every $s \in T$: $\langle \Gamma(s, \cdot), h \rangle = h(s)$. Show next that the correspondence

$$\Gamma(s, \cdot) \leftrightarrow X_s$$

extends (uniquely) to an isometry of $\overline{H}$ into the space $L_2(\Omega, \mathscr{A}, P)$ and that the image $X(h)$ of $h \in \overline{H}$ is again a centered Gaussian r.r.v.; we thus have $E[X(h)X(h')] = \langle h, h' \rangle$.

(b)* If T is a compact interval of R with the Lebesgue measure, denoted by dt, and if the kernel Γ is continuous on $T \times T$, there exists (at least) one complete orthonormal sequence $\{f_n, n \geqslant 1\}$ of eigenfunctions of the integral operator Γ in the space $L_2(T, dt)$ such that $\int_T \Gamma(s, t) f_n(t)\, dt = \lambda_n f_n(s)$ for λ_n necessarily positive or zero; moreover these functions f_n are continuous on T (if $\lambda_n \neq 0$) and the series $\sum_n \lambda_n f_n(s) f_n(t)$ converges uniformly to $\Gamma(s, t)$ on $T \times T$ [theorems of Hilbert-Schmidt and Mercer]. Show that in this case the space $\overline{H}$ can be identified with the space of continuous functions h on T such that

$$\sum_n \lambda_n^{-1}\left(\int_T h(t) f_n(t)\, dt\right)^2 < \infty;$$

show also that

$$\langle h, h' \rangle = \sum_n \lambda_n^{-1} \int_T h(t) f_n(t)\, dt \int_T h'(t) f_n(t)\, dt.$$

[One first establishes that for every measure μ on T,

$$\Gamma_\mu = \int \Gamma(\cdot, t)\mu(dt)$$

is a function in $\overline{H}$ and $\langle \Gamma_\mu, h \rangle = \int_T \mu(dt) h(t)$; then one shows that $\{f_n; \lambda_n > 0\}$ is a complete orthogonal sequence in $\overline{H}$; one observes finally that $\sup |f_n| \leqslant C\lambda_n^{-1/2}$ for a constant C not depending on n.] The sequence

$$\{\tilde{X}_n = X(f_n); \lambda_n > 0\}$$

is a sequence of independent centered Gaussian r.r.v.'s with variances $E(\tilde{X}_n^2) = \lambda_n^{-1}$; express $X(h)$ and in particular the X_t $(t \in T)$ as functions of the $\tilde{X}_n$.

(c) If $T = R$, the kernel Γ is of the form

$$\Gamma(s, t) = \gamma(s - t) = \int \exp\,[2\pi i(s - t)u] F(du)$$

for a positive, bounded and symmetric measure F on R, if and only if Γ is continuous and depends only on $(s - t)$ [Bochner's theorem]. Show the existence of a unique isometry, say Φ, of the space $L_2^{\mathbf{C}}(R, F)$ (of equivalence classes of complex measurable functions whose absolute squares are F-integrable) onto the space $\overline{H}$ such that $\Phi[\exp(2\pi i t \cdot)] = \gamma(\cdot - t)$.

(d) If $\mathscr{F}'$ denotes the set of equivalence classes of sets of finite measure of a measure space $(E, \mathscr{F}, \mu)$ [see Section IV.1], show that there exists a centered Gaussian family $\{X(F), F \in \mathscr{F}'\}$ with covariance $\Gamma(F_1, F_2) = \mu(F_1 \cap F_2)$. Show that for every countable family $\{F_i, i \in I\}$ of pairwise disjoint classes, the sequence

$$\{X(F_i), i \in I\}$$

is independent and such that $\sum_I X(F_i) = X(\sum_I F_i)$ in $L_2(P)$ whenever $\mu(\sum_I F_i) < \infty$ (*Gaussian "measure"*). Show that, in the present case, the space $\overline{H}$ introduced above is isometric to the space $L_2(E, \mu)$ under the mapping which associates, with $f \in L_2(E, \mu)$, the set function $f \cdot \mu$ defined on $\mathscr{F}'$.

III.4. SEPARABILITY AND MEASURABILITY OF RANDOM FUNCTIONS

Definition III.4.1. GIVEN A PROBABILITY SPACE $(\Omega, \mathscr{A}, P)$ AND AN INTERVAL T OF THE EXTENDED REAL LINE (REPRESENTING TIME, IN GENERAL), A REAL RANDOM FUNCTION (r.r.f.) ON T IS A MAPPING X OF $T \times \Omega$ INTO THE EXTENDED REAL LINE $\bar{R} = [-\infty, +\infty]$ SUCH THAT FOR EVERY $t \in T$, THE SECTION X_t IS A r.r.v. ON $(\Omega, \mathscr{A}, P)$. EACH OF THE FUNCTIONS $X(\cdot, \omega)$ DEFINED ON T AS THE SECTION AT ω OF THE r.r.f. $X(\omega \in \Omega)$ IS CALLED A REALIZATION OR TRAJECTORY OF X.

This definition generalizes in a natural way the notion of a sequence of r.r.v.'s, for which T is the half-line N of positive integers. (We say of such a sequence that it is a r.r.f. on N.) It is nevertheless insufficient, as by not imposing any a priori restriction on the irregularities of the realizations $X(\cdot, \omega)$, it does not allow one to define or handle such important expressions as:

(a) $\{X_t \in B\ (t \in T)\} = \bigcap_{t \in T} X_t^{-1}(B)$, this set not being necessarily measurable since T is uncountable;

(b) $\int_T dt\, X(t, \omega)$, the trajectories of a r.r.f. not being necessarily measurable in the time variable;

(c) $\lim_{t \to s} X(t, \omega)$, these limits possibly not existing for any ω (or if they do exist, not being measurable).

The present section (as well as the following one) is devoted to the study of three types of hypotheses which give meaning, respectively, to each of the preceding expressions and to other analogous ones.

Definition III.4.2. A r.r.f. $X = \{X_t, t \in T\}$ IS SAID TO BE SEPARABLE IF THERE EXISTS A COUNTABLE SUBSET S OF T (CALLED A SEPARANT) AND A NEGLIGIBLE SET N SUCH THAT IF $\omega \notin N$, THEN FOR EVERY $u \in T$ ONE HAS

$$X_u(\omega) \in \bigcap_{I: I \ni u} \overline{X(IS, \omega)}.$$

Here, I varies in the class $\mathscr{I}$ of relatively open intervals in T and $\overline{X(IS, \omega)}$ denotes the closure in $\bar{R}$ of the set of values assumed by the trajectory $X(\cdot, \omega)$ as t varies in IS. It is clear from the definition that the property of being a separant is not disturbed by the addition of a countable set of points to S; thus a separant is non-unique.

In a manner of speaking, a r.r.f. X is separable if almost all of its trajectories are as "regular" as their restriction to a suitably chosen countable set S; the above definition asserts in fact that *for every* $\omega \notin N$ *and every* $u \notin S$ *there exists a sequence* $\{s_j\}$ *in* S, *converging to* u, *such that* $X(u, \omega) = \lim_j X(s_j, \omega)$. The following proposition shows the usefulness of the notion of separability.

PROPOSITION III.4.1. *Let* $X = \{X_t, t \in T\}$ *be a separable* r.r.f. *and let* S *be a countable subset of* T *which is a separant for* X. *Then there exists a negligible set* N *such that for every compact set* $K \subset \bar{R}$ *and every relatively open interval* $I \subset T$ *we have*

$$\{X_t \in K\,(t \in I)\} \triangle \{X_t \in K\,(t \in IS)\} \subset N.$$

Consequently, the sets $\{X_t \in K\,(t \in I)\}$ *are measurable and*

$$P(X_t \in K\,(t \in I)) = P(X_t \in K\,(t \in IS)) = \inf_{U \subset I} P(X_t \in K\,(t \in U)),$$

where U *runs through the countable subsets of* $I \subset T$. *Moreover, for every* $\omega \notin N$ *we have*

$$\sup_I X_t(\omega) = \sup_{IS} X_t(\omega); \qquad \inf_I X_t(\omega) = \inf_{IS} X_t(\omega)$$

$$\limsup_{t \to u} X_t(\omega) = \limsup_{\substack{t \in S \\ t \to u}} X_t(\omega); \qquad \liminf_{t \to u} X_t(\omega) = \liminf_{\substack{t \in S \\ t \to u}} X_t(\omega)$$

as well as the analogous formulas when $t \uparrow u$ *or* $t \downarrow u$. *Consequently, in all of these formulas the left sides define* r.r.v.'s.

PROOF. Under the conditions of Definition III.4.2, we have $X(u, \omega) \in \overline{X(IS, \omega)}$ if $u \in I \in \mathscr{I}$ and if $\omega \notin N$; hence $\overline{X(I, \omega)} = \overline{X(IS, \omega)}$ for every $I \in \mathscr{I}$ and every $\omega \notin N$. The first part of the proposition now follows from the equivalence $\omega \in \{X_t \in K\,(t \in T_0)\} \Leftrightarrow \overline{X(T_0, \omega)} \subset K$ which holds for every closed set $K \subset \bar{R}$, every $\omega \in \Omega$ and every subset T_0 of T. The second part of the proposition follows in turn from the fact that $\sup_{T_0} X_t(\omega)$ ($\inf_{T_0} X_t(\omega)$) is the right-most (left-most) point of the set $\overline{X(T_0, \omega)}$. ∎

The preceding shows the basic role played by a set S which is a separant for X. Such a set is necessarily dense in T (in fact $\bigcap_{I \ni u} \overline{X(IS, \omega)}$ is nonempty for every $\omega \notin N$ and every $u \in T$ only under this condition); the following proposition establishes the converse in a particularly important case.

PROPOSITION III.4.2. *Every* r.r.f. $X = \{X_t, t \in T\}$ *which is separable and continuous in probability* (*see Definition* III.5.1) *admits every countable dense subset* S *of* T *as a separant.*

To prove this, we shall make use of the following lemma.

LEMMA. *For every* r.r.f. $X = \{X_t, t \in T\}$ *which is continuous in probability and for every countable dense set* S *in* T, *there exists a family* $\{N^u, u \in T\}$ *of negligible sets such that*

$$X_u(\omega) \in \bigcap_{I \ni u} \overline{X(IS, \omega)}$$

for every $u \in T$, *if* $\omega \notin N^u$.

PROOF. For every $u \in T$ and every sequence $\{s_j\}$ in S which converges to u, we have $X_{s_j} \xrightarrow[P]{} X_u$; by Proposition II.4.3, there exists a subsequence $\{s_k'\}$ of $\{s_j\}$ such that if ω does not belong to a negligible set N^u, one has $X_{s_k'}(\omega) \to X_u(\omega)$ and hence $X_u(\omega) \in \bigcap_{I \ni u} \overline{X(IS, \omega)}$. ∎

PROOF OF THE PROPOSITION. Let S_0 be a countable subset of T which is a separant for X, and let N be a negligible set such that

$$X_u(\omega) \in \overline{X(IS_0, \omega)}$$

if $u \in I$ and if $\omega \notin N$. Now if S is a countable dense set in T, we have $\overline{X(IS_0, \omega)} \subset \overline{X(IS, \omega)}$ as long as $\omega \notin \bigcup_{S_0} N^u$, by the lemma. It follows that for every $u \in I \in \mathscr{I}$, $X_u(\omega) \in \overline{X(IS, \omega)}$ except possibly for ω belonging to the negligible set $N \cup (\bigcup_{S_0} N^u)$; S is thus a separant for X. ∎

The following proposition, which is due to J. L. Doob, constitutes the fundamental result on the separability of random functions. After the following general proof, we shall give at the end of this section a simpler proof of this result in the case of a r.r.f. which is continuous in probability.

Definition III.4.3. TWO r.r.f.'s X AND X' DEFINED ON THE SAME PROBABILITY SPACE AND THE SAME INTERVAL T OF $\bar{R}$ ARE SAID TO BE EQUIVALENT IF $X_t = X_t'$ a.s. FOR EVERY $t \in T$.

The equivalence of X and X' implies in particular that the probability laws of the vectors $(X_{t_1}, X_{t_2}, \ldots, X_{t_n})$ and $(X_{t_1}', X_{t_2}', \ldots X_{t_n}')$ are identical for any $t_1, t_2, \ldots, t_n$. One should be warned, on the other hand, that two equivalent r.r.f.'s may have no trajectory in common: it does not in fact follow, from the assumption that the sets

$$\{\omega\colon X_t(\omega) \neq X'_t(\omega)\}$$

are negligible for every $t \in T$, that the set $\{\omega\colon X_t(\omega) \neq X'_t(\omega)$ for at least one $t \in T\}$ is negligible, nor even that it is different from Ω!

PROPOSITION III.4.3. *For any* r.r.f. $X = \{X_t, t \in T\}$ *defined on* $(\Omega, \mathscr{A}, P)$ *there exists a random function* $\tilde{X} = \{\tilde{X}_t, t \in T\}$, *defined on the same probability space, which is separable and equivalent to* X.

To prove this result we shall make use of the following lemma, which the reader can compare with the lemma following Proposition III.4.2.

LEMMA. *For every* r.r.f. $X = \{X_t, t \in T\}$ *there exists a countable subset* S *of* T *and a family* $\{N^u, u \in T\}$ *of negligible sets such that for every* $u \in T$, $X_u(\omega) \in \bigcap_{I \ni u} \overline{X(IS, \omega)}$ *if* $\omega \notin N^u$.

PROOF. The preceding relations, which can also be written as

$$X_u(\omega) \in \overline{X(IS, \omega)} \quad \text{if} \quad \omega \notin N^u \quad \text{and if} \quad u \in I \in \mathscr{I},$$

are equivalent to

$$\{X_t \in K \quad (t \in IS)\} \subset \{X_u \in K\} \bigcup N^u \qquad (u \in I \in \mathscr{I},\ K \text{ compact}).$$

It is in this form that we shall prove them.

For every $I \in \mathscr{I}$ and every $K \in \mathscr{K}$ (where $\mathscr{K}$ is the class of compact sets in $\bar{R}$) let $S_{I,K}$ be a countable subset of I for which the infimum

$$\inf_U P(X_t \in K \quad (t \in U))$$

is attained, where U runs through the countable subsets of I; the set

$$N^u_{I,K} = \{X_t \in K \quad (t \in S_{I,K})\} \bigcap \{X_u \notin K\}$$

is then negligible for every $u \in I$.

Let $\mathscr{I}_0$ be a countable subclass of $\mathscr{I}$ such that every $I \in \mathscr{I}$ is the union of those members of $\mathscr{I}_0$ which it contains; we can, for example, take for $\mathscr{I}_0$ the class of all open subintervals of T with rational endpoints. Similarly let $\mathscr{K}_0$ be a countable subclass of $\mathscr{K}$ such that every $K \in \mathscr{K}$ is the intersection of all those members of $\mathscr{K}_0$ which contain it. We set

$S = \bigcup S_{I_0,K_0}$ and $N^u = \bigcup N^u_{I_0,K_0}$, taking the unions over $\mathscr{I}_0 \times \mathscr{K}_0$, so that S is again a countable subset of T and the N^u $(u \in T)$ are again negligible sets. It now follows from the formulas

$$\{X_t \in K \quad (t \in IS)\} \subset \bigcap_{I_0 \subset I} \bigcap_{K_0 \supset K} \{X_t \in K_0 \quad (t \in S_{I_0,K_0})\}$$

$$\{X_u \in K\} = \bigcap_{K_0 \supset K} \{X_u \in K_0\},$$

and the definition of the sets $N^u_{I_0,K_0}$ and N^u that

$$\{X_t \in K \quad (t \in IS)\} \subset \{X_u \in K\} \bigcup N^u \qquad (u \in I \in \mathscr{I}, K \in \mathscr{K}). \quad \blacksquare$$

PROOF OF PROPOSITION III.4.3. We use the preceding lemma to choose a mapping $\tilde{X}$ of $T \times \Omega$ into $\bar{R}$ such that $\tilde{X}(u, \omega) = X(u, \omega)$ if $u \in S$ or if $\omega \notin N^u$, and $\tilde{X}(u, \omega) \in \bigcap_{I \ni u} \overline{X(IS, \omega)}$ if $u \notin S$ and $\omega \in N^u$; such a mapping always exists since the set $\bigcap_{I \ni u} \overline{X(IS, \omega)}$ cannot be empty for any $u \in T$ and $\omega \in \Omega$, being the intersection of a decreasing generalized sequence of nonempty compact sets. It is clear that $\tilde{X}_t = X_t$ a.s. for every $t \in T$ and hence that $\tilde{X}$ is a r.r.f. As $\tilde{X}_s = X_s$ on Ω if $s \in S$, we have $\overline{\tilde{X}(IS, \omega)} = \overline{X(IS, \omega)}$ for every $I \in \mathscr{I}$, $\omega \in \Omega$. Moreover, if $u \in I$, $\tilde{X}_u(\omega)$ belongs to this set; this is evident if $u \in S$ and follows from the choice of N^u $(\tilde{X})$ if $u \notin S$ and $\omega \notin N^u$ $(u \notin S$ and $\omega \in N^u)$. We have thus proved that $\tilde{X}$ is a separable r.r.f. and that S is a separant for $\tilde{X}$. $\blacksquare$

In the particular case where the r.r.f. X has been constructed by the method of product spaces (Section III.3), the preceding theorem admits the following variant, whose advantage is that it modifies the r.r.f. X only by a restriction of its domain of definition, and therefore preserves the interpretation of the X_t as coordinates of the space Ω.

PROPOSITION III.4.4. *Let P be a probability defined on*

$$(\Omega, \mathscr{A}) = (\bar{R}, \overline{\mathscr{R}})^T$$

and let X be the r.r.f. *on T whose sections at t are the coordinate mappings of $(\Omega, \mathscr{A})$. Then there exists a subset $\tilde{\Omega}$ of Ω with outer probability $P^*(\tilde{\Omega}) = 1$, such that the restriction of X to the trace probability space*

$$(\tilde{\Omega}, \tilde{\Omega} \cap \mathscr{A}, P(\cdot) = P^*(\tilde{\Omega} \cap \cdot))$$

is a separable r.r.f.

(The precise definition of a trace probability space was given in Problem I.4.4.)

PROOF. Let $\tilde{X}$ be a r.r.f. defined, starting from X, on $(\Omega, \mathscr{A}, P)$ as in the proof of the preceding proposition; we suppose in addition that the sets N^u have been chosen exactly equal to the complements of the sets on which $X(u, \cdot) \in \bigcap_{I \ni u} \overline{X(IS, \cdot)}$, which is evidently permissible. We now set $\tilde{\Omega} = \{\omega: X(\cdot, \omega) = \tilde{X}(\cdot, \omega) \text{ on } T\}$; to show that the outer probability of $\tilde{\Omega}$ equals 1, we have to show that every measurable subset A of $(\Omega, \mathscr{A})$ containing $\tilde{\Omega}$ has probability 1.

A measurable subset A of $(\Omega, \mathscr{A})$ depends only on a countable family of coordinates (Proposition III.3), say T_A. The hypothesis $\tilde{\Omega} \subset A$ implies that $\{\omega: X(\cdot, \omega) = \tilde{X}(\cdot, \omega) \text{ on } T_A\} \subset A$. In fact, by construction the trajectory $\tilde{\omega} = \{\tilde{X}(\cdot, \omega)\}$ of Ω does not belong to any one of the sets N^u; it therefore belongs to $\tilde{\Omega}$ and a fortiori to A; if moreover ω is such that $X(\cdot, \omega) = \tilde{X}(\cdot, \omega)$ on T_A, that is, if ω and $\tilde{\omega}$ coincide on T_A, then $\omega \in A$. As $\tilde{X}(t, \cdot) = X(t, \cdot)$ a.s. for every t and T_A is countable, we indeed have $P(A) = 1$.

On the other hand, it is clear that on $\tilde{\Omega}$, the r.r.f. $X = \tilde{X}$ is separable since the r.r.f. $\tilde{X}$ is separable on the entire space Ω. ∎

Definition III.4.4. LET $(T, \mathscr{T})$ BE AN INTERVAL OF $\bar{R}$ WITH THE σ-ALGEBRA $\mathscr{T} = T \cap \bar{\mathscr{R}}$ OF ITS BOREL SUBSETS AND LET $(\Omega, \mathscr{A}, P)$ BE A PROBABILITY SPACE. A MEASURABLE MAPPING X OF THE PRODUCT SPACE $(T \times \Omega, \mathscr{T} \otimes \mathscr{A})$ INTO $(\bar{R}, \bar{\mathscr{R}})$ IS CALLED A MEASURABLE r.r.f.

By Proposition III.1.2 such a mapping is effectively a r.r.f. in the sense of Definition III.4.1; the preceding terminology is thus justified. Besides, Proposition III.2.2 shows that for every probability λ on $(T, \mathscr{T})$, the following formula has a precise meaning as long as X is quasi-integrable (in particular, positive) on the product space $(T \times \Omega, \mathscr{T} \otimes \mathscr{A}, \lambda \times P)$:

$$E\left(\int_T \lambda(dt) X_t\right) = \int_T \lambda(dt) E(X_t).$$

This result is constantly used in probability theory.

THEOREM. *Let* $X = \{X_t, t \in T\}$ *be a* r.r.f. *defined and continuous in probability on the real interval* T. *Then there exists a* r.r.f. $\tilde{X}$, *defined on the same probability space, which is equivalent to* X *and separable and measurable.*

PROOF. We shall first suppose that the interval T is compact, say $T = [t_l, t_r]$, and use the hypothesis of the continuity in probability of X in the following form (see Proposition III.5.1):

$$\sup_{|t-s|<h} P(|X_t - X_s| > \epsilon) \downarrow 0 \quad \text{as} \quad h \downarrow 0.$$

For every integer $n > 0$ we choose a finite increasing sequence in T, say $t_0^n = t_l < t_1^n < \cdots < t_{k_n}^n = t_r$ such that $P(|X_u - X_v| > n^{-1}) < 2^{-n}$ if u and v belong to the same interval $[t_{i-1}^u, t_i^n]$; without loss of generality we may suppose that $\{t_i^n\} \subset \{t_j^{n+1}\}$ for every n and that the countable set S consisting of all the t_i^n is dense in T. We define a sequence $\{X^n, n > 0\}$ of mappings of $T \times \Omega$ into $\bar{R}$ by:

$$X^n(t, \omega) = X(t_i^n, \omega) \qquad \text{if} \qquad t_i^n \leqslant t < t_{i+1}^n.$$

These mappings are obviously measurable r.r.f.'s. Therefore the inequality $\sum_n P(|X_t - X_t^n| > n^{-1}) < \sum_n 2^{-n} < \infty$, which holds for every $t \in T$, implies that $\limsup_{n\to\infty} \{|X_t - X_t^n| > n^{-1}\} \underset{\text{a.s.}}{=} \varnothing$, and therefore that the limit $\lim \text{a.s.}_{n\to\infty} X_t^n$ exists and equals X_t a.s. for every $t \in T$. It follows that the mapping Y of $T \times \Omega$ into $\bar{R}$ defined by

$$Y(t, \omega) = \limsup_{n\to\infty} X^n(t, \omega)$$

is a measurable r.r.f. with the same temporal law as the r.r.f. X.

To conclude the proof of the theorem when T is compact, it remains to show that the r.r.f. Y is separable. By the definition of the X^n and of Y we have $Y_t = X_t$ for every $t \in S$; on the other hand, for every $t \in T$ and on all of Ω, Y_t is the limit superior of $\{X_{t^{(n)}}\}$ for a sequence $\{t^{(n)} = t_{i_n}^n\}$ which increases to t and whose values lie in S. It follows that Y satisfies the relations of Definition III.4.2 of separability (with $N = \varnothing$).

Finally, it is simple to extend the preceding argument to the case where T is not compact. In this case we choose an increasing sequence $\{T_n\}$ of compact intervals tending to T and define, as above, a r.r.f. X_n on $T_n \times \Omega$. The r.r.f. $Y = \limsup_{n\to\infty} X_n$ is then defined on all of the space $T \times \Omega$ and has the desired properties. ∎

Complements and problems

III.4.1. Show that a r.r.f. $X = \{X_t, t \in T\}$ is separable if and only if for every relatively open interval I in T and every compact set K in $\bar{R}$ the set

$$\{X_t \in K \quad (t \in I)\}$$

is measurable and has probability equal to $\inf_U P[X_t \in K\,(t \in U)]$, where U runs through the countable subsets of I. [To show that this condition is sufficient, use the argument of the lemma of Proposition III.4.3, taking the $N^u_{I,K}$ independent of u.]

III.5. CONTINUITY OF REAL RANDOM FUNCTIONS

Definition III.5.1. A r.r.f. $X = \{X_t, t \in T\}$ IS SAID TO BE CONTINUOUS IN PROBABILITY AT A POINT $s \in T$ IF X_s IS a.s. FINITE AND

$$\lim_{t \to s} P(|X_t - X_s| > \epsilon) = 0$$

FOR EVERY $\epsilon > 0$. IT IS SAID TO BE CONTINUOUS IN PROBABILITY ON T IF IT IS CONTINUOUS IN PROBABILITY AT EVERY POINT OF T.

A SEPARABLE r.r.f. $X = \{X_t, t \in T\}$ IS SAID TO BE CONTINUOUS a.s. AT A POINT $s \in T$ IF THE SET $N^s = \{X_s = \lim_{t \to s} X_t\}^c$ OF TRAJECTORIES WHICH ARE DISCONTINUOUS AT s IS NEGLIGIBLE. IT IS SAID TO BE CONTINUOUS a.s. ON T, IF IT IS CONTINUOUS a.s. AT EVERY POINT OF T.

A SEPARABLE r.r.f. $X = \{X_t, t \in T\}$ IS SAID TO HAVE a.s. CONTINUOUS TRAJECTORIES IF THE SET N OF ITS TRAJECTORIES WHICH ARE DISCONTINUOUS ON T IS NEGLIGIBLE.

It is clear that every separable r.r.f. which is continuous a.s. at a point s (respectively on T) is continuous in probability at s (respectively on T), but that the converse is false. If the separable r.r.f. X is not continuous a.s. at the point s, that is, if $P(N^s) > 0$, one says that s is a *fixed discontinuity* of X. Since we have $N = \bigcup_T N^s$ in the notation of the definitions, we see immediately that a r.r.f., almost all of whose trajectories are continuous, is necessarily continuous a.s. on T; however, the converse is false since it is not sufficient, for N to be negligible, that the N^s $(s \in T)$ be negligible. A simple and typical counterexample is furnished by the following r.r.f.:

Let P be the Lebesgue probability on the real interval $\Omega = (0, 1)$ and let X be the r.r.f. defined on $T = (0, 1)$ and Ω by

$$X(t, \omega) = 0 \quad \text{if} \quad t < \omega, \quad = 1 \quad \text{if} \quad t \geqslant \omega.$$

Each of the trajectories $X(\cdot, \omega)$ of this r.r.f. is continuous except at the point $t = \omega$; hence $N^t = \{t\}$ is negligible, but $N = \Omega$. The discontinuity at the point $t(\omega) = \omega$ of the r.r.f. of this example is called a *moving discontinuity*.

A CRITERION FOR CONTINUITY a.s. *In order that the separable* r.r.f. $X = \{X_t, t \in T\}$ *be continuous* a.s. *at the point* $s \in T$, *it is necessary and sufficient that*

$$\lim_{h \downarrow 0} \downarrow P[\sup_{t:|t-s|<h} |X_t - X_s| > \epsilon] = 0 \qquad \textit{for every} \quad \epsilon > 0.$$

PROOF. Indeed, in order that $X_t \xrightarrow[\text{a.s.}]{} X_s$, it is necessary and sufficient that $Z_h = \sup_{t:|t-s|<h} |X_t - X_s| \xrightarrow[\text{a.s.}]{} 0$ when $h \downarrow 0$; but the family $\{Z_h\}$ of positive r.r.v.'s decreases with h, and hence $\lim_{h \downarrow 0} \downarrow Z_h \underset{\text{a.s.}}{=} 0$ if and only if

$$P(Z_h > \epsilon) \downarrow 0 \qquad \text{as} \quad h \downarrow 0,$$

for every $\epsilon > 0$. ∎

PROPOSITION III.5.1. *If* $X = \{X_t, t \in T\}$ *is a* r.r.f. *defined on a compact interval* T *of* R, *the various types of continuity of* X *on* T *admit the following necessary and sufficient conditions, assuming in* (b) *and* (c) *that* X *is separable:*

(a) *continuity in probability on* T: $\sup_{|t-s|<h} P[|X_t - X_s| > \epsilon] \downarrow 0$,
(b) *continuity* a.s. *on* T: $\sup_s P[\sup_{t:|t-s|<h} |X_t - X_s| > \epsilon] \downarrow 0$.
(c) a.s. *continuous trajectories on* T: $P[\sup_{|t-s|<h} |X_t - X_s| > \epsilon] \downarrow 0$.

In these criteria $\epsilon > 0$ *is arbitrarily small,* s *and* t *vary in* T *as indicated, and the convergences hold as* $h \downarrow 0$.

PROOF. The reader can easily verify that these criteria are sufficient; their necessity follows from the following uniform continuity arguments.

If the r.r.f. X is continuous in probability on T, then for every fixed $\epsilon, \eta > 0$ and every $u \in T$ there exists an open interval I_u of R, centered on u, such that $\sup_{t \in I_u} P(|X_t - X_u| > \epsilon) < \eta$. Let $\{I_{u_1}, \ldots, I_{u_n}\}$ be a finite family of such intervals covering T and let h be a positive constant such that every interval $(s - h, s + h)$, $s \in T$, is contained in one of the I_{u_i}. Then it follows from

$$\{|X_t - X_s| > 2\epsilon\} \subset \{|X_t - X_u| > \epsilon\} \cup \{|X_s - X_u| > \epsilon\}$$

that the inequality

$$P[|X_t - X_s| > 2\epsilon] \leqslant 2\eta$$

holds as long as $|t - s| < h$. The criterion is deduced from this by letting η tend to 0.

If the r.r.f. X is continuous a.s. on T, then for every $\epsilon, \eta > 0$ and every $u \in T$ there exists an open interval I_u of R, centered at u, such that

$$P[\sup_{t \in I_u} |X_t - X_u| > \epsilon] < \eta.$$

Let $\{I_{u_1}, \ldots, I_{u_n}\}$ be a finite family of such intervals which covers T and let h be a positive constant such that every interval $(s - h, s + h)$, $s \in T$, is contained in some I_{u_i}. Then it follows from the triangle inequality

$$|X_t - X_s| \leqslant |X_t - X_u| + |X_s - X_u|$$

that

$$\sup_{t:|t-s|<h} |X_t - X_s| \leqslant 2 \sup_{t \in I_u} |X_t - X_u| \qquad \text{if} \qquad (s - h, s + h) \subset I_u$$

and hence $P[\sup_{t:|t-s|<h} |X_t - X_s| > 2\epsilon] < \eta$ for every $s \in T$. The criterion is deduced from this by letting η tend to 0.

Since every continuous function on T is uniformly continuous on T, a r.r.f. X which has a.s. continuous trajectories on T is such that

$$Z_h = \sup_{|t-s|<h} |X_t - X_s| \downarrow 0 \quad \text{a.s.} \qquad \text{as} \quad h \downarrow 0;$$

hence $P(Z_h > \epsilon) \downarrow 0$ for every $\epsilon > 0$ as $h \downarrow 0$. ∎

Proposition III.5.2. *Each of the two conditions below is sufficient to imply that the separable* r.r.f. *X defined on a compact interval T of R has* a.s. *continuous trajectories on T:*

(a) *for every $\epsilon > 0$*

$$\frac{1}{h} \sup_s P[\sup_{t:|t-s|<h} |X_s - X_t| > \epsilon] \to 0$$

as $h \downarrow 0$.

(b) *There exist two positive nondecreasing functions defined on an interval $(0, \delta)$, say $\epsilon(\cdot)$ and $\eta(\cdot)$, such that on the one hand*

$$\int_0^\delta \epsilon(h) \frac{dh}{h} < \infty, \qquad \int_0^\delta \eta(h) \frac{dh}{h^2} < \infty$$

and on the other

$$P[|X_{t+h} - X_t| \geqslant \epsilon(h)] \leqslant \eta(h) \qquad \textit{for every} \quad t \in T.$$

Proof. To lighten the notation we shall suppose that $T = [0, 1]$. For every integer $n \geqslant 1$ we set

$$Y_u^m = \sup_{m/n \leqslant s \leqslant (m+2)/n} |X_s - X_{m/n}|$$

when $0 \leqslant m < n$; then hypothesis (a) implies that

$$P(\sup_m Y_n^m > \epsilon) \leqslant \sum_m P(Y_n^m > \epsilon) \leqslant n \sup_m P(Y_n^m > \epsilon) \to 0$$

$$(n \to \infty, \epsilon > 0).$$

On the other hand, if u, v are two points of T such that $|u - v| < 1/n$, there exists at least one m such that $m/n \leqslant u \leqslant (m+2)/n$, $m/n \leqslant v \leqslant (m+2)/n$ and consequently such that $|X_u - X_v| \leqslant 2Y_n^m$; it follows that

$$\sup_{|u-v|<1/n} |X_u - X_v| \leqslant 2 \sup_m Y_n^m,$$

and therefore that $P(\sup_{|u-v|<1/n} |X_u - X_v| > \epsilon) \to 0$ as $n \to \infty$, for every $\epsilon > 0$.

(b) For every integer $m \geqslant 0$ we set

$$Z_m = \sup_{0 \leqslant k < 2^m} |X_{(k+1)2^{-m}} - X_{k2^{-m}}| \geqslant 0;$$

hypothesis (b) implies, first of all, that

$$P[Z_m \geqslant \epsilon(2^{-m})] \leqslant \sum_{0 \leqslant k < 2^m} P[|X_{(k+1)2^{-m}} - X_{k2^{-m}}| \geqslant \epsilon(2^{-m})] \leqslant 2^m \eta(2^{-m}).$$

Proposition II.4.2 and the inequalities

$$\sum_{m>n} \epsilon(2^{-m}) \leqslant \frac{1}{\log 2} \int_0^{2^{-n}} \epsilon(h) \frac{dh}{h} < \infty,$$

$$\sum_{m>n} 2^m \eta(2^{-m}) \leqslant \int_0^{2^{-n}} \eta(h) \frac{dh}{h^2} < \infty,$$

which are obtained by breaking up the interval $(0, 2^{-n})$ into the intervals $(2^{-(m+1)}, 2^{-m})$, show next that $\sum_m Z_m < \infty$ a.s.; more precisely, there exists a r.v. N with positive integer values, and defined a.s., such that

$$\sum_{m>n} Z_m(\omega) \leqslant \sum_{m>n} \epsilon(2^{-m}) \qquad \text{if} \qquad n \geqslant N(\omega).$$

We note on the other hand that hypothesis (b) implies that the r.r.f. X is continuous in probability (for, $\epsilon(h) \to 0$, $\eta(h) \to 0$ if $h \to 0$); the set S of real numbers t of the form $t = k2^{-n}$ (k, n integers $\geqslant 0$; $k < 2^n$) is dense in [0, 1] and is therefore a separant for the r.r.f. X; it follows that

$$\sup_{|t-s| \leqslant h} |X_t - X_s|$$

does not change when s and t are restricted to belong to S. If $t \in S$ and if k is an integer such that $|t - k2^{-n}| < 2^{-n}$ for a given n, we can write $t = k2^{-n} \pm \sum_{n+1}^{n'} \tau_m 2^{-m}$ with $n' \geqslant n$ and $\tau_m = 0$ or 1; repeated application of the triangle inequality then shows that

$$|X_t - X_{k2^{-n}}| \leqslant \sum_{n+1}^{n'} Z_m \leqslant \sum_{m>n} Z_m.$$

If s and t belong to S and if $|t - s| < 2^{-n}$, there exists an integer k such that $|s - k2^{-n}| < 2^{-n}$, $|t - k2^{-n}| < 2^{-n}$; it follows that

$$|X_t - X_s| \leqslant |X_t - X_{k2^{-n}}| + |X_s - X_{k2^{-n}}| \leqslant 2 \sum_{m>n} Z_m.$$

We have thus shown that

$$\sup_{|t-s|<2^{-n}} |X_t - X_s| \leqslant 2 \sum_{m>n} Z_m \xrightarrow[\text{a.s.}]{} 0 \qquad (n \to \infty),$$

that is, the continuity of almost all of the trajectories of X. ∎

A more precise result can be obtained. If $h > 0$ and if n is the integer such that $h/2 \leqslant 2^{-n} < h$, then for every trajectory such that $h \leqslant 2^{-N(\omega)}$ we have

$$\sup_{|t-s|<h/2} |X_t - X_s| \leqslant \sup_{|t-s|<2^{-n}} |X_t - X_s| \leqslant 2 \sum_{m>n} Z_m$$

$$\leqslant \frac{2}{\log 2} \int_0^{2^{-n}} \epsilon(u)\, \frac{du}{u} \leqslant \frac{2}{\log 2} \int_0^h \epsilon(u)\, \frac{du}{u}.$$

Since $\sup_{|t-s|<h} |X_t - X_s| \leqslant 2 \sup_{|t-s|<h/2} |X_t - X_s|$, we obtain the following corollary on setting $H(\omega) = 2^{-N(\omega)}$.

Corollary. *Under the conditions of hypothesis* (b) *of the preceding proposition, there exists a* r.r.v. H a.s. *strictly positive such that*

$$\sup_{|t-s|<h} |X_t(\omega) - X_s(\omega)| \leqslant \left(\frac{4}{\log 2}\right) \int_0^h \epsilon(u)\, \frac{du}{u} \qquad \textit{if} \qquad h \leqslant H(\omega).$$

By way of an application, we shall derive from the preceding results the following proposition, due to Kolmogorov.

Proposition III.5.3. *If the separable* r.r.f. X *defined on a compact interval T of R is such that*

$$E|X_{t+h} - X_t|^\alpha \leqslant Ch^{1+\beta}$$

for three strictly positive constants α, β, C, then for every constant γ such that $\gamma < \beta/\alpha$ one has

$$\frac{1}{h^\gamma} \sup_{|t-s|<h} |X_t - X_s| \xrightarrow[\text{a.s.}]{} 0 \qquad (h \downarrow 0).$$

In particular, almost all of the trajectories of X are continuous.

PROOF. For any constants $c > 0$ and γ such that $0 < \gamma < \beta/\alpha$, the functions $\epsilon(h) = ch^{\gamma}$ and $\eta(h) = Cc^{-\alpha}h^{1+(\beta-\alpha\gamma)}$ satisfy hypothesis (b) of Proposition III.5.5; to this end we observe that

$$P[|X_{t+h} - X_t| > ch^{\gamma}] \leqslant (ch^{\gamma})^{-\alpha}E(|X_{t+h} - X_t|^{\alpha}) \leqslant (Cc^{-\alpha})h^{1+(\beta-\gamma\alpha)}$$

Since

$$\int_0^h \epsilon(u)\frac{du}{u} = \frac{c}{\gamma}h^{\gamma},$$

the corollary above shows that

$$\frac{1}{h^{\gamma}} \sup_{|t-s|<h} |X_t - X_s| \leqslant c\frac{4}{\gamma \log 2}$$

if h is sufficiently small; the proposition follows from this, as c can be chosen arbitrarily small. ▮

Complements and problems

III.5.1. A random function $X = \{X_t, t \in T\}$ is said to be *continuous in the mean of order p* at the point s (on T) if $\lim_{t\to s} \|X_t - X_s\|_p = 0$ at the point s (for every $s \in T$). Prove a result analogous to Proposition III.5.1 for this type of continuity; show that if T is compact, the r.r.f. X is continuous in the mean of order p on T if and only if it is continuous in probability and $\{|X_t|^p, t \in T\}$ is uniformly integrable ($p \in [1, \infty)$).

III.5.2. **Gaussian random functions.** Let $X = \{X_t, t \in T\}$ be a separable r.r.f. defined on the space $(\Omega, \mathscr{A}, P)$ and the interval T of R, which is centered Gaussian with covariance $\Gamma = \{\Gamma(s, t); s, t \in T\}$; by this is meant that every vector $(X_{t_1}, \ldots, X_{t_n})$ has a centered Gaussian law with covariance

$$\{\Gamma(t_i, t_j); 1 \leqslant i, j \leqslant n\}.$$

Show that the following conditions are all equivalent: (a) the r.r.f. X is continuous in probability on T; (b) the r.r.f. X is continuous in the mean of order p on T ($1 \leqslant p < \infty$); (c) the function $\Gamma(s, t)$ is continuous on $T \times T$; (d) the function $\Gamma(s, t)$ is continuous at every point of the diagonal of $T \times T$.

If T is compact and if there exist two constants $C > 0$ and $\delta > 0$ such that

$$E[(X_t - X_s)^2] \leqslant C|t - s|^{\delta}$$

for any $s, t \in T$, show that the r.r.f. X has a.s. continuous trajectories; show more precisely that $\lim \text{a.s.}_{h\downarrow 0}\, h^{-\gamma} \sup_{|t-s|\leqslant h} |X_t - X_s| = 0$ for every constant $\gamma < \delta/2$. [Use Proposition III.5.3, taking account of the fact that every centered Gaussian r.r.v. Y has absolute moments of the form $E(|Y|^p) = K(p)[E(Y^2)]^{p/2}$, where $K(p)$ is a constant which does not depend on Y.]

The r.f. of *Brownian movement* is defined as the separable Gaussian centered r.r.f. $X = \{X_t, t \in R_+\}$ with covariance $\Gamma(s, t) = \min(s, t)$. Deduce from the preceding that

$$\lim_{h \downarrow 0} h^{-(1/2)+\epsilon} \sup_{\substack{|t-s| \leqslant h \\ s,t \leqslant u}} |X_t - X_s| = 0 \text{ a.s.}$$

for every $\epsilon > 0$ and $u < \infty$.

III.6. STOPPING TIMES

Let $(\Omega, \mathscr{A}, P)$ be a probability space which we shall consider fixed throughout this section, and let T be an interval of the extended line $\overline{Z}$ of integers (the discrete case) or of the extended real line $\overline{R}$ (the continuous case) representing the domain of variation of "time."

Definition III.6.1. A r.r.f. $X = \{X_t, t \in T\}$ DEFINED ON T AND AN INCREASING FAMILY $\{\mathscr{A}_t, t \in T\}$ OF σ-SUBALGEBRAS OF $\mathscr{A}$ ARE SAID TO BE ADAPTED IF FOR EVERY $t \in T$, THE r.r.v. X_t IS $\mathscr{A}_t$-MEASURABLE (THE EVENTS IN $\mathscr{A}_t$ ARE THEN SAID TO BE PRIOR TO t).

If X is a r.r.f. defined on T, obviously the family

$$\{\mathscr{B}_t = \mathscr{B}(X_s, s \leqslant t); t \in T\}$$

is adapted to it in the sense of the preceding definition. If $\{X_t\}$ and $\{\mathscr{A}_t\}$ are adapted, the same is evidently true of $\{f_t(X_t)\}$ and $\{\mathscr{A}_t\}$; this result, which can be generalized, shows the interest of the preceding definition: every property which can be defined relative to the family $\{\mathscr{A}_t\}$ rather than relative to $\{X_t\}$ will automatically be independent of any transformations which may be carried out on each of the variables X_t.

Definition III.6.2. GIVEN AN INCREASING FAMILY $\{\mathscr{A}_t, t \in T\}$ OF σ-SUBALGEBRAS OF $\mathscr{A}$, A MAPPING τ OF A NON-NEGLIGIBLE SUBSET Ω_τ OF Ω INTO T IS CALLED A STOPPING TIME IF IT SATISFIES THE CONDITION $\{\tau \leqslant t\} \in \mathscr{A}_t$ FOR EVERY $t \in T$. WE ASSOCIATE WITH IT THE σ-ALGEBRA $\mathscr{A}_\tau$ OF SUBSETS A OF Ω_τ SUCH THAT $A \cap \{\tau \leqslant t\} \in \mathscr{A}_t$ FOR EVERY $t \in T$ (THE EVENTS IN $\mathscr{A}_\tau$ ARE SAID TO BE PRIOR TO τ).

In the case where τ assumes only a countable number of values, in particular in the discrete case, Definition III.6.2 can be given the following equivalent form: τ is a stopping time relative to the family $\{\mathscr{A}_t, t \in T\}$

if and only if $\{\tau = t\} \in \mathscr{A}_t$ for every possible value $t \in T$ of τ; the σ-algebra $\mathscr{A}_\tau$ consists of the subsets A of Ω_τ such that $A \cap \{\tau = t\} \in \mathscr{A}_t$ for every possible value t of τ. (The σ-algebra $\mathscr{A}_\tau$ is thus characterized in this particular case by the property of having the same trace on each of the sets $\{\tau = t\}$ as does $\mathscr{A}_t$.)

To show the equivalence of the two preceding definitions, we start with the two identities

$$\{\tau = t\} = \{\tau \leqslant t\} - \bigcup_{n>0} \left\{\tau \leqslant t - \frac{1}{n}\right\}; \qquad \{\tau = t\} = \bigcup_{s \leqslant t} \{\tau = s\}.$$

Then if τ is a stopping time in the sense of Definition III.6.2, the sets $\{\tau \leqslant t\}$ and $\{\tau \leqslant t - 1/n\}$ and thus also the set $\{\tau = t\}$ belong to $\mathscr{A}_t$; likewise $A \cap \{\tau = t\} \in \mathscr{A}_t$ if $A \in \mathscr{A}_\tau$. Conversely, if the mapping τ assumes only a countable number of values and if $\{\tau = s\} \in \mathscr{A}_s$ for every s, then the set $\{\tau \leqslant t\}$ is the union of a countable number of sets in $\mathscr{A}_t$, namely those sets $\{\tau = s\}$ for $s \leqslant t$ which are nonempty; similarly $A \in \mathscr{A}_\tau$ as long as $A \cap \{\tau = s\} \in \mathscr{A}_s$ for every s and $\tau(\Omega_\tau)$ is countable.

Definition III.6.2 also calls for the following comments. First of all, every constant time, say $\tau = t_0$ on $\Omega_\tau = \Omega$, is a stopping time for which $\mathscr{A}_\tau = \mathscr{A}_{t_0}$; this in particular justifies the terminology used. It is easy to verify that $\mathscr{A}_\tau$ is a σ-subalgebra of $\Omega_\tau \cap \mathscr{A}$ and that the set Ω_τ necessarily belongs to $\mathscr{A}$; to show this one expresses Ω_τ as a countable union of sets $\{\tau \leqslant t\}$; moreover, *the mapping τ of $(\Omega_\tau, \mathscr{A}_\tau)$ into T with the σ-algebra of its Borel subsets is measurable*, as one can verify directly.

When the interval T of $\bar{Z}$ or $\bar{R}$ has the point $+\infty$ as a limit point but does not contain this point, it is frequently convenient, and conforms with one's intuition, to extend the definition of a stopping time τ to all of the space Ω by setting $\tau = +\infty$ on Ω_τ^c; the variable τ will then be a stopping time with values in $T + \{\infty\}$ if we take for $\mathscr{A}_\infty$ a σ-subalgebra of $\mathscr{A}$ containing all the $\mathscr{A}_t$ $(t \in T)$. One can then define the σ-algebra $\mathscr{A}_\tau$ as the σ-algebra of subsets A of Ω such that $A \cap \{\tau \leqslant t\} \in \mathscr{A}_t$ for every $t \in T$, this definition implying automatically that $A \cap \{\tau = +\infty\} \in \mathscr{A}$.

If τ is a stopping time relative to $\{\mathscr{A}_t, t \in T\}$, the same is true of $\tau + t_0$ if $t_0 \geqslant 0$ and more generally of $\theta(\tau)$ if $\theta(\cdot)$ is a measurable mapping of T or a subset of T into T such that $\theta(t) \geqslant t$ for every $t \in T$. It is also easy to show that $\Omega_{\theta(\tau)} \cap \mathscr{A}_\tau \subset \mathscr{A}_{\theta(\tau)}$.

The following relation, defined for stopping times relative to a fixed increasing family $\{\mathscr{A}_t\}$ of σ-algebras, is evidently an order relation: $\tau_1 \leqslant \tau_2$ if $\Omega_{\tau_1} \supset \Omega_{\tau_2}$ and if $\tau_1(\omega) \leqslant \tau_2(\omega)$ for every $\omega \in \Omega_{\tau_2}$. The supremum and infimum (for the preceding order) of two stopping times τ and τ' is defined by the formulas:

$$\tau \vee \tau'(\omega) = \max[\tau(\omega), \tau'(\omega)] \quad \text{on} \quad \Omega_{\tau \vee \tau'} = \Omega_\tau \cap \Omega_{\tau'};$$

$$\tau \wedge \tau'(\omega) = \begin{cases} \tau(\omega) & \text{on} \quad \Omega_\tau \cap \Omega_{\tau'}^c, \\ \min[\tau(\omega), \tau'(\omega)] & \text{on} \quad \Omega_\tau \cap \Omega_{\tau'}, \\ \tau'(\omega) & \text{on} \quad \Omega_\tau^c \cap \Omega_{\tau'}, \end{cases}$$

$$\Omega_{\tau \wedge \tau'} = \Omega_\tau \cup \Omega_{\tau'}.$$

In particular, one frequently has to consider the stopping time $\tau \wedge t_0$ which is everywhere defined and equals τ on $\{\tau \leqslant t_0\}$ and t_0 on the complementary set. Note that if $T = |\cdot, +\infty)$ and if we agree to extend every stopping time by setting $\tau = +\infty$ on Ω^c, the stopping times $\tau \vee \tau'$ and $\tau \wedge \tau'$ are equal on Ω to the supremum and infimum, respectively, of the functions τ and τ'; $\tau \vee \tau' = +\infty$ if $\tau = +\infty$ or if $\tau' = +\infty$, and $\tau \wedge \tau' = +\infty$ if $\tau = +\infty$ and $\tau' = +\infty$.

Let $\{\tau_n\}$ be an increasing sequence of stopping times defined relative to a fixed family $\{\mathscr{A}_t, t \in T\}$:

$$\cdots \Omega_{\tau_n} \supset \Omega_{\tau_{n+1}} \supset \cdots; \qquad \tau_n(\omega) \leqslant \tau_{n+1}(\omega) \quad \text{on} \quad \Omega_{\tau_{n+1}}.$$

Then the limit τ defined by $\Omega_\tau = \{\lim \tau_n \in T\}$, $\tau(\omega) = \lim \uparrow \tau_n(\omega)$ is again a stopping time; in fact $\{\tau \leqslant t\} = \lim_n \downarrow \{\tau_n \leqslant t\} \in \mathscr{A}_t$ for every $t \in T$. It is not true in general that the limit of a decreasing sequence of stopping times defined relative to a family $\{\mathscr{A}_t, t \in T\}$ is again a stopping time relative to this same family (see Problem III.6.1).

PROPOSITION III.6.1. *In the probability space $(\Omega, \mathscr{A}, P)$ let τ be a stopping time defined on Ω_τ relative to an increasing family $\{\mathscr{A}_t, t \in T\}$ of σ-subalgebras of $\mathscr{A}$ and let $X = \{X_t, t \in T\}$ be a* r.r.f. *defined on T which is adapted to the family $\{\mathscr{A}_t, t \in T\}$. Then each of the conditions below is sufficient to imply that the mapping X_τ of Ω_τ into $\bar{R}$ (defined by $X_\tau(\omega) = X_{\tau(\omega)}(\omega)$) is an $\mathscr{A}_\tau$-measurable* r.r.v.*:*

(a) *the stopping time τ assumes only a countable set of distinct values (this condition is always met in the discrete case),*

(b) *(in the continuous case) the trajectories of the* r.r.f. *X are right continuous on T,*

(c) *for every $u \in T$, the restriction of the mapping X of $T \times \Omega$ into $\bar{R}$ to the set $T_u \times \Omega$ is $\mathscr{T}_u \otimes \mathscr{A}_u$-measurable, if T_u denotes the interval $\{t: t \in T, t \leqslant u\}$ and $\mathscr{T}_u$ is the trace of $\bar{\mathscr{R}}$ on T_u.*

(Observe that a mapping X of $T \times \Omega$ into $\bar{R}$ satisfying condition (c) above is necessarily a r.r.f. which is adapted to $\{\mathscr{A}_t, t \in T\}$ by virtue of Proposition III.1.2.)

PROOF. In the case where the stopping time τ assumes only a countable number of distinct values, the relation

$$\{X_\tau \in B\}\{\tau \leqslant t\} = \bigcup_{s \leqslant t} \{X_t \in B\}\{\tau = s\} \in \mathscr{A}_t,$$

which holds for every $t \in T$ and every Borel set $B \subset \bar{R}$, implies at once, because the union in the right side has only a countable number of non-empty terms, that X_τ is $\mathscr{A}_\tau$-measurable.

Next we show that in the continuous case *condition* (b) *implies condition* (c). To simplify the notation let us take

$$T_u = (0, 1] \quad \text{or} \quad [0, 1]$$

and set $X^n(t, \omega) = X(q2^{-n}, \omega)$, where q is the smallest integer such that $q2^{-n} \geqslant t$. The right continuity of the trajectories of X implies that

$$X(t, \omega) = \lim_n X^n(t, \omega)$$

for every $t \in T$ and $\omega \in \Omega$; but the mappings X_n are obviously $\mathscr{T}_u \otimes \mathscr{A}_u$-measurable, and the same is then true of X.

Let us assume that condition (c) is satisfied, and show that the restriction of X_τ to the set $A_u = \{\tau \leqslant u\}$ is $\mathscr{A}_u$-measurable for any $u \in T$; the proposition will follow from this. The mapping τ of $(A_u, A_u \cap \mathscr{A}_u)$ into $(T_u, \mathscr{T}_u)$ being measurable, as one can easily verify, the mapping of $(A_u, A_u \cap \mathscr{A}_u)$ into $(T_u \times \Omega, \mathscr{T}_u \otimes \mathscr{A}_u)$ which associates $(\tau(\omega), \omega)$ with ω is also measurable. But the mapping X_τ of A_u into $\bar{R}$ is obtained as the composition of the preceding mapping with the mapping X of $(T_u \times \Omega, \mathscr{T}_u \otimes \mathscr{A}_u)$ into $\bar{R}$ which is measurable by hypothesis; it follows that X_τ is indeed $\mathscr{A}_u$-measurable on A_u and hence $\mathscr{A}_\tau$-measurable on Ω_τ. ∎

REMARK. If one assumes that the σ-algebras $\mathscr{A}_t$ contain all the negligible subsets of $(\Omega, \mathscr{A}, P)$, Proposition III.6.1 remains valid if we assume that condition (a) or condition (b) is only satisfied a.s.

Complements and problems

III.6.1. Let T be an interval of $\bar{R}$ and let $\{\mathscr{A}_t, t \in T\}$ be an increasing family of σ-algebras in the probability space $(\Omega, \mathscr{A}, P)$. Show that for every mapping τ of a subset Ω_τ of Ω into T the following conditions are equivalent:

(a) $\{\tau < t\} \in \mathscr{A}_t$ for every $t \in T$; (b) $\{\tau \leqslant t\} \in \mathscr{A}_{t+0}$ for every $t \in T$; (c) $\{\tau < t\} \in \mathscr{A}_{t-0}$ for every $t \in T$; we have denoted by $\mathscr{A}_{t+0}$ the σ-algebra which is the intersection of the $\mathscr{A}_s$ $(s > t)$ and by $\mathscr{A}_{t-0}$ the σ-algebra generated by the $\mathscr{A}_s$ $(s < t)$. Show next that the limit of any increasing or decreasing sequence of stopping times defined relative to $\{\mathscr{A}_{t+0}, t \in T\}$ is again a stopping time.

III.6.2. If $X = \{X_t, t \in T\}$ is a r.r.f. which is continuous in probability and adapted to the increasing family $\{\mathscr{A}_t, t \in T\}$ in $(\Omega, \mathscr{A}, P)$, show that there exists a measurable r.r.f. equivalent to X and which satisfies condition (c) of Proposition III.6.1. [Use the proof of the theorem of Section III.4.]

III.6.3. **(Waiting times.)** Let X be a r.r.f. defined on $(\Omega, \mathscr{A}, P)$ and satisfying condition (c) of Proposition III.6.1 relative to a family $\{\mathscr{A}_t, t \in T\}$; we assume that T is closed at the left. For every subset B of $\bar{R}$ we define the function $\tau_B(\omega) = \inf\{t\colon X_t(\omega) \in B\}$, with values in T, on the set

$$\Omega_B = \bigcup_T \{X_t \in B\};$$

if the trajectories of X are right continuous and if the set B is closed, τ_B is the first instant t at which $X_t \in B$. Deduce from Problem III.1.2 and the equality

$$\{\tau_B \leqslant u\} = \bigcap_{\epsilon > 0} \mathrm{proj}_\Omega \{(t, \omega)\colon t \leqslant u + \epsilon, X(t, \omega) \in B\}$$

that τ_B is a stopping time relative to $\{\mathscr{A}_{t+0}, t \in T\}$ at least for every Borel set B in $\bar{R}$. What can one say about X_{τ_B}?

Extend the preceding results to the variables τ_A defined by

$$\tau_A(\omega) = \inf\{t\colon (t, X(t, \omega)) \in A\},$$

when A is a measurable set of $(T \times \bar{R}, \mathscr{T} \otimes \bar{\mathscr{R}})$.

CHAPTER IV

CONDITIONAL EXPECTATIONS AND MARTINGALES

IV.1. MEASURES

Definition IV.1.1. A MEASURE μ ON A σ-ALGEBRA $\mathscr{A}$ OF SUBSETS OF A SET Ω IS A MAPPING OF $\mathscr{A}$ INTO $(-\infty, +\infty]$ SUCH THAT $\mu(\varnothing) = 0$ AND

$$\mu\Big(\sum_I A_i\Big) = \sum_I \mu(A_i) \qquad (\sigma\text{-additivity})$$

FOR EVERY COUNTABLE FAMILY $\{A_i, i \in I\}$ OF PAIRWISE DISJOINT SUBSETS OF Ω IN $\mathscr{A}$.

We have excluded the value $-\infty$ from the set of possible values of a measure in order to avoid the introduction of expressions of the form $\infty - \infty$ (if one had $\mu(A) = +\infty$ and $\mu(B) = -\infty$, one could not assign meaning to

$$\mu(A) + \mu(A^c B) = \mu(B) + \mu(B^c A) = \mu(A \cup B)).$$

A measure μ is said to be *positive* if $\mu(A) \geqslant 0$ $(A \in \mathscr{A})$, *bounded* if

$$\sup\{|\mu(A)|;\quad A \in \mathscr{A}\} < \infty;$$

a positive measure such that $\mu(\Omega) = 1$ (therefore bounded) is a probability.

PROPOSITION IV.1.1. (Jordan-Hahn.) *If μ is a measure on $(\Omega, \mathscr{A})$, the formulas*

$$\mu^+(A) = \sup\{\mu(B), B \subset A\}, \qquad \mu^-(A) = \sup\{-\mu(B), B \subset A\}$$

define two positive measures on $(\Omega, \mathscr{A})$. The measure μ^- is moreover bounded, and $\mu = \mu^+ - \mu^-$ on $\mathscr{A}$.

There exists at least one subset D of Ω in $\mathscr{A}$ such that

$$A \subset D \Rightarrow \mu(A) \geqslant 0, \qquad A \subset D^c \Rightarrow \mu(A) \leqslant 0,$$

and hence such that $\mu^+(A) = \mu(AD)$, $\mu^-(A) = -\mu(AD^c)$.

PROOF. We shall begin by proving the existence of D; the other properties of the proposition will follow almost immediately. Let $\mathscr{B}$ be the subclass of $\mathscr{A}$ defined by $\mathscr{B} = \{B: \mu^+(B) = 0\}$; this class is closed under countable union, for if $A \subset \bigcup_n B_n$ where $B_n \in \mathscr{B}$, we have

$$\mu(A) = \sum_n \mu\left[A\left(B_n - \bigcup_{m<n} B_m\right)\right] \leqslant \sum_n \mu^+(B_n) = 0.$$

It follows that the infimum $\beta = \inf\{\mu(B), B \in \mathscr{B}\}$ is attained and is therefore finite; in fact, if the sequence $\{B_n, n \geqslant 1\}$ in $\mathscr{B}$ is such that $\mu(B_n) \to \beta$, then $\bigcup_n B_n \in \mathscr{B}$ and hence, for every p

$$\beta \leqslant \mu\left(\bigcup_n B_n\right) = \mu(B_p) + \mu\left(\bigcup_n B_n - B_p\right) \leqslant \mu(B_p) \to \beta \qquad (p \to \infty).$$

Thus $\mu(\bigcup_n B_n) = \beta$ and, setting $D = (\bigcup_n B_n)^c$, we have thus shown the existence of a $D \in \mathscr{A}$ such that $D^c \in \mathscr{B}$ and $\mu(D^c) = \beta$, therefore such that (1) $A \subset D^c \Rightarrow \mu(A) \leqslant 0$, (2) $A \subset D$, $\mu(A) < 0 \Rightarrow 0 < \mu^+(A) < \infty$. (In fact, if $\mu^+(A)$ equalled zero, the set $A + D^c$ would belong to $\mathscr{B}$ and we would have $\mu(A + D^c) < \mu(D^c) = \beta$!; if $\mu^+(A)$ were infinite, there would exist a subset B of A such that $\mu(B) > -\beta$ and we would have

$$\mu(A - B) = \mu(A) - \mu(B) < \beta!)$$

We shall now show by contradiction that $A \subset D \Rightarrow \mu(A) \geqslant 0$. If, to the contrary, there exists a subset A of D such that $\mu(A) < 0$, we can find, by property (2) of D above, a subset A_1 of A such that

$$\mu(A_1) \geqslant \tfrac{1}{2}\mu^+(A) > 0.$$

The subset $A - A_1$ of D is then such that $\mu(A - A_1) = \mu(A) - \mu(A_1) < 0$. Proceeding by induction, we construct a sequence $\{A_n, n \geqslant 1\}$ of subsets of D such that

$$A_{n+1} \subset A - \sum_1^n A_m, \qquad \mu(A_{n+1}) \geqslant \tfrac{1}{2}\mu^+\left(A - \sum_1^n A_m\right) > 0.$$

This is possible by virtue of the second property of D and of the inequality $\mu(A - \sum_1^n A_m) < 0$ which one can easily prove at every step of the induction. The equality $\mu(A) = \mu(A - \sum_1^\infty A_m) + \sum_1^\infty \mu(A_m)$, where $\mu(A) < 0$ and $\mu(A_m) > 0$, implies, on the one hand, that

$$\mu\left(A - \sum_1^\infty A_m\right) < 0,$$

and on the other hand that $\sum \mu(A_m) < \infty$ and thus that $\lim_m \mu(A_m) = 0$; hence we have $\mu^+(A - \sum_1^\infty A_m) \leqslant \mu^+(A - \sum_1^n A_m) \to 0$ $(n \to \infty)$. The properties of $A - \sum_1^\infty A_m$ are incompatible with property (2) of D. The existence of D and the first of its properties stated in the proposition are thus established.

If $B \subset A$, then $\mu(B) = \mu(AD) + \mu(BD^c) - \mu[(A - B)D] \leqslant \mu(AD)$; it follows that $\mu^+(A) = \mu(AD)$ and it is now evident that μ^+ is a positive measure on $\mathscr{A}$. In the same way, we have $\mu^-(A) = -\mu(AD^c)$, and it follows that μ^- is a positive measure, which is bounded because

$$\sup\{\mu^-(A), A \in \mathscr{A}\} = \mu^-(\Omega) = -\mu(D^c) < +\infty.$$

Finally, the identity $\mu(A) = \mu(AD) + \mu(AD^c)$ implies that

$$\mu = \mu^+ - \mu^-. \blacksquare$$

Let us remark that the measures μ^+ and μ^- can also be characterized as the smallest positive measures which majorize μ and $-\mu$ respectively.

COROLLARY. *In order that the measure μ on $(\Omega, \mathscr{A})$ be bounded, it is (necessary and) sufficient that $\mu(\Omega) < \infty$.*

PROOF. The preceding proposition shows that for every $A \in \mathscr{A}$ we have

$$-\infty < -\mu^-(\Omega) \leqslant -\mu^-(A) \leqslant \mu(A) \leqslant \mu^+(A) \leqslant \mu^+(\Omega) = \mu(D) \leqslant \infty.$$

It follows that μ is bounded if and only if $\mu^+(\Omega) < \infty$. Since

$$\mu(\Omega) = \mu^+(\Omega) - \mu^-(\Omega),$$

this condition is equivalent to that of the corollary. $\blacksquare$

The *total variation* $|\mu|$ of a measure μ on $(\Omega, \mathscr{A})$ is by definition the positive measure $|\mu| = \mu^+ + \mu^-$. It is bounded if and only if the measure μ is. (It takes its name from the fact that

$$|\mu|(A) = \sup\left\{\sum_I |\mu(A_i)|\right\},$$

where $\{A_i, i \in I\}$ runs through all countable partitions of A.)

If μ_1 and μ_2 are two bounded measures on $(\Omega, \mathscr{A})$, the measures defined by $\mu_1 \vee \mu_2 = \mu_1 + (\mu_2 - \mu_1)^+$ and $\mu_1 \wedge \mu_2 = \mu_1 - (\mu_2 - \mu_1)^-$ are respectively the supremum and infimum of μ_1 and μ_2, that is, the smallest (largest) measure which is a majorant (minorant) of the measures μ_1 and μ_2. If D is the set appearing in the Jordan-Hahn decomposition of $(\mu_2 - \mu_1)$, the reader can verify from Proposition IV.1.1 that for every $A \in \mathscr{A}$,

$$\begin{aligned}(\mu_1 \vee \mu_2)(A) &= \sup\{\mu_1(B) + \mu_2(A - B);\quad B \subset A\}\\ &= \mu_1(AD^c) + \mu_2(AD),\\ (\mu_1 \wedge \mu_2)(A) &= \inf\{\mu_1(B) + \mu_2(A - B);\quad B \subset A\}\\ &= \mu_1(AD) + \mu_2(AD^c).\end{aligned}$$

Two positive bounded measures μ_1 and μ_2 on $(\Omega, \mathscr{A})$ are said to be *mutually singular* when $\mu_1 \wedge \mu_2 = 0$; by the preceding, *in order for μ_1 and μ_2 to be mutually singular, it is necessary and sufficient that there exist a set D in $(\Omega, \mathscr{A})$ such that $\mu_1(D) = 0 = \mu_2(D^c)$.*

PROPOSITION IV.1.2. *The vector space $\mathscr{M}(\Omega, \mathscr{A})$ of bounded measures on $(\Omega, \mathscr{A})$ is a complete lattice. With the norm $\|\mu\|_1 = |\mu|(\Omega)$, $\mathscr{M}(\Omega, \mathscr{A})$ is a Banach space.*

PROOF. We have already shown that $\mathscr{M}(\Omega, \mathscr{A})$ is a lattice. To show that it is a complete lattice, it suffices to show that for every increasing generalized sequence $\{\mu_\alpha\}$ of positive measures majorized by a positive bounded measure ν, the formula $\mu(A) = \lim \uparrow \mu_\alpha(A)$ defines a positive bounded measure (which is then necessarily the supremum of $\{\mu_\alpha\}$). But if $\{A_i, i \in I\}$ is a countable family of pairwise disjoint sets in A, for every $\epsilon > 0$ there exists an index α such that

$$\mu\Big(\sum_I A_i\Big) \leqslant \epsilon + \mu_\alpha\Big(\sum_I A_i\Big);$$

since $\mu_\alpha(\sum_I A_i) = \sum_I \mu_\alpha(A_i) \leqslant \sum_I \mu(A_i)$, it follows that

$$\mu\Big(\sum_I A_i\Big) \leqslant \sum_I \mu(A_i).$$

Conversely, it follows from $\sum_I \mu(A_i) \leqslant \sum_I \nu(A_i) = \nu(\sum_I A_i) < \infty$ and the fact that $\{\mu_\alpha\}$ is a generalized sequence, that we can find a finite subset I_0 of I and an index α such that

$$\sum_I \mu(A_i) \leqslant \epsilon + \sum_{I_0} \mu_\alpha(A_i);$$

since

$$\sum_{I_0} \mu_\alpha(A_i) \leqslant \mu_\alpha\Big(\sum_I A_i\Big) \leqslant \mu\Big(\sum_I A_i\Big),$$

we conclude that

$$\sum_I \mu(A_i) \leqslant \mu\Big(\sum_I A_i\Big).$$

This proves that μ is σ-additive. It is easy to verify that $\|\mu\|_1$ defines a norm on $\mathscr{M}(\Omega, \mathscr{A})$; we shall prove that this space, thus normed, is complete following Corollary 3 of the following proposition. ∎

PROPOSITION IV.1.3. (Lebesgue.) *Let* $(\Omega, \mathscr{A}, P)$ *be a probability space and let* μ *be a bounded (and positive) measure on* $(\Omega, \mathscr{A})$. *Then there exists an integrable (and positive)* r.r.v. X *on* $(\Omega, \mathscr{A}, P)$ *and a negligible set* N *of* $(\Omega, \mathscr{A}, P)$ *such that*

$$\mu(A) = \int_A X\,dP + \mu(AN) \qquad (A \in \mathscr{A}).$$

This decomposition of μ *into the sum of an indefinite integral with respect to* P *and a measure which is singular with respect to* P *is unique.*

In the case where μ *is positive,* X *is the largest* r.r.v., *up to equivalence, such that* $\int_A X\,dP \leqslant \mu(A)$ *for every* $A \in \mathscr{A}$.

PROOF. By virtue of Proposition IV.1.1 we can restrict ourselves to the case where μ is positive and bounded. Let $\mathscr{L}$ be the class of all (equivalence classes of) positive r.r.v.'s Y such that $\int_A Y\,dP \leqslant \mu(A)$ for every $A \in \mathscr{A}$. We shall show that this class has the following properties:

(a) $0 \in \mathscr{L}$;
(b) $Y_1, Y_2 \in \mathscr{L} \Rightarrow \sup(Y_1, Y_2) \in \mathscr{L}$;
(c) $Y_n \in \mathscr{L}$ $(n \geqslant 1)$ and $Y_n \uparrow Y \Rightarrow Y \in \mathscr{L}$.

Property (b) follows from

$$\begin{aligned}\int_A \sup(Y_1, Y_2) &= \int_{AB} Y_1 + \int_{AB^c} Y_2 \\ &\leqslant \mu(AB) + \mu(AB^c) = \mu(A) \qquad (A \in \mathscr{A}),\end{aligned}$$

where $B = \{Y_1 \geqslant Y_2\}$. Property (c) follows from the monotone convergence properties of the integral.

The preceding suffices to show, imitating the proof of Proposition II.4.1, that $\mathscr{L}$ has a maximal element X. We next introduce the positive bounded measure defined by $\mu'(A) = \mu(A) - \int_A X\,dP$. Let D_n be a Jordan-Hahn decomposition set for the measure $\mu' - n^{-1}P$; this set is therefore such that

$$\mu'(AD_n) \geqslant n^{-1}P(AD_n), \qquad \mu'(AD_n^c) \leqslant n^{-1}P(AD_n^c)$$

for every $A \in \mathscr{A}$. Since the r.r.v. $X + n^{-1}\,1_{D_n}$ belongs to $\mathscr{L}$, as

$$\int_A (X + n^{-1}1_{D_n})\,dP \leqslant \int_A X\,dP + \mu'(AD_n) \leqslant \mu(A) \qquad (A \in \mathscr{A}),$$

it follows from the maximality property of X that $P(D_n) = 0$; the set $N = \bigcup_n D_n$ is thus negligible in $(\Omega, \mathscr{A}, P)$. On the other hand, for every n we have $\mu'(N^c) \leqslant \mu'(D_n^c) \leqslant n^{-1}P(D_n^c) \leqslant n^{-1}$; consequently.

$$\mu'(N^c) = 0 \qquad \text{and} \qquad \mu'(A) = \mu'(AN) = \mu(AN) \qquad \text{for every } A \in \mathscr{A}.$$

Having proved the existence of a Lebesgue decomposition of μ with respect to P, we show that this decomposition is unique. Let

$$\mu(A) = \int_A Z\,dP + \nu(A) \qquad (A \in \mathscr{A})$$

be a decomposition of μ of the preceding type. Since $\int_A Z\,dP \leqslant \mu(A)$ on $\mathscr{A}$, we deduce that $Z \leqslant X$ a.s., where X is the r.r.v. of the preceding proof; hence

$$\nu(A) \geqslant \int_A (X - Z)\,dP \qquad (A \in \mathscr{A}).$$

Since ν is singular with respect to P, there exists a set $D \in \mathscr{A}$ such that $P(D^c) = 0$, $\nu(D) = 0$; we conclude from this that

$$\int (X - Z)\,dP = \int_D (X - Z)\,dP \leqslant \nu(D) = 0,$$

and therefore $Z = X$ a.s. ∎

COROLLARY 2. *Let $(\Omega, \mathscr{A}, P)$ be a probability space. For every bounded measure μ on $(\Omega, \mathscr{A})$, the following three conditions are equivalent:*

(a) $\mu(N) = 0$ *for every negligible set* N *of* $(\Omega, \mathscr{A}, P)$*;*
(b) *for every* $\epsilon > 0$ *there exists a* $\delta > 0$ *such that*
$$P(A) \leqslant \delta \Rightarrow |\mu(A)| \leqslant \epsilon \qquad (A \in \mathscr{A});$$
(c) $\mu(A) = \int_A X\,dP$ *for an integrable* r.r.v. X *defined on* $(\Omega, \mathscr{A}, P)$.

PROOF. The preceding proposition shows that (a) ⇒ (c). The implication (c) ⇒ (b) was proved in Section II.5. Finally (b) ⇒ (a) is obvious. ∎

We may observe that the measure μ satisfies condition (b) [(c)] on $\mathscr{A}$ as long as it satisfies it on an algebra [on a semialgebra] which generates $\mathscr{A}$; in fact, the class on which this condition is satisfied is monotone [monotone and additive].

A bounded measure μ satisfying condition (b) above is said to be *absolutely continuous* with respect to P, which is written as $\mu \ll P$; for this to be the case, it is necessary and sufficient that μ^+, μ^- be $\ll P$, or that $|\mu| \ll P$. The equivalence class of the r.r.v. X introduced in (c) is then given the name *derivative* of μ with respect to P, and is also denoted by $d\mu/dP$; the justification for this terminology lies in the fact that μ is the integral (with respect to P) of its derivative. (This terminology is also carried over to the case where the measure μ is not absolutely continuous with respect to P; in this case one should be cautioned that μ is no longer the integral of its derivative.) Lastly, it is often convenient to write condition (c) in the abbreviated form: $\mu = X \cdot P$ on $(\Omega, \mathscr{A})$.

COROLLARY 3. *The mapping $X \to X \cdot P$ which associates, with every class of integrable* r.r.v.'s *on $(\Omega, \mathscr{A}, P)$, the bounded measure $X \cdot P$, is an isometry of the space $L_1(\Omega, \mathscr{A}, P)$ onto the subspace of $\mathscr{M}(\Omega, \mathscr{A})$ consisting of those measures absolutely continuous with respect to P ($\mathscr{M}$ being taken with the norm $\|\cdot\|_1$ of Proposition* IV.1.2).

PROOF. This result is deduced at once from Corollary 2 by observing that the total variation of $X \cdot P$ is $|X| \cdot P$ and hence

$$\|X \cdot P\|_1 = \int |X| \, dP. \quad \blacksquare$$

This corollary enables us to complete the proof of Proposition IV.1.2 by showing that the normed space $\mathscr{M}(\Omega, \mathscr{A})$ is complete. In fact, if $\{\mu_n, n \geqslant 1\}$ is a Cauchy sequence in $\mathscr{M}$, let P be the probability

$$P = \sum_1^\infty \frac{1}{2^n \|\mu_n\|_1} \mu_n;$$

it is obvious that the measures μ_n are absolutely continuous with respect to P. By the preceding corollary, the derivatives $d\mu_n/dP$ form a Cauchy sequence in the space $L_1(\Omega, \mathscr{A}, P)$; the limit $X = \lim_{n\to\infty} d\mu_n/dP$ exists in $L_1(\Omega, \mathscr{A}, P)$, this space being complete, and it is clear that

$$X\cdot P = \lim_{n\to\infty} \mu_n \quad \text{in} \quad \mathscr{M}(\Omega, \mathscr{A}).$$

The following result is a slight generalization of Corollary 2 above, and is useful in probability theory.

PROPOSITION IV.1.4. (RADON–NIKODYM.) *Let $(\Omega, \mathscr{A}, P)$ be a probability space and let μ be a measure on $(\Omega, \mathscr{A})$ such that $\mu(N) = 0$ for every negligible set of $(\Omega, \mathscr{A}, P)$. Then there exists a* r.r.v. *X, unique up to equivalence, such that X^- is integrable on $(\Omega, \mathscr{A}, P)$ and such that*

$$\mu(A) = \int_A X\,dP \qquad (A \in \mathscr{A}).$$

In order that X be positive (integrable) it is necessary and sufficient that μ be positive (bounded). In order that X be finite, it is necessary and sufficient that there exist an increasing sequence $\{C_n, n \geqslant 1\}$ with union Ω, and such that $\mu(C_n) < \infty$ $(n \geqslant 1)$ (μ is a σ-finite measure).

PROOF. In the case where μ is positive and bounded, this proposition reduces to Corollary 1. If μ is a positive measure such that $\mu(\Omega) = \infty$, let $\mathscr{C} = \{C: \mu(C) < \infty\}$; this class being closed under union, it is possible to find an increasing sequence $\{C_n, n \geqslant 1\}$ in $\mathscr{C}$ such that $\lim \uparrow P(C_n) = \sup\{P(C), C \in \mathscr{C}\}$. Let μ_n be the positive bounded measure defined by $\mu_n(A) = \mu[A(C_n - C_{n-1})]$ for every $n \geqslant 1$ $(C_0 = \varnothing)$; it is easily seen that

$$\mu(A) = \sum_n \mu_n(A) \qquad \text{if} \qquad P\left[A \cap \left(\bigcup_n C_n\right)^c\right] = 0$$

and that $\mu(A) = \infty$ otherwise. By Corollary 1 applied to μ_n, there exists a positive integrable r.r.v. X_n such that

$$\mu_n(A) = \int_A X_n\,dP, \qquad X_n = 0 \quad \text{a.s. on} \quad (C_n - C_{n-1})^c.$$

It remains now to define the positive r.r.v. X by: $X = X_n$ on $(C_n - C_{n-1})$ for every $n \geqslant 1$ and $X = +\infty$ on $(\bigcup_n C_n)^c$, and to observe that $\mu(A) = \int_A X\,dP$ for every $A \in \mathscr{A}$. Moreover X is integrable if and only if μ is bounded, and X is a.s. finite if and only if $P(\bigcup_n C_n) = 1$.

The case where the measure μ is not positive can be reduced to the case where $\mu \geqslant 0$ by means of Proposition IV.1.1. Observe that if $\mu(A) = \int_A X\,dP$ on $\mathscr{A}$, then $\mu^+(A) = \int_A X^+\,dP$ on $\mathscr{A}$. ∎

Complements and problems

IV.1.1. Let μ be a *bounded* measure on $(\Omega, \mathscr{A})$. Prove directly without referring to the results of this section that:

(1) μ^+ and μ^- are positive bounded measures, and $\mu = \mu^+ - \mu^-$;

(2) there exists a set D such that $\mu^+(A) = \mu(AD)$, $\mu^-(A) = -\mu(AD^c)$. (If $\{D_n\}$ is a sequence in $\mathscr{A}$ such that $\sum_n [\mu^+(\Omega) - \mu(D_n)] < \infty$, show that one can take $D = \limsup D_n$.)

IV.1.2. If P and Q are two probabilities on $(\Omega, \mathscr{A})$ and if $Q = X \cdot P$, give the Lebesgue decomposition of P with respect to Q in terms of X. Show that $u_p(f) = f \cdot X^{1/p}$ defines an isometry of $L_p(\Omega, \mathscr{A}, Q)$ into $L_p(\Omega, \mathscr{A}, P)$ for any p, $1 \leqslant p \leqslant \infty$ (define $X^{1/\infty}$ as $1_{\{X \neq 0\}}$).

Two probabilities are said to be *equivalent* if they have the same family of negligible sets. (This is the equivalence associated with the partial order $\ll$.) In order that P and Q be equivalent, it is necessary and sufficient that $Q \ll P$ and that $\{dQ/dP = 0\}$ be P-negligible. Show also that u_p is an isometry of $L_p(Q)$ onto $L_p(P)$ if and only if P and Q are equivalent.

IV.1.3. Let $\{P_\theta, \theta \in \Theta\}$ be an arbitrary family of probabilities on $(\Omega, \mathscr{A})$. If there exists a probability with respect to which all the P_θ are absolutely continuous, show that there exists such a probability having the special form

$$P = \sum_\theta a_\theta P_\theta \qquad \text{where} \qquad a_\theta \geqslant 0 \quad \text{and} \quad \sum_\theta a_\theta = 1.$$

[If $P_\theta \ll Q$, choose the a_θ so that the countable set $\Theta_0 = \{\theta; a_\theta \neq 0\}$ has the property that $\operatorname{ess\,sup}_\Theta \{dP_\theta/dQ > 0\} = \operatorname{ess\,sup}_{\Theta_0} \{dP_\theta/dQ > 0\}$.] If Θ is countable, there always exists a probability P with respect to which the P_θ are absolutely continuous; show that the same is true when there exists a countable subset Θ_0 of Θ such that $\{P_\theta, \theta \in \Theta_0\}$ is dense in $\{P_\theta, \theta \in \Theta\}$ in the sense of the Banach space topology of $\mathscr{M}(\Omega, \mathscr{A})$.

IV.1.4. Let $(\Omega, \mathscr{A})$ be a measurable space. We consider pairs (X, P) consisting of a probability P and a r.r.v. X such that $\int X^2\, dP < \infty$; two pairs (X, P) and (X', P') are said to be equivalent if for one (equivalently, for every) probability Q such that $P \ll Q$ and $P' \ll Q$, the set

$$\left\{X\sqrt{\frac{dP}{dQ}} \neq X'\sqrt{\frac{dP'}{dQ}}\right\}$$

is Q-negligible. Since we then have $(X, Y \cdot P) = (XY^{1/2}, P)$ if $Y \geqslant 0$, it is more suggestive to denote a pair (X, P) by $X\sqrt{dP}$. Show that the space of equivalence classes of the $X\sqrt{dP}$ is a Hilbert space H for the scalar product

$$\langle X\sqrt{dP}, X'\sqrt{dP'}\rangle = \int XX' \sqrt{\frac{dP}{dQ}}\sqrt{\frac{dP'}{dQ}}\, dQ,$$

which is independent of the probability Q chosen so that $P \ll Q$, $P' \ll Q$. Show that for every P, the mapping $X \to X\sqrt{dP}$ is an isometry of $L_2(\Omega, \mathscr{A}, P)$ into H. For every $p \neq 2$ define the Banach space $X\sqrt[p]{dP}$ similarly and in such a way that it isometrically extends each of the spaces $L_p(\Omega, \mathscr{A}, P)$.

IV.1.5. If $\mathscr{A}$ is a Boolean algebra of subsets of Ω and if m is an additive mapping of $\mathscr{A}$ into R_+, the infimum

$$\mu(A) = \inf \sum_I m(A_i),$$

taken over the collection of countable partitions $\{A_i, i \in I\}$ of A in $\mathscr{A}$, defines, as A varies in $\mathscr{A}$, a positive measure on $(\Omega, \mathscr{A})$ which can be characterized as the smallest positive measure on $(\Omega, \mathscr{A})$ which is majorized by m. Show, moreover, that if $\mathscr{A}$ is a σ-algebra and if ν is a positive measure on $\mathscr{A}$ which is singular with respect to μ, then for any $\epsilon > 0$ there exists a set A_ϵ in $\mathscr{A}$ such that $m(A_\epsilon) < \epsilon$ and $\nu(A_\epsilon^c) = 0$.

IV.1.6. The vector space $B(\Omega, \mathscr{A})$ of bounded r.r.v.'s defined on $(\Omega, \mathscr{A})$, taken with the norm $\|X\| = \sup_\Omega |X(\omega)|$, is a Banach space (in general, distinct from the spaces $L_\infty(\Omega, \mathscr{A}, P)$). Show that the integral $\int X\,d\mu$ defines a bilinear functional on the Banach spaces $B(\Omega, \mathscr{A})$ and $\mathscr{M}(\Omega, \mathscr{A})$ such that

$$\|\mu\| = \sup_{X \neq 0} \frac{|\int X\,d\mu|}{\|X\|}, \qquad \|X\| = \sup_{\mu \neq 0} \frac{|\int X\,d\mu|}{\|\mu\|}.$$

Deduce from this that the space $\mathscr{M}(\Omega, \mathscr{A})[B(\Omega, \mathscr{A})]$ is isometric to a closed vector subspace (in general, a proper subspace) of the strong dual of the space $B(\Omega, \mathscr{A})[\mathscr{M}(\Omega, \mathscr{A})]$.

IV.2. DUALITY OF L_p SPACES, AND THE WEAK TOPOLOGY ON THE SPACE L_1

The following proposition, which is a corollary of the Radon-Nikodym theorem, shows that the dual of the Banach space $L_p(\Omega, \mathscr{A}, P)$ of classes of r.r.v.'s with integrable p-th powers $(1 \leqslant p < \infty)$ is the space $L_{p'}(\Omega, \mathscr{A}, P)$, if p' is given by $1/p + 1/p' = 1$. The dual of the space $L_\infty(\Omega, \mathscr{A}, P)$ contains the space $L_1(\Omega, \mathscr{A}, P)$ but is in general distinct from it (L_1 is the dual of L_∞ only if the Boolean metric algebra $\mathscr{A}/P$ is finite, in which case all the spaces L_p are isomorphic to a Euclidean space).

PROPOSITION IV.2.1. *Let $1 \leqslant p \leqslant \infty$ and let p' be given by $1/p + 1/p' = 1$. Every (equivalence class of a)* r.r.v.

$$Y \in L_{p'}(\Omega, \mathscr{A}, P)$$

defines a continuous linear functional F on L_p according to the formula

$$F(X) = \int XY\,dP \qquad (X \in L_p).$$

Moreover, the norm of F, defined by $\|F\| = \sup\{|F(X)|;\ \|X\|_p \leqslant 1\}$ *equals* $\|Y\|_{p'}$.

Conversely, when $1 \leqslant p < \infty$, *all the continuous linear functionals on* L_p *are given by the above formula.*

PROOF. It follows first from Hölder's inequality that if $Y \in L_{p'}$, the r.r.v. XY is integrable if $X \in L_p$, and $|\int XY| \leqslant \|X\|_p \|Y\|_{p'}$. It obviously follows that the formula of the proposition defines a continuous linear functional on L_p and that $\|F\| \leqslant \|Y\|_{p'}$. Let us show that the opposite inequality is satisfied if $Y \neq 0$. If $p > 1$, we easily verify that $Z = \varepsilon(Y)|Y|^{p'-1}$ (where $\varepsilon(Y) = +1$ if $Y \geqslant 0$ and -1 if $Y < 0$) is a r.r.v. in L_p such that $\|Z\|_p = (\|Y\|_{p'})^{p'-1}$ and

$$\|F\|\ \|Z\|_p \geqslant |F(Z)| = \int |Y|^{p'} = (\|Y\|_{p'})^{p'};$$

hence $\|F\| \geqslant \|Y\|_{p'}$. This argument is valid even if $p = \infty$; in this case Z is taken as $\varepsilon(Y)$ and now $\|Z\|_\infty = 1$. When $p = 1$, we similarly put $Z_\eta = \varepsilon(Y)1_{\{|Y| \geqslant \|Y\|_\infty - \eta\}}$ for every $\eta > 0$, so that

$$\|Z_\eta\|_1 = P(|Y| \geqslant \|Y\|_\infty - \eta) > 0$$

and $\|F\|\ \|Z_\eta\|_1 \geqslant |F(Z_\eta)| \geqslant \int_{\{|Y| \geqslant \|Y\|_\infty - \eta\}} |Y|$; hence $\|F\| \geqslant \|Y\|_\infty - \eta$ for any $\eta > 0$.

Conversely if $p < \infty$ and if F is a continuous linear functional on L_p, the formula $\varphi(A) = F(1_A)$ $(A \in \mathscr{A})$ defines a set function on $\mathscr{A}$ which is additive and such that $|\varphi(A)| \leqslant \|F\|[P(A)]^{1/p}$. This inequality implies that this function is a measure (it is continuous at $\varnothing$) which is bounded and absolutely continuous with respect to P; by the Radon-Nikodym theorem there exists an integrable r.r.v. Y such that $\varphi(A) = \int_A Y\,dp$ and consequently such that $F(X) = \int YX$ for every step r.r.v. X.

We shall show next that $Y \in L_p$, assuming first that $p > 1$, i.e., $p' < \infty$.

Let $\{X_n, n \geqslant 1\}$ be an increasing sequence of step r.r.v.'s such that $|Y| = \lim_{n\to\infty} \uparrow X_n$; since $\varepsilon(Y)(X_n)^{p'-1}$ is a step r.r.v., we have as before

$$\int (X_n)^{p'} \leqslant F[\varepsilon(Y)X_n^{p'-1}] \leqslant \|F\|(\|X_n\|_{p'})^{p'-1},$$

that is $\|X_n\|_{p'} \leqslant \|F\|$; it follows that $Y \in L_{p'}$, since

$$\|Y\|_{p'} = \lim_{n\to\infty} \uparrow \|X_n\|_{p'}.$$

If $p' = \infty$, we similarly have $\| Y \|_\infty \leqslant \|F\|$. In fact, otherwise the step r.r.v. $X = \varepsilon(Y)1_{\{|Y| > \|F\|\}}$ would be different from 0 and such that

$$F(X) = \int_{\{|Y| > \|F\|\}} |Y| > \|F\| P(|Y| > \|F\|) = \|F\| \int |X|;$$

but this strict inequality contradicts the definition of $\|F\|$. Under these conditions, $F(X)$ and $\int YX$ $(X \in L_p)$ are two continuous linear functionals on L_p which are equal on the dense subspace in L_p consisting of the step r.r.v.'s; hence they are necessarily equal everywhere on L_p. ▮

The preceding proof also shows that:

COROLLARY. *In order that a continuous linear functional F on* $L_\infty(\Omega, \mathscr{A}, P)$ *be of the form* $F(X) = \int YX$ *for some* $Y \in L_1$, *it is necessary and sufficient that the additive set function* $F(1_A)$ *be* σ*-additive on* $\mathscr{A}$.

In the rest of this section,† we intend to study the weak topology $\sigma(L_1, L_\infty)$ induced on the space L_1 by the space L_∞, the strong dual of L_1, and particularly to obtain a criterion for compactness in L_1 for this topology. Let us recall in this connection that in every space L_p $(p > 1)$ a set H is relatively compact in the weak topology $\sigma(L_p, L_{p'})$ if and only if it is bounded; this results from the fact that L_p is the dual of $L_{p'}$ and from a general theorem of the theory of Banach spaces.

PROPOSITION IV.2.2. *Every sequence* $\{X_n, n \geqslant 1\}$ *of integrable* r.r.v.'s *such that the limits* $\lim_{n\to\infty} \int_A X_n$ *exist and are finite for every* $A \in \mathscr{A}$ *is uniformly integrable. Moreover, the sequence* $\{X_n, n \geqslant 1\}$ *converges in the sense of* $\sigma(L_1, L_\infty)$ *to an integrable* r.r.v. X*; in particular we therefore have* $\lim_{n\to\infty} \int_A X_n = \int_A X$.

(This proposition, when stated for a generalized sequence of integrable r.r.v.'s, is false if the sequence does not have a countable base.)

PROOF. This very deep result is proved by applying the Baire category theorem to the complete metric space consisting of the Boolean metric algebra $\mathscr{A}/P$; let us recall that the elements of this space are P-equivalence classes of sets $A \in \mathscr{A}$ and that the metric in this space is

† The remainder of this section consists of results which will not be used in the sequel.

defined by the distance $P(A \triangle A')$. We also note that for every integrable r.r.v. X the mapping $A \to \int_A X$ of $\mathscr{A}/P$ into R is (uniformly) continuous, as

$$\left|\int_A X - \int_{A'} X\right| \leqslant \int_{A \triangle A'} |X| \to 0 \quad \text{if} \quad P(A \triangle A') \to 0.$$

Consequently, the set $\{A: |\int_A X| \leqslant \epsilon\}$ is closed in $\mathscr{A}/P$ for every $\epsilon > 0$.

Fix $\epsilon > 0$. By virtue of the hypothesis, the union of the closed sets

$$F_N = \bigcap_{\substack{m \geqslant N \\ n \geqslant N}} \left\{A: \left| \int_A (X_m - X_n) \right| \leqslant \epsilon\right\}$$

in $\mathscr{A}/P$ is equal to the entire space. The Baire category theorem now implies the existence of an integer, say N_0, such that F_{N_0} has an interior point; in other words, there exists an integer N_0, an element $A_0 \in \mathscr{A}/P$ and a real number $r > 0$ such that

$$\left| \int_A (X_m - X_n) \right| \leqslant \epsilon \quad \text{if} \quad m, n \geqslant N_0 \text{ and } P(A \triangle A_0) \leqslant r.$$

This implies that

$$\int_B |X_m - X_n| \leqslant 4\epsilon \quad \text{if} \quad m, n \geqslant N_0 \text{ and } P(B) \leqslant r.$$

In fact, the identities

$$(A_0 \cup B) \triangle A_0 \subset B, \qquad (A_0 \cap B^c) \triangle A_0 \subset B,$$

$$\int_B X = \int_{A_0 \cup B} X - \int_{A_0 \cap B^c} X$$

and the condition $P(B) \leqslant r$ imply that $\left|\int_B (X_m - X_n)\right| \leqslant 2\epsilon$ if $m, n \geqslant N_0$; upon applying this inequality separately to the sets $B\{X_m \geqslant X_n\}$ and $B\{X_m < X_n\}$, we obtain the result stated.

Since the finite sequence $\{X_m, 1 \leqslant m \leqslant N_0\}$ is uniformly integrable, for every $r' > 0$ sufficiently small we can write

$$\int_B |X_m| \leqslant \epsilon \quad \text{if} \quad m \leqslant N_0 \text{ and } P(B) \leqslant r'.$$

Combining this result with the preceding and using the triangle inequality, we see that for every $m \geqslant 1$

$$\int_B |X_m| \leqslant 5\epsilon \quad \text{if} \quad P(B) \leqslant \min(r, r');$$

this shows the uniform absolute continuity of the sequence $\{X_m, m \geqslant 1\}$, as ϵ is arbitrary.

To prove the uniform integrability of this sequence, it remains to show that $\sup_n \int |X_n| < \infty$ (see Proposition II.5.2). To this end, let us consider a finite partition of the space $(\Omega, \mathscr{A}, P)$ consisting of sets A_i, $i \in I$ of probability $\leqslant r$ and of atoms A_j, $j \in J$ (see Problem I.4.3). We now have

$$\sup_n \int_{A_j} |X_n| < \infty \qquad \text{if} \qquad j \in J,$$

as the X_n are constants on the A_j and the limits $\lim_{n\to\infty} \int_{A_j} X_n$ exist. Adding, we obtain the desired result.

Last, we set $Q(A) = \lim_{n\to\infty} \int_A X_n$ on $\mathscr{A}$; this set function is obviously additive. The uniform absolute continuity of the sequence $\{X_n, n \geqslant 1\}$ implies that Q is a measure, absolutely continuous with respect to P. By the Radon-Nikodym theorem, there exists an integrable r.r.v. X such that $Q(A) = \int_A X$. We have thus shown that $\lim_{n\to\infty} \int X_n Y = \int XY$ for every indicator r.v. $Y = 1_A$ and hence for every step r.r.v. Y. Since every bounded r.r.v. Z is the limit in L_∞ norm of at least one sequence of step r.r.v.'s $\{Y_q, q \geqslant 1\}$, we have, taking into account that $\{X_n\}$ is bounded in L_1,

$$\begin{aligned}\left|\int X_n Z - \int XZ\right| &\leqslant \left|\int X_n Y_q - \int XY_q\right| + \int |X_n|\,|Z - Y_q| \\ &\quad + \int |X|\,|Z - Y_q| \\ &\leqslant \left|\int X_n Y_q - \int XY_q\right| \\ &\quad + \left[\sup_n \int |X_n| + \int |X|\right] \|Z - Y_q\|_\infty \to 0\end{aligned}$$

as $n \to \infty$ and then $q \to \infty$. ∎

The following corollary simply expresses the results of the proposition in terms of measures.

COROLLARY 1. (THEOREM OF VITALI–HAHN–SAKS.) *If the sequence* $\{P_n, n \geqslant 1\}$ *of probabilities defined on a measurable space* $(\Omega, \mathscr{A})$ *is such that the limit* $Q(A) = \lim_{n\to\infty} P_n(A)$ *exists for every* $A \in \mathscr{A}$, *then* Q *is a probability on* $(\Omega, \mathscr{A})$. *Moreover,* $\sup_n P_n(A) \downarrow 0$ *as* $A \downarrow \varnothing$ *in* $(\Omega, \mathscr{A})$.

PROOF. Let P be the probability on $(\Omega, \mathscr{A})$ defined by

$$P = \sum_{n \geqslant 1} 2^{-n} P_n.$$

By the Radon-Nikodym theorem, there exist integrable r.r.v.'s X_n $(n \geqslant 1)$ such that $P_n = X_n \cdot P$. It remains only to apply the proposition to the sequence $\{X_n, n \geqslant 1\}$. ∎

COROLLARY 2. *In order that a sequence* $\{X_n, n \geqslant 1\}$ *of integrable* r.r.v.'s *converge in the sense of the topology* $\sigma(L_1, L_\infty)$ *to an integrable* r.r.v. X, *it is necessary and sufficient that* $\lim_{n\to\infty} \int_A X_n = \int_A X$ *for every* $A \in \mathscr{A}$.

PROOF. The condition is trivially necessary; it is sufficient by virtue of the proposition. ∎

COROLLARY 3 (SEQUENTIAL CAUCHY CRITERION FOR $\sigma(L_1, L_\infty)$). *In order that a sequence* $\{X_n, n \geqslant 1\}$ *of integrable* r.r.v.*'s be convergent in the sense of the topology* $\sigma(L_1, L_\infty)$, *it is necessary and sufficient that it be a Cauchy sequence for this topology.*

(The space L_1 with the topology $\sigma(L_1, L_\infty)$ is thus sequentially complete.)

PROOF. The condition is evidently necessary. Conversely, if $\{X_n, n \geqslant 1\}$ is a Cauchy sequence for the topology $\sigma(L_1, L_\infty)$, then $\lim_{n\to\infty} \int X_n Y$ exists for every $Y \in L_\infty$; therefore Proposition IV.2.2 establishes a result stronger than the sufficiency of the sequential Cauchy criterion. ∎

PROPOSITION IV.2.3. *A subset H of $L_1(\Omega, \mathscr{A}, P)$ is relatively compact for the weak topology $\sigma(L_1, L_\infty)$ if and only if it is uniformly integrable.*

PROOF. To show that the condition is necessary, let us consider a subset H of L_1 which is not uniformly integrable. Then we can find a sequence $\{X_n, n \geqslant 1\}$ in H such that

$$\int_{\{|X_n| > n\}} X_n \geqslant \eta$$

for every $n \geqslant 1$ and for some $\eta > 0$. Then no subsequence of $\{X_n, n \geqslant 1\}$ is uniformly integrable or, by virtue of Proposition IV.2.2, convergent for the topology $\sigma(L_1, L_\infty)$. By Eberlein's theorem, the set H cannot therefore be relatively compact in L_1.

To show that the condition is sufficient, we imbed the space L_1 into the dual of L_∞; the set H, being uniformly integrable, is bounded in L_1 and therefore also in the dual of L_∞. Consequently the closure $\overline{H}$ of H in the dual of L_∞ for the topology $\sigma((L_\infty)', L_\infty)$ is compact in the sense of this topology. As this topology induces the weak topology $\sigma(L_1, L_\infty)$ on L_1 ($\subset L'_\infty$), it suffices to prove that $\overline{H} \subset L_1$. But every element $F \in \overline{H}$ is a continuous linear functional on L_∞, the limit (of a generalized sequence) of functionals

$$F_\alpha(Y) = \int X_\alpha Y \qquad (Y \in L_\infty;\ X_\alpha \in H),$$

and consequently, by the uniform absolute continuity of H, we have

$$P(A) \leqslant \delta \Rightarrow \sup_{X \in H} \int_A |X| \leqslant \epsilon \Rightarrow F(1_A) \leqslant \epsilon.$$

By the corollary of Proposition IV.2.1, this implies that $F \in L_1$ and hence that $\overline{H} \subset L_1$. ▮

COROLLARY. *In order that a bounded subset H of $\mathcal{M}(\Omega, \mathscr{A})$ be relatively compact for the weak topology $\sigma(\mathcal{M}, \mathcal{M}')$ of $\mathcal{M}$, it is necessary and sufficient that there exist a probability P on $(\Omega, \mathscr{A})$ such that*

$$P(A) \leqslant \delta(\epsilon) \Rightarrow |\lambda(A)| \leqslant \epsilon \qquad \textit{for every } \lambda \in H$$

for every $\epsilon > 0$ and for $\delta(\epsilon) > 0$ sufficiently small. [The set H is thus necessarily contained in the subspace $L_1(\Omega, \mathscr{A}, P)$ of $\mathcal{M}$.]

PROOF. The condition is obviously sufficient, as it implies that H is contained in $L_1(\Omega, \mathscr{A}, P)$ and is relatively compact in the topology $\sigma(L_1, L_\infty)$. [We know that the topology $\sigma(L_1, L_\infty)$ is identical with the topology induced on L_1 by the topology $\sigma(\mathcal{M}, \mathcal{M}')$.]

To show that the condition is necessary, we shall first show the existence for every $\epsilon > 0$ of a $\delta > 0$ and a finite number of measures $\lambda_1, \ldots, \lambda_m$ in H such that

$$|\lambda_l|(A) \leqslant \delta \quad (1 \leqslant l \leqslant m) \Rightarrow |\lambda(A)| \leqslant \epsilon \quad \text{for every } \lambda \in H.$$

In fact, if such a constant δ and such measures did not exist, it would be possible to choose by induction a sequence $\{\lambda_p\}$ of measures in H and a sequence $\{A_p\}$ of sets such that

$$|\lambda_m|(A_p) \leqslant 2^{-p} \quad (1 \leqslant m \leqslant p), \qquad |\lambda_{p+1}(A_p)| \geqslant \epsilon.$$

Setting $P = \sum_1^\infty (1/2^p\|\lambda_p\|)|\lambda_p|$, we would obtain a sequence $\{\lambda_p\}$ in $L_1(\Omega, \mathscr{A}, P)$ which is contained in H and is thus relatively compact for $\sigma(L_1, L_\infty)$; the sequence $\{d\lambda_p/dP\}$ would therefore be uniformly integrable in $L_1(\Omega, \mathscr{A}, P)$, which is impossible as $P(A_p) \to 0$ and $|\lambda_{p+1}(A_p)| \geqslant \epsilon$.

Having introduced for each $\epsilon = 1/n$ a constant δ_n and measures $\lambda_1^{(n)}, \ldots, \lambda_{m_n}^{(n)}$ having the above properties, we choose constants $a_j^{(n)} > 0$ $(1 \leqslant j \leqslant m_n; n \geqslant 1)$ such that $P = \sum_{j,n} a_j^{(n)}|\lambda_j^{(n)}|$ is a probability. Choosing δ sufficiently small, for every previously fixed integer n we will have

$$P(A) \leqslant \delta \Rightarrow |\lambda_j^{(n)}|(A) \leqslant \delta_n \quad (1 \leqslant j \leqslant m_n) \Rightarrow |\lambda(A)| \leqslant 1/n$$

for every $\lambda \in H$. The necessity of the condition is thus proved. ▌

Complements and problems

*IV.2.1. **Vector measures.** Let $(\Omega, \mathscr{A})$ be a measurable space and let E be a Banach space. A mapping μ of $\mathscr{A}$ into E is called a vector measure if for every $x' \in E'$ (E' the dual of E) the set function $\langle x', \mu(\cdot)\rangle$ is a bounded measure on $(\Omega, \mathscr{A})$. Show that there exists at least one probability P on $(\Omega, \mathscr{A})$ such that $P(A) = 0 \Rightarrow \mu(A) = 0$ in E and such that for every countable family $\{A_i, i \in I\}$ of pairwise disjoint sets in $(\Omega, \mathscr{A})$, one has $\mu(\sum_I A_i) = \sum_I \mu(A_i)$ in the strong sense in E. [Observe that when x' runs through the unit ball of E', the family $\{\langle x', \mu(\cdot)\rangle\}$ is compact in $\mathscr{M}(\Omega, \mathscr{A})$; to show this, use Eberlein's theorem and Proposition IV.2.2.]

IV.2.2. Show that the space of continuous linear mappings of $L_p(\Omega, \mathscr{A}, P)$ into $L_{p'}(\Omega', \mathscr{A}', P')$ is a Banach space and a complete lattice for the natural order; the supremum $T_1 \vee T_2$ of two such mappings T_1 and T_2 can be defined on $(L_p)_+$ by

$$T_1 \vee T_2(f) = \sup\{T_1 g + T_2(f - g); 0 \leqslant g \leqslant f\} \qquad (f \in (L_p)_+).$$

If $p, p' < \infty$ and if T is a mapping of the preceding type, we denote by T^* the adjoint of T, mapping $L_{q'}(\Omega', \mathscr{A}', P')$ into $L_q(\Omega, \mathscr{A}, P)$; show that $(T_1 \vee T_2)^* = T_1^* \vee T_2^*$.

IV.3. CONDITIONAL EXPECTATIONS

Throughout this section, the probability space $(\Omega, \mathscr{A}, P)$ will be fixed and $\mathscr{B}$ will denote an arbitrary σ-subalgebra of $\mathscr{A}$.

If μ is a positive measure on $(\Omega, \mathscr{A})$, absolutely continuous with respect to P, the restriction $\mu_{\mathscr{B}}$ of μ to $(\Omega, \mathscr{B})$ is absolutely continuous with respect to the restriction $P_{\mathscr{B}}$; if X is the positive r.r.v., unique up to equivalence, such that $\mu = X \cdot P$, we set $\mu_{\mathscr{B}} = E^{\mathscr{B}}X \cdot P$ on $(\Omega, \mathscr{B})$. This definition of $E^{\mathscr{B}}X$ (sometimes the notation $E(X \mid \mathscr{B})$, rather than $E^{\mathscr{B}}X$, is used) and the following one which is equivalent to it are thus justified by the Radon-Nikodym theorem.

Definition IV.3.1. IF X IS AN (EQUIVALENCE CLASS OF) POSITIVE r.r.v. X ON $(\Omega, \mathscr{A}, P)$, THE CONDITIONAL EXPECTATION $E^{\mathscr{B}}X$ OF X WITH RESPECT TO THE σ-SUBALGEBRA $\mathscr{B}$ OF $\mathscr{A}$ IS THE UNIQUE POSITIVE (EQUIVALENCE CLASS OF) r.r.v. ON $(\Omega, \mathscr{B}, P_{\mathscr{B}})$ SUCH THAT

$$\int_B X\, dP = \int_B E^{\mathscr{B}}X\, dP_{\mathscr{B}} \qquad (B \in \mathscr{B})$$

OR, WHAT IS EQUIVALENT, SUCH THAT $\int XZ\, dP = \int (E^{\mathscr{B}}X)Z\, dP_{\mathscr{B}}$ FOR EVERY POSITIVE AND $\mathscr{B}$-MEASURABLE r.r.v. Z.

(The first equality of this definition implies the second for every $Z = 1_B$ $(B \in \mathscr{B})$, therefore by linearity for every positive $\mathscr{B}$-measurable step r.r.v., and therefore by monotone continuity for every positive $\mathscr{B}$-measurable r.r.v.)

Since $E(E^{\mathscr{B}}X) = E(X)$, the positive r.r.v. $E^{\mathscr{B}}X$ is integrable if and only if X is. This remark allows us to extend the preceding definition to every quasi-integrable r.r.v. by setting $E^{\mathscr{B}}X = E^{\mathscr{B}}(X^+) - E^{\mathscr{B}}(X^-)$.

Let B be an atom of $(\Omega, \mathscr{B}, P_{\mathscr{B}})$ if there is one. Since every $\mathscr{B}$-measurable r.r.v. is necessarily a.s. constant on B, we must have

$$E^{\mathscr{B}}X \underset{\text{a.s.}}{=} \frac{1}{P(B)} \int_B X\, dP \qquad \text{on} \quad B.$$

In the particular case where the σ-algebra $\mathscr{B}$ is generated by a countable partition $\{B_i, i \in I\}$ of $(\Omega, \mathscr{A})$, the preceding formula completely determines $E^{\mathscr{B}}X$ on Ω; the result is that which is set up as a definition in elementary probability theory.

The conditional expectation of a (class of) r.r.v. is a (class of) r.r.v., while the expectation of a (class of) r.r.v. is a real number; with this single difference the properties of the conditional expectation are analogous to those of the expectation [observe, by the way, that $E^{\mathscr{B}_0}(X) = E(X)$ if $\mathscr{B}_0 = \{\varnothing, \Omega\}$]. We shall simply cite them, leaving it to the reader to verify them by using Definition IV.3.1:

(a) $E^{\mathscr{B}}X \geqslant 0$ a.s. if $X \geqslant 0$ a.s.; $E^{\mathscr{B}}X \underset{\text{a.s.}}{=} 0$ if $X \underset{\text{a.s.}}{=} 0$.

$E(E^{\mathscr{B}}X) = E(X)$; $E^{\mathscr{B}}X$ is integrable if and only if X is;

$E^{\mathscr{B}}(1) \underset{\text{a.s.}}{=} 1$;

(b) $E^{\mathscr{B}}(cX) \underset{\text{a.s.}}{=} cE^{\mathscr{B}}X$ if $c \in R$,

$E^{\mathscr{B}}(X_1 + X_2) \underset{\text{a.s.}}{=} E^{\mathscr{B}}X_1 + E^{\mathscr{B}}X_2$ if X_1^- and X_2^-, or X_1^+ and X_2^+, are integrable;

(c) $X_1 \leqslant X_2$ a.s. $\Rightarrow E^{\mathscr{B}}X_1 \leqslant E^{\mathscr{B}}X_2$ a.s.;

(d) $X_n \uparrow X$ a.s. $\Rightarrow E^{\mathscr{B}}X_n \uparrow E^{\mathscr{B}}X$ a.s. if $E(X_n^-) < +\infty$ for at least one n;

$X_n \downarrow X$ a.s. $\Rightarrow E^{\mathscr{B}}X_n \downarrow E^{\mathscr{B}}X$ a.s. if $E(X_n^+) < +\infty$ for at least one n.

(The statements of these results are a little simpler when one only considers integrable r.r.v.) Properties (c) and (d) imply the generalized *Fatou-Lebesgue* lemma:

If $\{X_n, n \geqslant 1\}$ *is a sequence of* r.r.v.'s *and if* Y *and* Z *are integrable* r.r.v.'s, *then the following implications are valid:*

$$Y \leqslant X_n \text{ a.s. } (n \geqslant 1) \Rightarrow E^{\mathscr{B}}(\liminf_n X_n) \leqslant \liminf_n E^{\mathscr{B}}(X_n) \text{ a.s.},$$

$$X_n \leqslant Z \text{ a.s. } (n \geqslant 1) \Rightarrow \limsup_n E^{\mathscr{B}}(X_n) \leqslant E^{\mathscr{B}}(\limsup_n X_n) \text{ a.s.}$$

If the sequence $\{X_n, n \geqslant 1\}$ *of* r.r.v.'s *is convergent and is majorized in absolute value by an integrable* r.r.v. U, *that is,* $|X_n| \leqslant U$ $(n \geqslant 1)$, *then*

$$E^{\mathscr{B}}(\lim_n X_n) \underset{\text{a.s.}}{=} \lim_n E^{\mathscr{B}}X_n.$$

The following properties are peculiar to the conditional expectation:

(1) If X is $\mathscr{B}$-measurable, then $E^{\mathscr{B}}X \underset{\text{a.s.}}{=} X$ and more generally, for every r.r.v. Y on $(\Omega, \mathscr{A}, P)$, $E^{\mathscr{B}}(XY) \underset{\text{a.s.}}{=} X \cdot E^{\mathscr{B}}Y$;

(2) $\mathscr{B}_1 \subset \mathscr{B}_2 \Rightarrow E^{\mathscr{B}_1}(E^{\mathscr{B}_2}X) = E^{\mathscr{B}_1}X = E^{\mathscr{B}_2}(E^{\mathscr{B}_1}X)$.

Since, as an easy generalization of Lemma II.6.1, we have $E^{\mathscr{B}}[\varphi(X)] \geqslant \varphi(E^{\mathscr{B}}X)$ for every r.r.v. $X \geqslant 0$ and every real continuous convex function φ defined on $[0, \infty]$, the conditional moments $E^{\mathscr{B}}(|X|^p)$ of a r.r.v. have properties analogous to those of the moments of a r.r.v. We can thus show, for example, that $E^{\mathscr{B}}(|X|^p) \geqslant (E^{\mathscr{B}}|X|)^p$ for every p $(1 \leqslant p \leqslant \infty)$ and that $E^{\mathscr{B}}|X| \geqslant |E^{\mathscr{B}}X|$. On combining these two results, we see that $E(|X|)^p = E(E^{\mathscr{B}}(|X|^p)) \geqslant E(|E^{\mathscr{B}}X|^p)$, that is, $\|X\|_p \geqslant \|E^{\mathscr{B}}X\|_p$ for every (class of) r.r.v. $X \in L_p$ $(\Omega, \mathscr{A}, P)$. The preceding, together with properties (b) and (2) of $E^{\mathscr{B}}$, implies the following result.

PROPOSITION IV.3.1. *The conditional expectation* $E^{\mathscr{B}}$, *restricted to the space* $L_p(\Omega, \mathscr{A}, P)$, *is for every* $p \geqslant 1$ *a linear idempotent transformation with norm* 1 *(a projection) of the space* $L_p(\Omega, \mathscr{A}, P)$ *onto the subspace* $L_p(\Omega, \mathscr{B}, P_{\mathscr{B}})$. *In particular, on the Hilbert space* $L_2(\Omega, \mathscr{A}, P)$ *the conditional expectation* $E^{\mathscr{B}}$ *is the orthogonal projection of* $L_2(\Omega, \mathscr{A}, P)$ *onto the subspace* $L_2(\Omega, \mathscr{B}, P_{\mathscr{B}})$.

This last property is sometimes taken as the definition, on $L_2(\Omega, \mathscr{A}, P)$, of the conditional expectation $E^{\mathscr{B}}$; this operator is then extended to the r.r.v.'s having an integral, and the various results of this section are then established without difficulty.

When the σ-algebra $\mathscr{B}$ with respect to which one conditions is generated by a r.r.v. Z on $(\Omega, \mathscr{A}, P)$, that is, $\mathscr{B} = \mathscr{B}(Z)$, the r.r.v. $E^{\mathscr{B}}X$ is also denoted by $E(X \mid Z)$. By Proposition II.2.5, $E(X \mid Z)$ is a real measurable function of Z; such a function is sometimes called, by abuse of language, the conditional expectation of X with respect to Z (this function, by the way, is only determined up to equivalence with respect to the induced measure $P \circ Z^{-1}$).

Complements and problems

IV.3.1. Show that for every closed vector subspace H of $L_2(\Omega, \mathscr{A}, P)$ such that $1 \in H$, the following conditions are equivalent:

(1) there exists a σ-subalgebra $\mathscr{B}$ of $\mathscr{A}$ such that $H = L_2(\Omega, \mathscr{B}, P_{\mathscr{B}})$ [in this case, automatically, $1 \in H$];

(2) the projection P_H of L_2 onto H is a positive operator;

(3) H is a subspace of L_2 and a lattice;

(4) $H \cap L_\infty(\Omega, \mathscr{A}, P)$ is an algebra which is L_2-dense in H. [Show first that (1) $\Rightarrow$ (2), (3) and (4); to show that (2) $\Rightarrow$ (3), observe that for every $f \in H$, $P_H(f^+) \geqslant (P_H f)^+ = f^+$ and thus that $P_H f^+ = f^+$ since $\|P_H\| \leqslant 1$; to prove that (3) $\Rightarrow$ (1) and (4) $\Rightarrow$ (1), show that $\mathscr{B} = \{B\colon 1_B \in H\}$ is a σ-algebra and that $H = L_2(\Omega, \mathscr{B}, P_{\mathscr{B}})$.]

Show that an endomorphism T of $L_2(\Omega, \mathscr{A}, P)$ is a conditional expectation if and only if it satisfies the three conditions

(a) $T[L_\infty(\Omega, \mathscr{A}, P)] \subset L_\infty(\Omega, \mathscr{A}, P)$;

(b) $T[f \cdot Tg] = Tf \cdot Tg$ when $f \in L_2(\Omega, \mathscr{A}, P)$ and $g \in L_\infty(\Omega, \mathscr{A}, P)$;

(c) $E(Tf) = E(f)$ for every $f \in L_2$. [Note that the first two conditions imply that $\{g\colon g \in L_\infty, T(fg) = Tf \cdot g \text{ for every } f \in L_2\}$ is an algebra which is closed under monotone limits, and therefore of the form $L_\infty(\Omega, \mathscr{B}, P_{\mathscr{B}})$ for some σ-subalgebra $\mathscr{B}$ of $\mathscr{A}$. Deduce from this that $T[L_\infty(\mathscr{A})] \subset L_\infty(\mathscr{B})$ and that $Tf = E^{\mathscr{B}}(f \cdot T^*1)$; finally, use (c).]

Show that every positive idempotent contraction T of $L_2(\Omega, \mathscr{A}, P)$ which satisfies $T1 = 1$ is a conditional expectation. [Deduce from the first part of the problem that the space $\{f;\ Tf = f\}$ is of the form $L_2(\Omega, \mathscr{B}, P_{\mathscr{B}})$ for some σ-subalgebra $\mathscr{B}$ of $\mathscr{A}$. Show next that if $E^{\mathscr{B}}f = 0$, Tf and f are orthogonal and consequently $Tf = 0$.]

IV.3.2. **Strong convergence of conditional expectations on L_p.** Show that for every $p \in [1, \infty)$ and every $X \in L_p(\Omega, \mathscr{A}, P)$ the family

$$\{[E^{\mathscr{B}}(X)]^p;\ \mathscr{B} \subset \mathscr{A}\}$$

obtained by letting $\mathscr{B}$ vary among the σ-subalgebras of $\mathscr{A}$ is uniformly integrable. Given a sequence (or a generalized sequence) $\{\mathscr{B}_n\}$ of σ-subalgebras of $\mathscr{A}$ such that the limit $\lim_n E^{\mathscr{B}_n}(1_A)$ exists for every $A \in \mathscr{A}$ (or only for every A of a semialgebra generating $\mathscr{A}$) in the sense of convergence in probability, show that for every $p \in [1,\infty)$ and every $X \in L_p$ the limit $\lim_n E^{\mathscr{B}_n}(X)$ exists in the sense of convergence in L_p. Show, moreover, by using Problem IV.3.1, that there exists a σ-subalgebra $\mathscr{B}$ of $\mathscr{A}$ such that the above limits equal $E^{\mathscr{B}}(1_A)$ and $E^{\mathscr{B}}(X)$ respectively.

Show that for every monotone sequence (or generalized sequence) $\{\mathscr{B}_n\}$ of σ-subalgebras of $\mathscr{A}$ we have $\lim_n E^{\mathscr{B}_n}(X) = E^{\mathscr{B}}(X)$ for every $X \in L_p$ and every $p \in [1,\infty)$, where $\mathscr{B}$ denotes the intersection of the $\mathscr{B}_n$ in the case of a decreasing sequence, and the σ-algebra generated by the $\mathscr{B}_n$ in the case of an increasing sequence. [Reduce it to the case $p = 2$; in the case of an increasing sequence, for example, observe that the aforementioned convergence is obvious if X belongs to one of the spaces $L_2(\Omega, \mathscr{B}_n, P_{\mathscr{B}_n})$ or is orthogonal to $L_2(\Omega, \mathscr{B}, P_{\mathscr{B}})$.]

IV.3.3. Show that for every positive r.r.v. X defined on a probability space $(\Omega, \mathscr{A}, P)$ and for every σ-subalgebra $\mathscr{B}$ of $\mathscr{A}$ containing the negligible sets of $\mathscr{A}$, $\{E^{\mathscr{B}}(X) > 0\}$ is the smallest equivalence class of sets of $\mathscr{B}$ containing the support $\{X > 0\}$ of the r.r.v. X. For the validity of this result, the assumption that $\mathscr{B}$ contains the negligible sets in $\mathscr{A}$ is essential (consider the case where $\mathscr{B} = \{\varnothing, \Omega\}$ and where X is a.s. zero but not identically zero).

IV.3.4. Let $(\Omega, \mathscr{A}, P)$ be a probability space. Given the probability $Q = X \cdot P$ on $(\Omega, \mathscr{A})$, express the conditional expectation $E_Q^{\mathscr{B}}$ defined on $(\Omega, \mathscr{A}, Q)$ in terms of the conditional expectation $E_P^{\mathscr{B}}$ defined on $(\Omega, \mathscr{A}, P)$. Under what conditions is it true that $E_Q^{\mathscr{B}}(Z) = E_P^{\mathscr{B}}(Z)$ a.s. for Q, for every positive r.r.v. Z?

IV.3.5. **(Sufficient σ-algebras.)** Let $\{P(\theta, \cdot), \theta \in \Theta\}$ be a family of probabilities defined on $(\Omega, \mathscr{A})$ and absolutely continuous with respect to an auxiliary probability chosen (see Problem IV.1.3) of the form

$$P = \sum_{\theta} a_\theta P(\theta, \cdot),$$

where $a_\theta \geqslant 0$ and $\sum a_\theta = 1$; we set $p_\theta = dP(\theta, \cdot)/dP$. Show that the σ-algebra $\mathscr{B}(p_\theta, \theta \in \Theta)$ is the smallest σ-subalgebra $\mathscr{B}$ of $\mathscr{A}$ having the following property: for every positive r.r.v. Y on $(\Omega, \mathscr{A})$, there exists a positive $\mathscr{B}$-measurable r.r.v. Y' such that $E_{P(\theta,\cdot)}^{\mathscr{B}}(Y) = Y'$ a.s. for $P(\theta, \cdot)$, for every θ. [Solve Problem IV.3.4 and observe that if $\mathscr{B}$ has the preceding property, we have $E^{\mathscr{B}}[Y(p_\theta - E^{\mathscr{B}}p_\theta)] = 0$ a.s. for P, for every r.r.v. Y; take

$$Y = p_\theta - E^{\mathscr{B}}p_\theta.]$$

For any function f of θ and any integrable r.r.v. Y, we have

$$\int [E_P^{\mathscr{B}}(Y) - f(\theta)]^2 \, dP_\theta \leqslant \int [Y - f(\theta)]^2 \, dP_\theta$$

for every θ. This says, in the language of decision theory (Problem III.2.3), that the class of $\mathscr{B}$-measurable estimators is complete for the quadratic loss function. The same result holds if we restrict ourselves to unbiased estimators, that is to r.r.v.'s Y such that $\int Y \, dP_\theta = f(\theta)$; in fact, $E^{\mathscr{B}}(Y)$ is unbiased whenever Y is.

Application. Given k r.r.v.'s $U_1, \ldots, U_k$ on $(\Omega, \mathscr{A}, P)$, show that the subset Θ of R^k where $\varphi(\theta) = \int \exp(\sum_i \theta_i U_i) \, dP$ is finite is a convex set; we suppose that this set contains at least one interior point; this is not a restriction of generality, for when necessary we can reduce the number of parameters. Show that the "sufficient" σ-algebra $\mathscr{B}$ associated with the family of probabilities $\{P_\theta, \theta \in \Theta\}$ with P-densities on $(\Omega, \mathscr{A})$ equal to

$$P_\theta = [\varphi(\theta)]^{-1} \exp\left(\sum_i \theta_i U_i\right)$$

is identical with $\mathscr{B}(U_i, 1 \leqslant i \leqslant k)$. If Π denotes the probability induced on R^k by the U_i, that is $\Pi(S) = P[(U_1, \ldots, U_k) \in S]$, show that a function f of θ has an unbiased estimator if and only if there exists a measurable function g defined on R^k such that $f(\theta) = \int \exp(\theta u) g(u) \Pi(du)$. If it exists, the function g is unique up to Π-equivalence and, moreover, one can show that $g(U_1, \ldots, U_k)$ is an unbiased estimator of $f(\theta)$ which is preferable to every other unbiased estimator of $f(\theta)$.

IV.3.6. Show that if $X_n \downarrow X$ a.s., then $E^{\mathscr{B}} X_n \downarrow E^{\mathscr{B}} X$ a.s. on the set $\bigcup_n \{E^{\mathscr{B}} X_n < \infty\}$; deduce from this a generalization of the Fatou-Lebesgue lemma of the present section.

IV.4. INDEPENDENCE

We take a fixed probability space $(\Omega, \mathscr{A}, P)$ throughout this section.

Definition IV.4.1. A FINITE FAMILY $\{\mathscr{B}_i, i \in I\}$ OF σ-SUBALGEBRAS OF $\mathscr{A}$ IS SAID TO BE INDEPENDENT (RELATIVE TO P) IF

$$P\left(\bigcap_I B_i\right) = \prod_I P(B_i)$$

FOR EVERY CHOICE OF $B_i \in \mathscr{B}_i$ $(i \in I)$ OR, WHAT IS EQUIVALENT, IF

$$E\left(\prod_I Y_i\right) = \prod_I E(Y_i)$$

FOR EVERY CHOICE OF POSITIVE $\mathscr{B}_i$-MEASURABLE r.r.v.'s Y_i $(i \in I)$. AN

INFINITE FAMILY $\{\mathscr{B}_i, i \in I\}$ OF σ-SUBALGEBRAS OF $\mathscr{A}$ IS SAID TO BE INDEPENDENT IF EVERY FINITE SUBFAMILY IS INDEPENDENT.

We leave it to the reader to verify the equivalence of the two preceding definitions of independence by using the properties of linearity and monotone continuity of the expectation.

PROPOSITION IV.4.1. (CRITERION FOR INDEPENDENCE.)
Let $\{\mathscr{C}_i, i \in I\}$ be an arbitrary family of nonempty subclasses of $\mathscr{A}$ having the following properties:

(a) *each of the classes $\mathscr{C}_i$ is closed under intersection;*

(b) *the family of $\mathscr{C}_i$ $(i \in I)$ is independent in the sense that for every choice of $C_j \in \mathscr{C}_j$ $(j \in J \subset I;\ J$ finite) we have*

$$P\left(\bigcap_J C_j\right) = \prod_J P(C_j).$$

Then the family $\{\mathscr{B}_i, i \in I\}$ of σ-algebras generated by the classes $\mathscr{C}_i$ $(i \in I)$ is independent; every family $\{\mathscr{B}'_i, i \in I\}$, where the $\mathscr{B}'_i$ differ from the $\mathscr{B}_i$ only by negligible sets, is again independent.

PROOF. It suffices to prove the proposition when I is finite. Let us choose an $i \in I$ and denote by $\mathscr{D}$ the subclass of $\mathscr{A}$ consisting of sets D such that $P[D \cap \bigcap_{j \neq i} C_j] = P(D) \prod_{j \neq i} P(C_j)$ for every choice of $C_j \in \mathscr{C}_j$ $(j \neq i)$. It is easy to see that $\mathscr{D}$ contains $\mathscr{C}_i$ and is a σ-additive class in the sense of Problem I.4.8; it follows that $\mathscr{D}$ contains $\mathscr{B}_i$. Thus, the family $\{\mathscr{B}_i, \mathscr{C}_j\ (j \neq i)\}$ has properties (a) and (b) of the proposition; repeating the preceding argument once for each remaining $i \in I$, $i \neq j$, we obtain the independence of $\{\mathscr{B}_i, i \in I\}$. Finally, it is evident that the family $\{\mathscr{B}'_i, i \in I\}$ is independent if every member of $\mathscr{B}'_i$ is of the form $B \cup N$ for some $B \in \mathscr{B}_i$ and some negligible set N. ∎

COROLLARY. *If $\{\mathscr{B}_i, i \in I\}$ is an independent family of σ-subalgebras of $\mathscr{A}$ and if $\{I_j, j \in J\}$ is a family of pairwise disjoint subsets of I, the family $\{\mathscr{B}_{I_j}, j \in J\}$ is again independent, where $\mathscr{B}_{I_j}$ denotes the σ-algebra generated by the $\mathscr{B}_i$ $(i \in I_j)$.*

PROOF. Let $\mathscr{C}_{I_j}$ be the subclass of $\mathscr{A}$ consisting of sets of the form $\bigcap_{i \in K} B_i$ $(B_i \in \mathscr{B}_i)$, where K is an arbitrary finite subset of I_j. The family $\{\mathscr{C}_{I_j}, j \in J\}$ satisfies the hypotheses of the preceding proposition; on the other hand, each of the classes $\mathscr{C}_{I_j}$ (is a semialgebra which) generates $\mathscr{B}_{I_j}$. The corollary follows from this. ▮

PROPOSITION IV.4.2. *In order that two σ-subalgebras $\mathscr{B}_1$ and $\mathscr{B}_2$ of $\mathscr{A}$ be independent in the probability space $(\Omega, \mathscr{A}, P)$, it is necessary and sufficient that*

$$E^{\mathscr{B}_1}(Y) = E(Y) \quad \text{a.s.}$$

for every $\mathscr{B}_2$-measurable positive r.r.v. *Y.*

PROOF. By the definition of the conditional expectation, the equality $E^{\mathscr{B}_1}(Y) = E(Y)$ is equivalent, for a fixed positive r.r.v. Y, to the validity of the relation $E(X)E(Y) = E(XY)$ for every positive $\mathscr{B}_1$-measurable r.r.v. X. The result of the proposition now follows at once from the definition of independence (taken in its second form). ▮

Definition IV.4.2. A FAMILY $\{X_i, i \in I\}$ OF r.r.v.'S IS SAID TO BE INDEPENDENT (RELATIVE TO P) IF THE FAMILY $\{\mathscr{B}(X_i), i \in I\}$ OF σ-SUBALGEBRAS OF $\mathscr{A}$ IS INDEPENDENT. A FAMILY $\{A_i, i \in I\}$ OF EVENTS IS SAID TO BE INDEPENDENT IF $\{1_{A_i}, i \in I\}$ IS INDEPENDENT.

The foregoing criterion for independence implies the following result, if we take for $\mathscr{C}_i$ $(i \in I)$ the class of sets $\{X_i < a\}$ $(a \in R)$, or the class $\mathscr{C}_i = \{A_i\}$.

The family $\{X_i, i \in I\}$ of r.r.v.'s *is independent if and only if*

$$P\left[\bigcap_J \{X_j < a_j\}\right] = \prod_J P(X_j < a_j)$$

for every choice of real a_j $(j \in J)$ and every finite subset J of I. The family $\{A_i, i \in I\}$ of events is independent if and only if $P(\bigcap_J A_j) = \prod_J P(A_j)$ for every finite subset J of I.

The following definition is not related to independence; we introduce it here for the result which follows. There is no difficulty in generalizing the following notions to generalized sequences of σ-algebras or of r.r.v.'s.

Definition IV.4.3. GIVEN A SEQUENCE $\{\mathscr{B}_n, n \geqslant 1\}$ OF σ-SUBALGEBRAS OF $\mathscr{A}$, THE EVENTS OF THE σ-ALGEBRA $\mathscr{B}_\infty$, THE INTERSECTION OVER N OF THE σ-ALGEBRAS GENERATED BY THE $\mathscr{B}_n$ $(n \geqslant N)$, ARE CALLED ASYMPTOTIC (OR TERMINAL) EVENTS.

In particular, if $\mathscr{B}_n = \mathscr{B}(X_n)$ for r.r.v.'s X_n, one has

$$\mathscr{B}_\infty = \bigcap_N \mathscr{B}\{X_n, n \geqslant N\}.$$

PROPOSITION IV.4.3. ZERO-ONE LAW. *The probability of every event which is asymptotic relative to a sequence* $\{\mathscr{B}_n, n \geqslant 1\}$ *of independent* σ-*algebras, equals* 0 *or* 1. (*In other words* $\mathscr{B}_\infty = \{\varnothing, \Omega\}$ *up to negligible sets.*)

PROOF. It suffices to apply the corollary of Proposition IV.4.1 twice. In fact, the independence of $\{\mathscr{B}_n, n \geqslant 1\}$ implies that of $\{\mathscr{B}_m\ (m \leqslant M), \mathscr{A}_N\}$ if $\mathscr{A}_N$ denotes the σ-algebra generated by the $\mathscr{B}_n\ (n \geqslant N)$ and if $N > M$; since $\mathscr{B}_\infty \subset \mathscr{A}_N$, it follows that $\{\mathscr{B}_n\ (m \leqslant M), \mathscr{B}_\infty)$ is independent, and thus also that $\{\mathscr{B}_n, 1 \leqslant n \leqslant \infty\}$ is. Hence $\mathscr{A}_1$ and $\mathscr{B}_\infty$ are independent, and in particular $\mathscr{B}_\infty$ is independent of itself; in other words

$$P(B \cap B) = P(B)P(B)$$

for every $B \in \mathscr{B}_\infty$, which is equivalent to $P(B) = 0$ or 1 $(B \in \mathscr{B}_\infty)$. ∎

COROLLARY 1. *A* r.r.v. X *which is asymptotic relative to a sequence* $\{\mathscr{B}_n, n \geqslant 1\}$ *of independent* σ-*algebras (i.e.,* $\mathscr{B}_\infty$-*measurable) is* a.s. *constant.*

COROLLARY 2. *For every sequence* $\{X_n, n \geqslant 1\}$ *of finite independent* r.r.v.'s *and every sequence* $\{\varphi_n\}$ *of real numbers tending to zero, the series* $\sum_n X_n$ *converges or diverges* a.s., *and the sequences* $\{X_n\}$ *and* $\{\varphi_n(\sum_1^n X_m)\}$ *converge or diverge* a.s.

In concluding this section, let us recall the following classical result, which is as important as its proof is simple and direct.

PROPOSITION IV.4.4. (BOREL-CANTELLI.) *For any sequence*

$$\{A_n, n \geqslant 1\}$$

of events one has

$$\sum_n P(A_n) < \infty \Rightarrow \limsup_n A_n \underset{\text{a.s.}}{=} \varnothing,$$

$$\sum_n P\left[A_n \,\middle|\, \bigcap_1^{n-1} A_m^c\right] = \infty \Rightarrow \sup_n A_n \underset{\text{a.s.}}{=} \Omega.$$

In particular, for every independent sequence $\{A_n, n \geqslant 1\}$ *of events one has* $\limsup_n A_n \underset{\text{a.s.}}{=} \varnothing$ *or* Ω *according as the series* $\sum_n P(A_n)$ *converges or diverges.*

PROOF. The first two implications follow, respectively, from

$$P(\sup_{m \geqslant n} A_m) \leqslant \sum_{m \geqslant n} P(A_m)$$

upon letting $n \to \infty$, and from

$$P(\sup_n A_m) = 1 - P(\inf_n A_n^c) = 1 - \prod_n \left[P\left(\bigcap_1^n A_m^c\right)\Big/P\left(\bigcap_1^{n-1} A_m^c\right)\right]$$
$$= 1 - \prod_n \left\{1 - P\left[A_n \,\Big|\, \bigcap_1^{n-1} A_m^c\right]\right\}.$$

Since $P(A_n|\bigcap_1^{n-1} A_m^c) = P(A_n)$ if the sequence $\{A_n, n \geqslant 1\}$ is independent, the second part of the proposition follows at once from the first. ∎

Complements and problems

IV.4.1. If $\{\mathscr{B}_i, i \in I\}$ is an arbitrary independent family of σ-algebras in $(\Omega, \mathscr{A}, P)$, the family $\{\mathscr{B}_i', i \in I\}$ is again independent if $\mathscr{B}_i' \subset \mathscr{B}_i$ $(i \in I)$. Deduce from this that $\{f_i(X_i), i \in I\}$ is a family of independent r.r.v.'s if the family $\{X_i, i \in I\}$ is independent and if the f_i are measurable. In order that the family $\{X_i, i \in I\}$ of r.r.v.'s be independent, it is necessary and sufficient that

$$E\left[\prod_J f_j(X_j)\right] = \prod_J Ef_j(X_j)$$

for every finite family $\{f_j, j \in J\}$ of bounded measurable functions.

IV.4.2. **Conditional independence.** On the probability space $(\Omega, \mathscr{A}, P)$, the family $\{\mathscr{B}_i, i \in I\}$ of σ-subalgebras of $\mathscr{A}$ is said to be conditionally independent with respect to $\mathscr{B}$, if $E^{\mathscr{B}}(\prod_J X_j) = \prod_J E^{\mathscr{B}}(X_j)$ for every finite family $\{X_j, j \in J\}$ of positive r.r.v.'s such that X_j is $\mathscr{B}_j$-measurable, and for every $J \subset I$. Generalize the results of this section, in particular the zero-one law, to conditional independence.

IV.4.3. **Markovian dependence.** Given an interval T of R or of Z, a family $\{\mathscr{B}_t, t \in T\}$ of σ-subalgebras of $\mathscr{A}$ is said to have Markovian dependence in $(\Omega, \mathscr{A}, P)$ if for every $t \in T$, the σ-algebras $\sigma(\mathscr{B}_s; s \leqslant t)$ and $\sigma(\mathscr{B}_s; s \geqslant t)$ are conditionally independent with respect to $\mathscr{B}_t$. To this end; (1) it is necessary that for every t and every quasi-integrable r.r.v. Y measurable with respect to

$$\sigma(\mathscr{B}_s; s \geqslant t),$$

we have $E(Y \mid \mathscr{B}_t) = E[Y \mid \sigma(\mathscr{B}_s; s \leqslant t)]$; (2) it is sufficient that for every t and every A belonging to one of the σ-algebras $\mathscr{B}_u$ $(u > t)$ we have

$$E(1_A \mid \mathscr{B}_t) = E[1_A \mid \sigma(\mathscr{B}_{s_1}, \ldots, \mathscr{B}_{s_n}, \mathscr{B}_t)]$$

for any finite number of s_j which are less than t. Show, in addition, that if the family $\{\mathscr{B}_t, t \in T\}$ has Markovian dependence and if $u < v$ in T, the σ-algebras $\sigma(\mathscr{B}_t, t \leqslant u)$ and $\sigma(\mathscr{B}_t, t \geqslant v)$ are conditionally independent with respect to $\sigma(\mathscr{B}_t, u \leqslant t \leqslant v)$. [Here σ stands for "σ-algebra generated by."]

IV.4.4. **Gaussian spaces.** A closed subspace H of the L_2 space constructed on a probability space $(\Omega, \mathscr{A}, P)$ is said to be Gaussian if for every

$X \in H$ the probability induced by X on R is a (possibly degenerate) Gaussian law or, what is the same, if for every $X \in H$ we have

$$\log E(\exp(itX)) = itE(X) - (1/2)t^2\{E(X^2) - [E(X)]^2\}.$$

In order that H be Gaussian, show: (1) that it is necessary that every vector $(X_1, \ldots, X_n)$ with coordinates $X_m \in H$ have a Gaussian law in R^n; (2) that it is sufficient that there exist a subset G of H whose linear span is dense in H and such that every vector $(X_1, \ldots, X_n)$ with coordinates $X_m \in G$ has a Gaussian law.

Let H be a Gaussian space consisting of centered r.r.v.'s (that is, orthogonal to 1) and let $\mathscr{H}$ be the smallest σ-subalgebra of $\mathscr{A}$ with respect to which all the r.r.v.'s of H are measurable. If $\{X_i, i \in I\}$ is an orthonormal system in H which is complete in H, show that the products $\prod_I [1/\sqrt{n_i!}]H_{n_i}(X_i)$ of Hermite polynomials form a complete orthonormal system in $L_2(\Omega, \mathscr{H}, P)$ when the n_i run through the nonnegative integers, but are such that $\sum_I n_i < \infty$. [Use the formula defining the Hermite polynomials:

$$\exp(ux - \tfrac{1}{2}u^2) = \sum_{n \geq 0} (u^n/n!)H_n(X).]$$

Let H_1 be a closed subspace of a Gaussian space H consisting of centered r.r.v.'s and let $\mathscr{H}_1$ be the σ-algebra generated by H_1. Show that the restrictions to H of the operators proj_{H_1} and $E^{\mathscr{H}_1}$ are identical. [Reduce it to considering only the r.r.v.'s orthogonal to H_1.] Deduce from this that two Gaussian subspaces H_1 and H_2 which are orthogonal to 1 are mutually orthogonal if and only if the σ-algebras $\mathscr{H}_1$ and $\mathscr{H}_2$ which they generate are independent.

IV.4.5. If, in a probability space $(\Omega, \mathscr{A}, P)$, three σ-subalgebras $\mathscr{A}_1$, $\mathscr{A}_2$, $\mathscr{A}_3$ of $\mathscr{A}$ satisfy the conditions (1) $\mathscr{A}_1$ is contained in the σ-algebra generated by $\mathscr{A}_2$ and $\mathscr{A}_3$, (2) the σ-algebra generated by $\mathscr{A}_1$ and $\mathscr{A}_2$ is independent of $\mathscr{A}_3$, show that $\mathscr{A}_1 \subset \mathscr{A}_2$ up to negligible sets, that is, for any $A \in \mathscr{A}_1$ there is a $B \in \mathscr{A}_2$ such that $P(A \triangle B) = 0$. [Deduce from (2) that

$$E^{\mathscr{A}_2}(X) = E^{\mathscr{A}_2 \vee \mathscr{A}_3}(X)$$

for every $\mathscr{A}_1$-measurable integrable r.r.v. X.]

IV.5. MARTINGALE THEORY

Throughout this section, we are given a probability space $(\Omega, \mathscr{A}, P)$, an interval T of the extended line $\bar{Z}$ of integers (discrete case) or of the extended real line $\bar{R}$ (continuous case) whose endpoints (not necessarily in T) will be denoted by t_l and t_r, and an increasing family $\{\mathscr{A}_t, t \in T\}$ of σ-subalgebras of $\mathscr{A}$. The notion of stopping times introduced in Section III.6 will here play a fundamental role.

Definition IV.5.1. A r.r.f. $\{X_t, t \in T\}$ WHICH IS ADAPTED TO THE FAMILY $\{\mathscr{A}_t, t \in T\}$ IS CALLED A SUBMARTINGALE (RELATIVE TO $\{\mathscr{A}_t, t \in T\}$) IF $E(X_t^+) < \infty$ FOR EVERY $t \in T$ AND IF, FOR EVERY PAIR $s < t$ IN T, WE HAVE $X_s \leqslant E^{\mathscr{A}_s}(X_t)$. IT IS CALLED A MARTINGALE IF $E|X_t| < \infty$ FOR EVERY $t \in T$ AND IF, FOR EVERY PAIR $s < t$ IN T, WE HAVE $X_s = E^{\mathscr{A}_s}(X_t)$. IT IS CALLED A SUPERMARTINGALE IF $\{-X_t, t \in T\}$ IS A SUBMARTINGALE.

(N.B.: Henceforth, and without further mention, we shall in the continuous case consider only separable martingales and submartingales; by Proposition III.4.3 this does not restrict generality.)

A submartingale is thus a r.r.f. which "grows in conditional mean." The inequalities in the definition of a submartingale are frequently used in the following equivalent form: for every pair $s < t$ in T and every $A \in \mathscr{A}_s$ one has the inequality

$$\int_A X_s \leqslant \int_A X_t.$$

They also imply that $E(X_s Y) \leqslant E(X_t Y)$ for every positive and $\mathscr{A}_s$-measurable r.r.v. Y, when $s < t$ in T.

The following technical result will be used frequently (Problem IV.5.4 gives a more general form of this result).

PROPOSITION IV.5.1. *If* $\{X_t, t \in T\}$ *is a submartingale, the* r.r.f. $\{\max(X_t, a), t \in T\}$ *is a submartingale for any* $a \in R$; *moreover, for any subinterval* T_1 *of* T *which is closed at the right, the family*

$$\{\max(X_t, a), t \in T_1\}$$

is uniformly integrable.

If $\{X_t, t \in T\}$ *is a martingale consisting of* r.r.v's *in* $L_p(\Omega, \mathscr{A}, P)$ *for a* $p \in [1, \infty)$, *then* $\{|X|^p, t \in T\}$ *is a positive submartingale; moreover, the family* $\{|X_t|^p, t \in T_1\}$ *is uniformly integrable for every subinterval* T_1 *of* T *which is closed at the right.*

PROOF. Since $\{X_t - a, t \in T\}$ is a submartingale whenever $\{X_t, t \in T\}$ is, it suffices to prove the first part of the proposition when $a = 0$. To show that $\{X_t^+, t \in T\}$ is a submartingale if $\{X_t, t \in T\}$ is, it suffices to observe that $E^{\mathscr{A}_s}(X_t^+) \geqslant [E^{\mathscr{A}_s}(X_t)]^+ \geqslant X_s^+$ for every pair $s < t$ in T. If t_1 is the right endpoint of a subinterval T_1 of T which is closed at the right, it follows from the chain of inequalities

$$cP(X_t > c) \leqslant \int_{\{X_t > c\}} X_t^+ \leqslant \int_{\{X_t > c\}} X_{t_1}^+ \leqslant E(X_{t_1}^+) < \infty \qquad (t \in T_1)$$

which is valid for any $c > 0$, that $\sup_{T_1} P(X_t > c) \downarrow 0$ as $c \uparrow \infty$ and consequently, $X_{t_1}^+$ being integrable, that $\sup_{t \in T_1} \int_{\{X_t > c\}} X_{t_1}^+ \downarrow 0$ as $c \uparrow \infty$. The second inequality in the chain above then shows that $\{X_t^+, t \in T_1\}$ is uniformly integrable.

If $\{X_t, t \in T\}$ is a martingale, then for every pair $s < t$ in T we have $E^{\mathscr{A}_s}(|X_t|^p) \geqslant |E^{\mathscr{A}_s}(X_t)|^p = |X_s|^p$. Hence the positive r.r.v.'s $|X_s|^p$ form a submartingale, as t varies in T, as long as they are integrable. The last part of the proposition now follows from the foregoing. ∎

Under very general conditions the inequality

$$X_s \leqslant E^{\mathscr{A}_s}(X_t) \qquad \text{if} \qquad s \leqslant t$$

in the definition of a submartingale remains valid when s and t are replaced by stopping times σ and τ such that $\sigma \leqslant \tau$. This fundamental property of submartingales will be given a precise formulation in Proposition IV.5.5; here we shall state a particular case on which the rest of this section is based.

LEMMA. *Let $\{X_t, \mathscr{A}_t; t \in T\}$ be a submartingale. If τ_1 and τ_2 are two stopping times defined on all of the space Ω relative to $\{\mathscr{A}_t, t \in T\}$ such that $\tau_1 \leqslant \tau_2$, and which take on only a finite number of distinct values in T, then $X_{\tau_1} \leqslant E^{\mathscr{A}_{\tau_1}}(X_{\tau_2})$. It follows in particular that for every stopping time τ which is everywhere defined and takes on only a finite number of distinct values lying between t_0 and t_1 in T we have*

$$X_{t_0} \leqslant E^{\mathscr{A}_{t_0}}(X_\tau), \qquad X_\tau \leqslant E^{\mathscr{A}_\tau}(X_{t_1}).$$

If $\{X_t, \mathscr{A}_t; t \in T\}$ is a martingale, the preceding inequalities become equalities under the same hypotheses.

PROOF. Let us denote the possible values of τ_1 and τ_2 by

$$t_0 < t_1 < \cdots < t_p.$$

Since X_{τ_1} is $\mathscr{A}_{\tau_1}$-measurable, the inequality $X_{\tau_1} \leqslant E^{\mathscr{A}_{\tau_1}}(X_{\tau_2})$ is equivalent to $\int_A X_{\tau_1} \leqslant \int_A X_{\tau_2}$ for every $A \in \mathscr{A}_{\tau_1}$, that is, for every A such that $A\{\tau_1 = t_m\} \in \mathscr{A}_{t_m}$ for $m = 0, \ldots, p$. Taking into account that $A = \sum_m A\{\tau_1 = t_m\}$ and the additivity of integration, it suffices to prove that $\int_B X_{t_m} \leqslant \int_B X_{\tau_2}$ when B is contained in $\{\tau_1 = t_m\}$ and belongs to $\mathscr{A}_{t_m}$.

To this end, we shall show that for such a set B, the function $\int_B X_{\tau_2 \wedge t_n}$ of n, defined for $m \leqslant n \leqslant p$, is nondecreasing; since $\tau_2 \wedge t_m = t_m$ on B

and since $\tau_2 \wedge t_p = \tau_2$, the proposition will be proved. But if $m \leqslant n \leqslant p$, it follows from $B\{\tau_2 > t_n\} \in \mathscr{A}_{t_n}$ that

$$\int_B X_{\tau_2 \wedge t_n} = \int_{B\{\tau_2 \leqslant t_n\}} X_{\tau_2} + \int_{B\{\tau_2 > t_n\}} X_{t_n}$$
$$\leqslant \int_{B\{\tau_2 \leqslant t_n\}} X_{\tau_2} + \int_{B\{\tau_2 > t_n\}} X_{t_{n+1}} = \int_B X_{\tau_2 \wedge t_{n+1}}.$$

The first part of the lemma is thus proved. The particular case which was formulated is obtained by taking successively $\tau_1 = t_0$, $\tau_2 = \tau$ and $\tau_1 = \tau$, $\tau_2 = t_1$. Finally, in the case of a martingale, an immediate modification of the arguments gives equalities in place of inequalities. ∎

PROPOSITION IV.5.2. *Every submartingale $\{X_t, \mathscr{A}_t; t \in T\}$ satisfies the following inequalities, where c is a positive constant:*

$$cP(\sup_T X_t > c) \leqslant \sup_T E(X_t^+) \quad (= E(X_{t_r}^+) < \infty \quad \textit{if} \quad t_r \in T).$$

Hence $\sup_T X_t < \infty$ a.s. *whenever* $\sup_T E(X_t^+) < \infty$, *in particular whenever T is closed at the right.*

If $\{X_t, \mathscr{A}_t; t \in T\}$ is a martingale, we have, for every positive constant c,

$$cP(\sup_T |X_t| > c) \leqslant \sup_T E|X_t| \quad (= E|X_{t_r}| \quad \textit{if} \quad t_r \in T)$$

and $\sup_T |X_t| < \infty$ a.s. *whenever the second term in the preceding inequality is finite.*

PROOF. We first restrict ourselves to considering the submartingale X only at a finite sequence $t_0 < t_1 < \cdots < t_p$ of instants, and denote by τ the first of these instants, if it exists, such that $X_t > c$. The variable τ with values in $\{t_0, t_1, \ldots, t_p\}$ is then a stopping time defined on

$$\Omega_\tau = \{\sup_m X_{t_m} > c\};$$

we have, in fact, $\{\tau = t_m\} = \{X_{t_k} \leqslant c \text{ if } k < m, X_{t_m} > c\} \in \mathscr{A}_{t_m}$. Applying the preceding lemma to the stopping times $\tau \wedge t_p$ and t_p, and taking into account that $X_\tau > c$ on Ω_τ, we obtain the inequalities

$$cP(\Omega_\tau) \leqslant \int_{\Omega_\tau} X_\tau = \int_{\Omega_\tau} X_{\tau \wedge t_p} \leqslant \int_{\Omega_\tau} X_{t_p} \leqslant E(X_{t_p}^+).$$

The first part of the proposition is thus proved in the case of a finite submartingale $\{X_{t_0}, \ldots, X_{t_p}\}$. In the general case, if $s_0, s_1, \ldots$ is an enumeration of T (discrete case) or a separant in T (continuous case), then by a passage to the limit, taking into account that

$$\sup_T X_t \underset{\text{a.s.}}{=} \lim_n \uparrow (\sup_{m \leqslant n} X_{s_m}),$$

we obtain

$$cP(\sup_T X_t > c) = c \lim_n \uparrow P(\sup_{m \leqslant n} X_{s_m} > c)$$
$$\leqslant \lim_n \uparrow \sup_{m \leqslant n} E(X_{s_m}^+) = \sup_T E(X_t^+).$$

Moreover, since the function $E(X_t^+)$ of t is increasing, we have

$$\sup_T E(X_t^+) = E(X_{t_r}^+) \quad \text{if} \quad t_r \in T, \quad = \lim_{t \uparrow t_r} E(X_t^+) \quad \text{if} \quad t_r \notin T.$$

Letting c tend to ∞, we see that $\sup_T X_t < \infty$ a.s. whenever $\sup_T E(X_t^+) < \infty$. Finally, if $\{X_t, t \in T\}$ is a martingale, the preceding is applicable to the submartingale $\{|X_t|, t \in T\}$ and yields the second part of the proposition. ∎

The inequality of the following proposition limits the average number of oscillations of a submartingale; from this inequality will follow the important convergence and continuity properties of submartingales, which are the objects of the rest of the theorems of this section. Let us recall, first of all, the following results from the theory of functions of a real variable.

Given a real function f which maps an interval T of $\bar{Z}$ or $\bar{R}$ into $\bar{R}$, one defines the number of times $\gamma_{a,b}(f)$ which the function f of t crosses the interval (a, b) of R in the descending sense (or *downcrossings* of (a, b)) as the supremum of those integers $m \geqslant 0$ for which there exists an increasing sequence $s_1 < s_2 < \cdots < s_{2m}$ in T of length $2m$ such that

$$f(s_1) > b,\ f(s_2) < a,\ f(s_3) > b, \ldots, f(s_{2m}) < a.$$

The condition $\gamma_{a,b}(f) < \infty$ for every pair $a < b$ in R (or only for every pair $a < b$ of a dense sequence in R) is then necessary and sufficient for the function f to be without discontinuities of the second kind on $\bar{T}$.

Let us also recall that the function f defined on an interval T of $\bar{Z}$ or $\bar{R}$ is said to be without discontinuities of the second kind on $\bar{T}$ if it has a limit from the left (from the right) at every point t of $\bar{Z}$ or $\bar{R}$ which is a limit from the left (from the right) of points of T, that is: (1) in the discrete case, if $\lim_{s \uparrow +\infty} f(s)$ exists when $t_r = +\infty$ and $\lim_{s \downarrow -\infty} f(s)$ exists when $t_l = -\infty$; (2) in the continuous case, if $f(t - 0) = \lim_{s \uparrow t} f(s)$ exists for every $t \in (t_l, t_r]$ and $f(t + 0) = \lim_{s \downarrow t} f(s)$ exists for every $t \in [t_l, t_r)$.

(One proves that the condition above is sufficient by noting that if, for example, $\liminf_{s \uparrow t} f(s) < \limsup_{s \uparrow t} f(s)$ for some t, the number

$\gamma_{a,b}$ is infinite for every pair $a < b$ lying between the two preceding limits. To prove that the condition is necessary, we associate with every $t \in \overline{T}$ an open interval I_t such that the oscillation of f on $I_t \cap (-\infty, t)$ and on $I_t \cap (t, +\infty)$ is less than a given ϵ; a finite number of such intervals suffices to cover $\overline{T}$, and one can show that this number majorizes $\gamma_{a,b}(f)$ as long as $(b - a) > 2\epsilon$.)

PROPOSITION IV.5.3. *Given a submartingale* $\{X_t, \mathscr{A}_t; t \in T\}$, *we denote by* $\gamma_{a,b}(\omega)$ *the number of downcrossings of the interval* (a, b) *by the trajectory* $X_{.}(\omega)$ *on* T. *Then* $\gamma_{a,b}$ *is a* r.v. *satisfying the inequality*

$$(b - a)E(\gamma_{a,b}) \leqslant \sup_T E[(X_t - b)^+].$$

PROOF. To begin with, we restrict ourselves to considering the submartingale only at a finite sequence $t_0 < t_1 < \cdots < t_p$ of instants in T, and introduce, by induction on m, the following variables τ_m which are obviously stopping times with values in $\{t_0, \ldots, t_p\}$; τ_1 denotes the first instant t_q $(0 \leqslant q \leqslant p)$, if it exists, such that $X_{t_q} > b$; τ_m for $m > 1$ denotes the first instant $t_i > \tau_{m-1}$, if it exists, such that $X_{t_i} < a$ if m is even, and such that $X_{t_i} > b$ if m is odd. The sequence of sets $\Omega_m = \Omega_{\tau_m}$ in Ω on which these stopping times are defined is evidently a decreasing sequence and one has $t_0 \leqslant \tau_1 < \tau_2 < \cdots < \tau_m < t_p$ on Ω_m; moreover, if

$$\gamma_{a,b}(t_0, \ldots, t_p; \omega)$$

denotes the number of downcrossings of the interval (a, b) by the sequence $\{X_{t_0}(\omega), \ldots, X_{t_p}(\omega)\}$, we have

$$\Omega_{2m} = \{\gamma_{a,b}(t_0, \ldots, t_p) \geqslant m\}.$$

This equality shows, first of all, that $\gamma_{a,b}(t_0, \ldots, t_p)$ is a random variable.

Taking into account that

$$X_{\tau_{2m-1}} > b \quad \text{on} \quad \Omega_{2m-1}, \qquad X_{\tau_{2m}} < a \quad \text{on} \quad \Omega_{2m},$$

and applying the lemma above to the stopping times $\tau_{2m-1} \wedge t_p$ and $\tau_{2m} \wedge t_p$, we obtain the inequalities

$$0 \leqslant \int_{\Omega_{2m-1}} (X_{\tau_{2m-1}} - b) \leqslant \int_{\Omega_{2m-1}} (X_{\tau_{2m} \wedge t_p} - b)$$
$$\leqslant (a - b)P(\Omega_{2m}) + \int_{\Omega_{2m-1} - \Omega_{2m}} (X_{t_p} - b).$$

It follows that

$$(b - a)P[\gamma_{a,b}(t_0, \ldots, t_p) \geqslant m] \leqslant \int_{\Omega_{2m-1} - \Omega_{2m}} (X_{t_p} - b)^+,$$

and since the sets $(\Omega_{2m-1} - \Omega_{2m})$ are pairwise disjoint as m varies, adding the preceding inequality over m yields

$$(b - a)E(\gamma_{a,b}(t_0, \ldots, t_p)) = (b - a) \sum_{m \geqslant 1} P[\gamma_{a,b}(t_0, \ldots, t_p) \geqslant m]$$
$$\leqslant E[(X_{t_p} - b)^+].$$

This proves the inequality of the proposition for the restriction of the submartingale X to $\{t_0, \ldots, t_p\}$. But since it is easily verified that

$$\gamma_{a,b}(\omega) = \lim_n \uparrow \gamma_{a,b}(\{s_0, \ldots, s_n\}; \omega)$$

for every (almost every) ω if $\{s_0, s_1, \ldots\}$ is an enumeration of T in the discrete case (a separant in T in the continuous case), and since the function $E[(X_t - b)^+]$ is increasing in t, we obtain the inequality of the proposition in the general case by a passage to the limit. ∎

COROLLARY. *Let $\{X_t, t \in T\}$ be a submartingale such that*

$$\sup_T E(X_t^+) < \infty.$$

Then for every fixed s we have $\inf_{t \geqslant s} X_t > -\infty$ a.s. *on the set* $\{X_s > -\infty\}$*; in particular, we have* $\inf_{t \geqslant s} X_t > -\infty$ a.s. *on Ω whenever* $E(X_s) > -\infty$.

PROOF. By virtue of the hypothesis and the inequality

$$(X_t - b)^+ \leqslant X_t^+ + b^-,$$

we have $\sup_T E(X_t - b)^+ < +\infty$ for every $b \in R$. Since the variables $\gamma_{a,b}$ decrease as $a \downarrow -\infty$ and since $P(\gamma_{a,b} > 0) \leqslant E(\gamma_{a,b})$, the inequality of the preceding proposition shows that the sets $\{\gamma_{a,b} > 0\}$ decrease towards a negligible set as $a \downarrow -\infty$.

We observe, on the other hand, that for every trajectory of the submartingale such that $X_s(\omega) > b$, the equality $\gamma_{a,b}(\omega) = 0$ implies that $\inf_{t \geqslant s} X_t \geqslant a$. The preceding thus shows that we have $\inf_{t \geqslant s} X_t > -\infty$ a.s. on the set $\{X_s > b\}$; it remains only to let b tend to $-\infty$ to obtain the result of the corollary. ∎

THEOREM. *Almost all of the trajectories of a submartingale*

$$\{X_t, \mathscr{A}_t; t \in T\}$$

such that $\sup_T E(X_t^+) < \infty$, *are without discontinuities of the second kind on* $\bar{T}$. (If T is closed at the right, the condition $\sup_T E(X_t^+) < \infty$ is automatically satisfied).

PROOF. By virtue of the hypothesis and the inequality

$$(X_t - b)^+ \leqslant X_t^+ + b^-,$$

we have $\sup_T E[(X_t - b)^+] < +\infty$ for every $b \in R$; Proposition IV.5.3 then shows that the r.r.v.'s $\gamma_{a,b}$ are all integrable ($a < b$ in R). Hence there exists a negligible set N such that if $\omega \notin N$, then $\gamma_{a,b} < \infty$ for every pair $a < b$ (it suffices to define N as the countable union of the sets $\{\gamma_{a,b} = \infty\}$ where $a < b$ run through the rationals; since with every pair $a < b$ of real numbers one can always associate rational numbers a', b' such that $a \leqslant a' < b' \leqslant b$ and hence such that $\gamma_{a,b} \leqslant \gamma_{a',b'}$, we will indeed have $\gamma_{a,b} < \infty$ on N^c for every pair $a < b$ in R). Consequently all the trajectories $\omega \notin N$ of the submartingale X are without discontinuities of the second kind. ∎

In the discrete case, the preceding theorem is equivalent to the following two results which are obtained by considering the limits of the trajectories at the points $+\infty$ and $-\infty$ respectively:

(1) *If* $\{X_n, \mathscr{A}_n; n = 1, 2, \ldots\}$ *is a submartingale, then*

$$\lim_{n \to +\infty} \text{a.s. } X_n$$

exists whenever $\sup_n E(X_n^+) < \infty$;

(2) *If* $\{X_n, \mathscr{A}_n; n = \cdots, -2, -1\}$ *is a submartingale, then*

$$\lim_{n \to -\infty} \text{a.s. } X_n$$

always exists. Introducing the inverted sequence

$$\{Z_n = X_{-n}, \mathscr{B}_n = \mathscr{A}_{-n}\} \qquad (n = 1, 2, \ldots),$$

this result can be stated in the following form:

(2b) *If* $\{\mathscr{B}_n, n \geqslant 1\}$ *is a decreasing sequence of σ-algebras and if* $\{Z_n, n \geqslant 1\}$ *is a sequence of* r.r.v.'s *respectively* $\mathscr{B}_n$*-measurable, such that* $E(Z_n^+) < \infty$ *for every* n *and* $Z_{n+1} \leqslant E^{\mathscr{B}_{n+1}}(Z_n)$ *for every* n, *then*

$$\lim_{n \to +\infty} \text{a.s. } Z_n$$

exists.

In the continuous case, applying the preceding theorem to the restrictions, to subintervals of T closed at the right, of a submartingale $\{X_t, t \in T\}$ defined on an interval T which is open at the right, we obtain the following result: almost all of the trajectories of a submartingale are without discontinuities of the second kind on $\overline{T}$ except possibly at t_r.

We thus see that the principal effect of the hypothesis $\sup_T E(X_t^+) < \infty$ in the theorem is to suppress possible discontinuities of the trajectories at t_r.

PROPOSITION IV.5.4. *Let $\{X_t, \mathscr{A}_t; t \in T\}$ be a submartingale such that the family $\{X_t^+, t \in T\}$ is uniformly integrable (this hypothesis is always satisfied if T is closed at the right). Then, except for a negligible set of trajectories, the limits $X_{t-}(\omega) = \lim_{s \uparrow t} X_t(\omega)$ exist at every point t which is the limit from the left of points in T; the limits X_{t-} are measurable with respect to the σ-algebras $\mathscr{A}_{t-}$ generated by the σ-algebras $\mathscr{A}_s$ $(s < t)$, and satisfy the inequalities*

$$X_s \leqslant E^{\mathscr{A}_s}(X_{t-}) \quad \textit{if} \quad s < t; \qquad X_{t-} \leqslant E^{\mathscr{A}_{t-}}(X_s) \quad \textit{if} \quad t \leqslant s.$$

Similarly the limits $X_{t+}(\omega) = \lim_{s \downarrow t} X_s(\omega)$ exist at every point t which is the limit from the right of points in T, except for a negligible set of trajectories; the limits X_{t+} are measurable with respect to the σ-algebras $\mathscr{A}_{t+}$, the intersections of the σ-algebras $\mathscr{A}_s$ $(s > t)$, and satisfy the inequalities

$$X_s \leqslant E^{\mathscr{A}_s}(X_{t+}) \quad \textit{if} \quad s \leqslant t; \qquad X_{t+} \leqslant E^{\mathscr{A}_{t+}}(X_s) \quad \textit{if} \quad t < s.$$

PROOF. We shall only carry out the proof in the case of the limits from the left. The existence of the X_{t-} results from the preceding theorem; it is also clear that X_{t-} is measurable with respect to $\mathscr{A}_{t-}$, since the r.r.v.'s X_s $(s < t)$ are. To prove the inequalities of the proposition, let us first observe that for every $a \in R$, the r.r.f. $\{\max(X_t, a), t \in T\}$ is a submartingale (Proposition IV.5.1) and that this family of r.r.v.'s is uniformly integrable because by hypothesis the family $\{X_t^+, t \in T\}$ is. Consequently we have, if $s < t$ and if $A \in \mathscr{A}_s$,

$$\int_A \max(X_s, a) \leqslant \lim_{u \uparrow t} \int_A \max(X_u, a) = \int_A \max(X_{t-}, a).$$

Letting $a \to -\infty$, we obtain the inequalities

$$\int_A X_s \leqslant \int_A X_{t-}$$

for every $A \in \mathscr{A}_s$, as X_s^+ and X_{t-}^+ are integrable (the second variable, by Fatou's lemma); these inequalities are equivalent to $X_s \leqslant E^{\mathscr{A}_s}(X_{t-})$. In the same way one obtains, when $t \leqslant s$,

$$\int_A \max(X_{t-}, a) = \lim_{u \uparrow t} \int_A \max(X_u, a) \leqslant \int_A \max(X_s, a)$$

for every $A \in \bigcup_{u<t} \mathscr{A}_u$. This inequality remains valid for every A in the

σ-algebra $\mathscr{A}_{t-}$ generated by $\bigcup_{u<t} \mathscr{A}_u$ since the r.r.v.'s max (X_{t-}, a) and max (X_s, a) are integrable. Letting a tend to $-\infty$, we find that

$$\int_A X_{t-} \leqslant \int_A X_s$$

for every $A \in \mathscr{A}_{t-}$, i.e., that $X_{t-} \leqslant E^{\mathscr{A}_{t-}}(X_s)$ if $t \leqslant s$. ∎

In the case of a submartingale $\{X_t, t \in T\}$ defined on an interval T which is open at the right and such that the family $\{X_t^+, t \in T\}$ is not uniformly integrable, we can nevertheless apply the preceding proposition to the restrictions of the submartingale X to the subintervals of T which are closed at the right. We thus obtain that the result stated in this proposition remains valid when the hypothesis of uniform integrability is omitted, except as concerns the limit at t_{r-}; the role of this hypothesis is moreover clarified by the following corollary.

COROLLARY. *Let $\{X_t, \mathscr{A}_t; t \in T\}$ be a submartingale. Then, in order that $\lim_{u \uparrow t_r} X_u$ exist* a.s. *and satisfy the inequality $X_s \leqslant E^{\mathscr{A}_s}(\lim_{u \uparrow t_r} X_u)$ for every $s < t_r$, it is necessary and sufficient that the family $\{X_t^+, t \in T\}$ be uniformly integrable.*

PROOF. The condition is sufficient by virtue of the preceding proposition. To show that it is necessary, we apply Proposition IV.5.1 to the submartingale consisting of the r.r.v.'s X_t $(t < t_r)$ and

$$\lim_{u \uparrow t_r} X_u. \quad ∎$$

In the discrete case, the preceding results can also be stated in the following form:

(1) *If $\{X_n, \mathscr{A}_n; n = 1, 2, \ldots\}$ is a submartingale, then*

$$X_\infty = \lim_{n \to \infty} \text{a.s. } X_n$$

exists and satisfies $X_n \leqslant E^{\mathscr{A}_n}(X_\infty)$ if and only if the family $\{X_n^+\}$ is uniformly integrable.

(2) If $\{\mathscr{B}_n, n \geqslant 1\}$ is a decreasing sequence of σ-algebras and if $\{Z_n, n \geqslant 1\}$ is a sequence of r.r.v.'s respectively $\mathscr{B}_n$-measurable, such that $E(Z_n^+) < \infty$ and $Z_{n+1} \leqslant E^{\mathscr{B}_{n+1}}(Z_n)$ for every n, then $\lim Z_n = Z_\infty$ always exists a.s. and satisfies $Z_\infty \leqslant E^{\mathscr{B}_\infty}(Z_n)$ for every n, where $\mathscr{B}_\infty$ denotes the intersection of the $\mathscr{B}_n$.

COROLLARY 2. (*Regularization from the right of a submartingale.*) *Let* $\{X_t, \mathscr{A}_t; t \in T\}$ *be a submartingale defined on an interval* T *of* $\bar{R}$. *Assuming that we set* $X_{t_r+} = X_{t_r}$ *if* $t_r \in T$, *the* r.r.f.

$$\{X_{t+}, \mathscr{A}_{t+}; t \in T \cup \{t_l\}\},$$

which is defined almost everywhere, is a submartingale whose trajectories are right continuous; moreover almost all of these trajectories have left limits on T. *We have* $X_{t+} = X_t$ a.s. *for every* $t \in T$ *at which the function* $E(X_t)$ *of* t *is right continuous and at which* $\mathscr{A}_t = \mathscr{A}_{t+0}$.

PROOF. The first part of this corollary follows immediately from the proposition. The second part follows from the inequality

$$X_t \leqslant E^{\mathscr{A}_t}(X_{t+}) \leqslant E^{\mathscr{A}_t}(X_s)$$

which is valid for $t < s$; in fact, by this inequality we cannot have $E(X_t) = \lim E(X_s) \neq \infty$ without having $X_t \underset{\text{a.s.}}{=} E^{\mathscr{A}_t}(X_{t+})$; if moreover $\mathscr{A}_t = \mathscr{A}_{t+}$, we have $X_{t+} = E^{\mathscr{A}_t}(X_{t+})$. ∎

An analogous result can be stated for the regularization from the left $\{X_{t-}, \mathscr{A}_{t-}; t \in T\}$ of a submartingale; nevertheless one can only define this regularization at the point t_r if the family $\{X_t^+, t \in T\}$ is uniformly integrable.

The following result is the generalization which we mentioned of the the fundamental lemma of this section.

PROPOSITION IV.5.5. *Let* $\{X_t, \mathscr{A}_t; t \in T\}$ *be a submartingale which we suppose, in the continuous case, to have almost all trajectories right continuous. If* τ_1 *and* τ_2 *are two stopping times defined on all of* Ω *relative to* $\{\mathscr{A}_t, t \in T\}$ *and if* $\tau_1 \leqslant \tau_2$, *each of the following two conditions is sufficient to imply the inequality* $X_{\tau_1} \leqslant E^{\mathscr{A}_{\tau_1}}(X_{\tau_2})$:

(a) *There exists a* $t_0 \in T$ *such that* $\tau_2 \leqslant t_0$ a.s. (*this condition is satisfied whenever* T *is closed at the right*).

(b) *The family* $\{X_t^+, t \in T\}$ *is uniformly integrable.*

PROOF. It suffices to prove the inequality of the proposition in the case where T is closed at the right. In fact, if condition (a) is satisfied, we can restrict ourselves to considering only $\{X_t, \mathscr{A}_t; t \leqslant t_0\}$; if condition (b) is satisfied without T being closed at the right, the "closure"

$$\{X_t\,(t \in T),\ \lim_{s \uparrow t_r} X_t\}$$

is a submartingale (Proposition IV.5.4) defined on the interval $T + \{t_r\}$ which is closed at the right.

The lemma at the beginning of this section shows that the inequality

$$X_{\tau_1} \leqslant E^{\mathscr{A}_{\tau_1}}(X_{\tau_2})$$

holds when $\tau_1 \leqslant \tau_2$ are two stopping times which take on only finitely many distinct values. For such stopping times, T being closed at the right, we thus have $X_\tau \leqslant E^{\mathscr{A}_\tau}(X_{t_r})$; arguing as in the proof of Proposition IV.5.1, we can then show that for every $a \in R$ the family $\{\max(X_\tau, a)\}$ obtained by letting τ run through all stopping times having a finite number of values is a uniformly integrable family of r.r.v.'s.

Let $\{\tau_1^n\}$ and $\{\tau_2^n\}$ be two sequences of stopping times having finitely many values, which decrease towards the given stopping times τ_1 and τ_2 respectively (the proof of Proposition III.6.1 contains an explicit construction of such sequences); we may suppose that $\tau_1^n \leqslant \tau_2^n$ by replacing, if necessary, τ_1^n by $\min(\tau_1^n, \tau_2^n)$. Since $\mathscr{A}_{\tau_1} \subset \mathscr{A}_{\tau_1^n}$, for every $A \in \mathscr{A}_{\tau_1}$ we have

$$\int_A \max(X_{\tau_1^n}, a) \leqslant \int_A \max(X_{\tau_2^n}, a).$$

As $n \uparrow \infty$, the uniformly integrable sequences $\{\max(X_{\tau_i^n}, a); n \geqslant 1\}_{i=1,2}$ converge a.s. to $\max(X_{\tau_i}, a)$ by virtue of the right continuity of the trajectories; hence we again have $\int_A \max(X_{\tau_1}, a) \leqslant \int_A \max(X_{\tau_2}, a) < \infty$. Letting $a \downarrow -\infty$, we obtain the desired inequality $\int_A X_{\tau_1} \leqslant \int_A X_{\tau_2}$ for every $A \in \mathscr{A}_{\tau_1}$, with Proposition III.6.1 showing that X_{τ_1} is measurable with respect to $\mathscr{A}_{\tau_1}$. ∎

Using the arguments of the proof of Proposition IV.5.1, we can deduce from the inequality $X_\tau \leqslant E^{\mathscr{A}_\tau}(X_{t_r})$, which holds for every stopping time τ, the following result.

COROLLARY 1. *Let $\{X_t, \mathscr{A}_t; t \in T\}$ be a submartingale which we suppose in the continuous case to have almost all trajectories right continuous. If the family $\{X_t^+, t \in T\}$ is uniformly integrable, in particular if T is closed at the right, the family* $\{\max(X_\tau, a)\}$, *where $a \in R$ is fixed and τ runs through all stopping times defined on Ω, is uniformly integrable.*

If $\{X_t, \mathscr{A}_t; t \in T\}$ is a submartingale and if $\{\tau_s, s \in S\}$ is an increasing family of stopping times defined on Ω, the preceding proposition gives conditions under which the r.r.f. $\{X_{\tau_s}, \mathscr{A}_{\tau_s}; s \in S\}$ is again a submartingale. A particularly interesting case is given by the following corollary.

COROLLARY 2. *Let* $\{X_t, \mathscr{A}_t; t \in T\}$ *be a submartingale which we suppose in the continuous case to have almost every trajectory right continuous. For any stopping time* τ *defined on* Ω *relative to* $\{\mathscr{A}_t, t \in T\}$, *the* r.r.f. $\{X_{\tau\wedge t}, \mathscr{A}_{\tau\wedge t}, t \in T\}$ *is again a submartingale.*

(One says of the r.r.f. $\{X_{\tau\wedge t}\}$ that it is obtained by stopping the r.r.f. $\{X_t\}$ at the instant τ.)

We shall conclude this section by applying the preceding results to a martingale. We remark that by definition $\{X_t, \mathscr{A}_t; t \in T\}$ is a martingale if and only if $\{X_t, t \in T\}$ and $\{-X_t, t \in T\}$ are submartingales; we observe also that in the formula

$$E(|X_t|) = 2E(X_t^+) - E(X_t),$$

the term $E(X_t)$ is finite and independent of t whenever $\{X_t, t \in T\}$ is a martingale. The theorem of this section therefore shows that *almost all trajectories of a martingale are without discontinuities of the second kind on* $\overline{T}$ whenever $\sup_T E(|X_t|) < \infty$, in particular whenever T is closed at the right. We see next that *the conclusions of Proposition* IV.5.4, *where the inequalities are replaced by equalities, are true whenever the martingale is uniformly integrable* (in particular, whenever T is closed at the right).

In the case where T is not closed at the right, one can nevertheless apply the preceding results to the restrictions of the martingale to every subinterval of T which is closed at the right; the above conclusions are thus valid, except possibly at the point t_r, for every martingale defined on T. With regard to the behavior of the martingale at the point t_r, we have the following result:

PROPOSITION IV.5.6. *For every martingale* $\{X_t, \mathscr{A}_t; t \in T\}$ *defined on an interval which is open at the right, the following three conditions are equivalent:*

(a) $\lim_{t\uparrow t_r} X_t$ *exists in the sense of* L_1;

(b) *there exists at least one* r.r.v. X *which is integrable and such that* $X_s = E^{\mathscr{A}_s}(X)$ *for every* $s \in T$;

(c) *the family* $\{X_t, t \in T\}$ *is uniformly integrable.*

If these conditions are satisfied, then $\lim_{t\uparrow t_r} X_t$ *exists* a.s. *and in the sense of* L_1 *and satisfies* $X_s = E^{\mathscr{A}_s}(\lim_{t\uparrow t_r} X_t)$ *for every* $s \in T$.

Moreover, if the martingale is such that $\sup_T E(|X_t|^p) < \infty$ *for some* $p > 1$, *the preceding conditions are satisfied and* $\lim_{t\uparrow t_r} X_t$ *exists in the sense of convergence in* L_p.

PROOF. Since conditional expectations are continuous operators on L_1, the implication (a) $\Rightarrow$ (b) follows immediately from the defining equality $X_s = E^{\mathscr{A}_s}(X_t)$ if $s < t$ in T, by taking $X = \lim_{t \uparrow\uparrow t_r} X_t$. The second part of Proposition IV.5.1, applied to the martingale

$$\{X_t\ (t \in T),\ X\},$$

shows that (b) $\Rightarrow$ (c). Finally, we know that $\lim_{t \uparrow\uparrow t_r} X_t$ exists a.s. as long as $\sup_T E|X_t| < \infty$; if $\{X_t, t \in T\}$ is, moreover, uniformly integrable, the preceding convergence also holds in L_1 (Proposition II.5.4).

To prove the second part of the proposition, we observe first that the condition $\sup E(|X_t|^p) < \infty$ for some $p > 1$ implies the uniform integrability of $\{X_t, t \in T\}$ (Problem II.5.2). Hence the limit $X = \lim_{t \uparrow\uparrow t_r} X_t$ exists and $\{X_t\ (t \in T), X\}$ is a martingale. On the other hand, Fatou's lemma shows that $E(|X|^p) \leqslant \sup_T E(|X_t|^p) < \infty$; hence Proposition IV.5.1 is applicable and shows that $\{|X_t|^p\ (t \in T), |X|^p\}$ is uniformly integrable; the convergence of X_t to X as $t \uparrow t_r$ therefore holds in L_p (Proposition II.6.1). ∎

Complements and problems

IV.5.1. If $\{X_t, t \in T\}$ is a submartingale consisting of integrable and centered r.r.v.'s and if we set $S = \sup_T E(X_t^2)$, show that the inequality $P(\sup_T X_t > c) \leqslant S/(S + c^2)$ holds for every constant $c > 0$. [First consider the case where T is finite; if τ denotes the first instant t such that $X_t > c$, use the inequality $(a + X_\tau)^2 \geqslant (a + c)^2$, choosing the positive constant a in the best possible way.]

If $\{X_t, t \in T\}$ is a martingale or a positive submartingale, and if

$$\sup_T E(|X_t|^p) < \infty$$

for some $p > 1$, show that $\|\sup_T |X_t|\,\|_p \leqslant p/(p-1) \sup_T \|X_t\|_p$. [Integrate the inequality $cP(A_c) \leqslant \int_{A_c} X_s$, where $A_c = \{\sup_{t \leqslant s} X_t > c\}$, over the variable c with respect to the measure $c^{p-2}\,dc$ and apply Hölder's inequality.]

IV.5.2. **The strong law of large numbers for sequences of symmetrically dependent r.r.v.'s.** A sequence $\{X_n, n \geqslant 1\}$ of r.r.v.'s is said to be symmetrically dependent if the probability law of every vector

$$(X_{n_1}, X_{n_2}, \ldots, X_{n_k})$$

is invariant with respect to permutations of the indices $n_1, n_2, \ldots, n_k$ (the indices $n_1, \ldots, n_k$ are assumed pairwise distinct). Every sequence of independent identically distributed r.r.v.'s is symmetrically dependent. We denote by $\mathscr{B}_n$ the σ-algebra generated by the events depending symmetrically upon $X_1, \ldots, X_n$ and arbitrarily upon $X_{n+1}, \ldots$; we denote the intersection of the decreasing $\mathscr{B}_n$ by $\mathscr{B}_\infty$.

Let $p \geqslant 1$. For every real measurable function f such that $f(X_1) \in L_p$, establish by a symmetry argument that if $m \leqslant n$, then

$$E^{\mathscr{B}_n}[f(X_m)] = (1/n) \sum_1^n f(X_j),$$

and deduce from this the strong law of large numbers:

$$\lim_{n \to \infty} \frac{1}{n} \sum_1^n f(X_j) = E^{\mathscr{B}_\infty}[f(X_1)] \text{ a.s.} \quad \text{and in } L_p.$$

Show that the sequence $\{X_n\}$ is conditionally independent and conditionally equidistributed with respect to $\mathscr{B}_\infty$ (one shows that

$$E^{\mathscr{B}_\infty}\left[\prod_{j=1}^k f_j(X_j)\right] = \prod_{j=1}^k E^{\mathscr{B}_\infty}[f_j(X_1)]$$

when the f_j $(1 \leqslant j \leqslant k)$ are bounded measurable functions, by first calculating

$$E^{\mathscr{B}_n}\left[\prod_{j=1}^k (f_j X_{n_j})\right] \qquad \text{for} \quad 1 \leqslant n_1, \ldots, n_k \leqslant n$$

by a symmetry argument). Establish, conversely, that a sequence of r.r.v.'s which are conditionally independent and conditionally equidistributed with respect to some σ-algebra is a symmetrically dependent sequence.

Show that the σ-algebra $\mathscr{B}_\infty$ differs from the σ-algebra

$$\mathscr{A}_\infty = \bigcap_N \mathscr{B}(X_n, n \geqslant N)$$

of asymptotic events only by negligible sets. [Note that $\lim_n (1/n) \sum_1^n f(X_j)$ is $\mathscr{A}_\infty$-measurable.] In the case of an independent sequence $\{X_n\}$, the operator $E^{\mathscr{B}_\infty}$ is thus equal to the ordinary expectation E.

IV.5.3. Let $\{\mathscr{A}_n, n \geqslant 1\}$ be an increasing sequence of σ-algebras in the space $(\Omega, \mathscr{A}, P)$; we denote by $\mathscr{B}$ the algebra $\bigcup \mathscr{A}_n$ and by $\mathscr{A}_\infty$ the σ-algebra generated by $\mathscr{B}$. Let Q be a mapping of $\mathscr{B}$ into $[0, 1]$ whose restriction Q_n to $\mathscr{A}_n$ is a probability for every n; we denote by X_n the derivative of Q_n with respect to the restriction of P to $\mathscr{A}_n$ [see Proposition IV.1.3].

Show that $\{X_n, \mathscr{A}_n; n \geqslant 1\}$ is a positive supermartingale which converges a.s. to the positive r.r.v. X_∞ defined as the largest $\mathscr{A}_\infty$-measurable r.r.v. such that $\int_B X_\infty \, dP \leqslant Q(B)$ for every $B \in \mathscr{B}$; in particular if Q is σ-additive on $\mathscr{B}$, X_∞ is equal to the derivative of the σ-additive extension of Q to $\mathscr{A}_\infty$ with respect to P_∞ (the restriction of P to $\mathscr{A}_\infty$). If $Q_n \ll P_n$ on $\mathscr{A}_n$ for every n, the sequence $\{X_n\}$ is a martingale; in this case, show that the set function Q can be extended to $\mathscr{A}_\infty$ as a probability which is absolutely continuous with respect to P_∞ if and only if the martingale $\{X_n\}$ is uniformly integrable; deduce from this that this extension is possible whenever the following condition is satisfied: $\sup_n E(X_n \log X_n) < \infty$.

We can restate the preceding results in the case where the σ-algebra $\mathscr{A}$ is of countable type and where one chooses for $\{\mathscr{A}_n\}$ an increasing sequence of finite algebras which generates $\mathscr{A}$, by giving an explicit expression for the X_n. In particular, one can consider the case where $(\Omega, \mathscr{A}, P)$ is the interval $[0, 1)$ of R with Lebesgue measure and where the algebras $\mathscr{A}_n$ are those generated by the dyadic partitions

$$\mathscr{P}_n = \{[k2^{-n}, (k + 1)2^{-n}]; 0 \leqslant k < 2^n\} \quad \text{of} \quad [0, 1).$$

IV.5.4. If $\{X_t, \mathscr{A}_t; t \in T\}$ is a submartingale and if f is a continuous increasing convex function, the r.r.f. $\{f(X_t), t \in T\}$ is again a submartingale as long only as $E[f^+(X_t)] < \infty$ for every $t \in T$; the same conclusion is valid if $\{X_t\}$ is a martingale and f is a continuous and convex (but not necessarily increasing) function. Thus if $\{X_t\}$ is a positive martingale, the r.r.f.

$$\{X_t \log X_t, t \in T\}$$

is a submartingale whenever $E[X_t \log X_t] < \infty$.

Let P and Q be two probabilities on $(\Omega, \mathscr{A})$ whose restrictions to any σ-subalgebra $\mathscr{B}$ of $\mathscr{A}$ we denote by $P_{\mathscr{B}}$ and $Q_{\mathscr{B}}$; we set

$$H(\mathscr{B}) = \int X_{\mathscr{B}} \log (X_{\mathscr{B}})\, dP \leqslant \infty$$

if $Q_{\mathscr{B}}$ is absolutely continuous with respect to $P_{\mathscr{B}}$, with density $X_{\mathscr{B}}$, and $H(\mathscr{B}) = +\infty$ if not. Show that $H(\mathscr{B})$ is a positive and increasing function of $\mathscr{B}$ and that $H(\mathscr{B}) = 0$ if and only if $Q_{\mathscr{B}} = P_{\mathscr{B}}$. If $\{\mathscr{B}_n\}$ is an increasing sequence of σ-algebras which generates $\mathscr{B}_\infty$, show that

$$H(\mathscr{B}_\infty) = \lim_n \uparrow H(\mathscr{B}_n).$$

If $\{\mathscr{B}_n\}$ is a decreasing sequence of σ-algebras with intersection $\mathscr{B}_\infty$, show that $H(\mathscr{B}_\infty) = \lim_n \downarrow H(\mathscr{B}_n)$ if the right side is not infinite. [Use the preceding problem.]

*IV.5.5. Let T be an abstract set, directed to the right for the relation $\leqslant$, and let $\{X_t, \mathscr{A}_t; t \in T\}$ be a martingale consisting of r.r.v.'s in L_p $(1 \leqslant p < \infty)$. Show the equivalence of the following conditions: (a) lim X_t along T exists in L_p; (b) the family $\{X_t, t \in T\}$ of r.r.v.'s is relatively compact in the weak sense in L_p (that is, uniformly integrable if $p = 1$, and bounded if $p > 1$); (c) there exists a r.r.v. X in L_p such that $X_t = E^{\mathscr{A}_t}(X)$. If these conditions are satisfied, show that $X_t = E^{\mathscr{A}_t}(\lim_T X_s)$.

IV.5.6. Let $\{X_t, \mathscr{A}_t; t \in T\}$ be a submartingale defined on the open interval $T = (0, 1)$ of R and such that $\sup_T E(X_t^+) < \infty$. Show that for almost all of the trajectories of this submartingale to be continuous, it is necessary and sufficient that for every pair $a < b$ in R

$$\lim_{h \downarrow 0} (1/h) \int_0^{1-h} dt\, P(X_t < a, X_{t+h} > b) = 0,$$

$$\lim_{h \downarrow 0} (1/h) \int_0^{1-h} dt\, P(X_t > b, X_{t+h} < a) = 0.$$

[Observe that the integrals $(1/h) \int_0^{1-h} dt\, 1_{\{X_t < a,\, X_{t+h} > b\}}$ define r.r.v.'s majorized by $\gamma_{a,b}$ which, as $h \downarrow 0$, have a limit superior bounded from above by

$$\sum_t 1_{\{X_{t-} \leqslant a, X_{t+} \geqslant b\}}$$

and a limit inferior bounded from below by

$$\sum_t 1_{\{X_{t-} < a, X_{t+} > b\}};$$

deduce from this that the first condition above is necessary and sufficient in order that $X_{t-} \geqslant X_{t+}$ for every t, for almost all of the trajectories of the submartingale.]

Consequently, the condition $\sup_t (1/h)P[|X_{t+h} - X_t| > \epsilon] \to 0$ as $h \downarrow 0$, for every $\epsilon > 0$, is sufficient for almost all of the trajectories of the finite submartingale $\{X_t, 0 < t < 1\}$ to be continuous on $(0, 1)$.

IV.6. CENTERED SEQUENCES OF RANDOM VARIABLES

In this section we intend to apply martingale theory to the study of centered sequences of random variables.

Definition IV.6.1. GIVEN AN INCREASING SEQUENCE $\{\mathscr{A}_n, n \geqslant 1\}$ OF σ-ALGEBRAS IN THE SPACE $(\Omega, \mathscr{A}, P)$, A SEQUENCE $\{Y_n, n \geqslant 1\}$ OF INTEGRABLE r.r.v.'s ADAPTED TO $\{\mathscr{A}_n\}$ IS SAID TO BE CENTERED IF $E^{\mathscr{A}_{n-1}}(Y_n) = 0$ FOR EVERY $n \geqslant 1$. (WE PUT $A_0 = \{\varnothing, \Omega\}$.)

Generally the σ-algebras $\mathscr{A}_n$ are those generated respectively by the Y_m $(m \leqslant n)$. One verifies immediately that the partial sums $X_n = \sum_1^n Y_m$ $(X_0 = 0)$ of a centered sequence form an integrable martingale; conversely, by the way, every integrable martingale $\{X_n, n \geqslant 0\}$ such that $X_0 = 0$ is of the preceding form, as can be seen by putting

$$Y_n = X_n - X_{n-1}.$$

We next remark that every sequence $\{Z_n, n \geqslant 1\}$ of integrable r.r.v.'s adapted to the sequence $\{\mathscr{A}_n, n \geqslant 1\}$ can be centered by putting

$$Y_n = Z_n - E^{\mathscr{A}_{n-1}}(Z_n);$$

in this way every result concerning centered sequences can be carried over to a result concerning arbitrary sequences of integrable r.r.v.'s. Let us remark, finally, that a sequence $\{Y_n, n \geqslant 1\}$ of independent r.r.v.'s is centered if and only if $E(Y_n) = 0$ for every $n \geqslant 1$.

PROPOSITION IV.6.1. *If* $\{Y_n, n \geqslant 1\}$ *is a centered sequence of* r.r.v.'s, *then:*

(1) *the convergence of the series* $\sum_{n \geqslant 1} E(Y_n^2)$ *implies the existence of the limit* $\lim_{n\to\infty} \sum_1^n Y_m$ *in the* a.s. *sense and in the sense of* L_2;

(2) *for every nondecreasing sequence* $\{u_n, n \geqslant 1\}$ *of real numbers tending to* ∞, *the convergence of the series* $\sum_{n \geqslant 1} u_n^{-2} E(Y_n^2)$ *implies that*

$$\lim_{n\to\infty} u_n^{-1} \sum_1^n Y_m = 0$$

in the a.s. *sense.*

Proof. The sequence $\{Y_n, n \geqslant 1\}$, being centered, is orthogonal since $E(Y_m Y_n) = E(Y_m E^{\mathscr{A}_m}(Y_n)) = 0$ if $m < n$; hence we have

$$E\left[\left(\sum_1^n Y_m\right)^2\right] = \sum_1^n E(Y_m^2).$$

It now suffices to apply Proposition IV.5.6 to the martingale $\{X_n = \sum_1^n Y_m\}$ to complete the proof of the first part of the proposition.

Since $\{u_n^{-1} Y_n\}$ is a centered sequence whenever $\{Y_n\}$ is, for any real $u_n \neq 0$, the convergence of the series $\sum_n u_n^{-2} E(Y_n^2)$ implies that the almost sure limit $\lim_{n\to\infty} \sum_1^n u_m^{-1} Y_m$ exists and is finite. The second part of the proposition follows from this on applying the following lemma due to Kronecker:

Lemma. *If* $\{u_n, n \geqslant 1\}$ *is a nondecreasing sequence of positive real numbers tending to* $+\infty$ *and if the sequence of real numbers* $\{y_n, n \geqslant 1\}$ *is such that* $\lim_{n\to\infty} \sum_1^n u_m^{-1} y_m$ *exists and is finite, then*

$$\lim_{n\to\infty} u_n^{-1} \sum_1^n y_m = 0.$$

Proof. The sequence $\{v_n = u_n - u_{n-1}\}$ consists of nonnegative real numbers and $\sum_1^n v_m = u_n \uparrow \infty$ as $n \uparrow \infty$. On the other hand the numbers $z_n = \sum_1^n u_m^{-1} y_m$ form a convergent sequence; since

$$\sum_1^n y_m = \sum_1^n u_m(z_m - z_{m-1}) = \sum_1^n v_m(z_n - z_{m-1})$$

we have, when $p < n$,

$$\left|\sum_1^n y_m\right| \leqslant \left|\sum_1^p v_m(z_n - z_{m-1})\right| + \left(\sum_{p+1}^n v_m\right) \sup_{p \leqslant m \leqslant n} |z_n - z_m|.$$

Dividing both sides of this inequality by u_n and letting n and then p tend to ∞, we obtain the stated result. ∎

Using the technique of stopping times, we can improve the results of the preceding proposition considerably. Nevertheless, a reading of the rest of this section is not necessary for the study of the following section.

PROPOSITION IV.6.2. *If* $\{Y_n, n \geqslant 1\}$ *is a centered sequence of* r.r.v.'s, *the limit* $\lim_{n\to\infty} \sum_1^n Y_m$ *exists in the* a.s. *sense and is* a.s. *finite on the set* $\Omega_0 = \{\sum_n E^{\mathscr{A}_{n-1}}(Y_n^2) < \infty\}$. *Moreover, if* $\sup_n |Y_n| \in L_2$, *the set* Ω_0 *is equal* a.s. *to the set where the series* $\sum Y_m$ *converges.*

On the other hand, if $\{U_n, n \geqslant 1\}$ *is an increasing sequence of positive* r.r.v.'s *such that* U_n *is measurable with respect to* $\mathscr{A}_{n-1}$ *for every* n, *then* $\lim \text{a.s.}_{n\to\infty} U_n^{-1} \sum_1^n Y_m = 0$ *on the set*

$$\Omega_1 = \left\{\lim \uparrow U_n = \infty,\ \sum_n U_n^{-2} E^{\mathscr{A}_{n-1}}(Y_n^2) < \infty\right\}.$$

This proposition does indeed constitute a generalization of the a.s. convergence results of Proposition IV.6.1. In fact, the convergence of the series

$$\sum_n E(Y_n^2)$$

implies that the variable $\sum_n E^{\mathscr{A}_{n-1}}(Y_n^2)$ is integrable, thus finite a.s. and hence that $\Omega_0 = \Omega$ a.s.; similarly, the convergence of the series

$$\sum_n u_n^{-2} E(Y_n^2)$$

implies that $\sum_n u_n^{-2} E^{\mathscr{A}_{n-1}}(Y_n^2) < \infty$ a.s. The proof of this proposition will rest on the following lemma:

LEMMA. *If* $\{Z_n, n \geqslant 0\}$ *is an arbitrary sequence of integrable* r.r.v.'s *adapted to the sequence* $\{\mathscr{A}_n, n \geqslant 0\}$, *then for every stopping time* ν *which is everywhere defined and bounded from above by an integer* N *we have the identity*

$$E(Z_\nu) - E(Z_0) = E\left[\sum_{n<\nu} (E^{\mathscr{A}_n}(Z_{n+1}) - Z_n)\right].$$

PROOF OF THE LEMMA. Since Z_n and $1_{\{\nu>n\}}$ are $\mathscr{A}_n$-measurable, we have

$$\begin{aligned} E(Z_{\nu\wedge n+1}) - E(Z_{\nu\wedge n}) &= E[1_{\{\nu>n\}}(Z_{n+1} - Z_n)] \\ &= E[1_{\{\nu>n\}}(E^{\mathscr{A}_n}(Z_{n+1}) - Z_n)]. \end{aligned}$$

The formula of the lemma is then obtained by summing over n from 0 to $N - 1$, on noting that $\nu \wedge 0 = 0$, $\nu \wedge N = \nu$. ∎

PROOF OF THE PROPOSITION. Let $\{Y_n, \mathscr{A}_n, n \geqslant 1\}$ be a centered sequence and let ν_a be the stopping time equal to the smallest integer m, if it exists, such that $\sum_{n \leqslant m} E^{\mathscr{A}_n}(Y_{n+1}^2) > a$ (a a positive constant). Then, if $X_n = \sum_1^n Y_m$, the martingale $\{X_{\nu_a \wedge N}, N \geqslant 1\}$ is such that

$$E(X_{\nu_a \wedge N}^2) = E\Big[\sum_{n < \nu_a \wedge N} (E^{\mathscr{A}_n}(X_{n+1}^2) - X_n^2)\Big] = E\Big[\sum_{n < \nu_a \wedge N} E^{\mathscr{A}_n}(Y_{n+1}^2)\Big] \leqslant a$$

as is seen by using the formula of the lemma and the definition of ν_a. By Proposition IV.5.6 lim a.s.$_{N \to \infty} X_{\nu_a \wedge N}$ exists and is finite a.s. on the entire space; it follows that $\lim_{N \to \infty} X_N$ exists a.s. on the set

$$(\Omega_{\nu_a})^c = \Big\{\sum_n E^{\mathscr{A}_n}(Y_{n+1}^2) \leqslant a\Big\}.$$

It remains to let a tend to ∞ to obtain the existence of lim X_N on Ω_0.

If $\{Y_n, \mathscr{A}_n, n \geqslant 1\}$ is a centered sequence such that $\sup |Y_n| \in L_2$, and if $X_n = \sum_1^n Y_m$, we denote by ν_a' the stopping time equal to the smallest integer m, if it exists, such that $|X_N| > a$ (a a positive constant). The equality

$$X_{\nu_a' \wedge N} = X_{(\nu_a' \wedge N) - 1} + Y_{\nu_a' \wedge N}$$

and the definition of ν_a' imply that $\|X_{\nu_a' \wedge N}\|_2 \leqslant a + \|\sup |Y_n|\,\|_2$. The formula of the lemma now shows that

$$E\Big[\sum_{n < \nu_a'} E^{\mathscr{A}_n}(Y_{n+1}^2)\Big] = \lim_N \uparrow E\Big[\sum_{n < \nu_a' \wedge N} E^{\mathscr{A}_n}(Y_{n+1}^2)\Big]$$

$$= \lim_N \uparrow E(X_{\nu_a' \wedge N}^2) < \infty.$$

Hence $\sum_n E^{\mathscr{A}_n}(Y_{n+1}^2) < \infty$ a.s. on the set $(\Omega_{\nu_a'})^c = \{\sup |X_n| \leqslant a\}$. Letting a tend to ∞, we find that the set Ω_0 of the proposition is contained in the set $\{\sup |X_n| < \infty\}$; this suffices to prove the first part of the proposition.

The hypotheses of the second part of the proposition imply that $\{U_n^{-1} Y_n\}$ is a centered sequence; since U_n is assumed $\mathscr{A}_{n-1}$-measurable, we in fact have $E^{\mathscr{A}_{n-1}}(U_n^{-1} Y_n) = U_n^{-1} E^{\mathscr{A}_{n-1}}(Y_n) = 0$. By the preceding, the series $\sum U_m^{-1} Y_m$ converges a.s. to a finite limit on the set where

$$\sum U_n^2 E^{\mathscr{A}_{n-1}}(Y_n^2) < \infty.$$

To complete the proof of the proposition, it now suffices to apply Kronecker's lemma. ▮

COROLLARY. *Given a centered sequence* $\{Y_n, \mathscr{A}_n, n \geqslant 1\}$, *let us put* $D_n = \sum_1^n E^{\mathscr{A}_{m-1}}(Y_m^2)$. *Then on the set* $\{\sum_m E^{\mathscr{A}_{m-1}}(Y_m^2) = \infty\}$ *we have*, a.s. *for every* $\epsilon > 0$,

$$\lim_n \frac{\sum_1^n Y_m}{D_n^{1/2}(\log D_n)^{(1/2)+\epsilon}} = 0.$$

(*On the complementary set, the series* $\sum Y_m$ *converges.*)

PROOF. We put $U_n = f(D_n)$, where f denotes the increasing function $f(t) = t^{1/2}(\log t)^{(1/2)+\epsilon}$. It is clear that $\lim \uparrow U_n = \infty$ on the set introduced in the corollary. On the other hand, since

$$U_n^{-2}E^{\mathscr{A}_{n-1}}(Y_n^2) = \frac{D_n - D_{n-1}}{f^2(D_n)} \leqslant \int_{D_{n-1}}^{D_n} \frac{dt}{f^2(t)},$$

the convergence at infinity of the integral $\int^\infty f^{-2}(t)\,dt$, whose verification is immediate, implies the convergence of the series $\sum U_n^{-2}E^{\mathscr{A}_{n-1}}(Y_n^2)$ everywhere; the preceding proposition is now applicable. ▮

The following proposition shows that the series $\sum_1^n Y_m$ oscillates indefinitely from $-\infty$ to $+\infty$ when it diverges, under the indicated hypothesis.

PROPOSITION IV.6.3. *For every centered sequence* $\{Y_n, n \geqslant 1\}$ *such that* $\sup |Y_n| \in L_1$, *we have*

$$\liminf_n \left(\sum_1^n Y_m\right) \underset{\text{a.s.}}{=} -\infty \quad \textit{and} \quad \limsup_n \left(\sum_1^n Y_m\right) \underset{\text{a.s.}}{=} +\infty$$

on the complement of the set where the series $\sum Y_m$ *converges to a finite limit.*

PROOF. Let ν_a be the stopping time equal to the smallest integer m, if it exists, such that the martingale $\{X_n = \sum_1^n Y_m\}$ is $> a$ at m; since we have $X_{\nu_a \wedge N}^+ \leqslant X_{\nu_a \wedge N-1}^+ + Y_{\nu_a \wedge N}^+ \leqslant a + \sup_n Y_n^+$, the hypothesis implies that the expectation $E(|X_{\nu_a \wedge N}|) = 2E(X_{\nu_a \wedge N}^+)$ remains bounded as $N \to \infty$. By Proposition IV.5.6 the martingale $\{X_{\nu_a \wedge N}\}$ then converges to a finite limit, and consequently the limit lim a.s.$_{n\to\infty} X_n$ exists and is finite a.s. on the set $(\Omega_{\nu_a})^c = \{\sup X_n \leqslant a\}$. Letting a tend to infinity, we thus see that lim X_n exists and is finite on the set

$$\{\sup_n X_n < \infty\} = \{\limsup_n X_n < \infty\},$$

hence also that $\limsup_n X_n \underset{\text{a.s.}}{=} \infty$ on the set of divergence of the sequence $\{X_n\}$. By symmetry we also must have $\liminf_n X_n \underset{\text{a.s.}}{=} -\infty$ on this set. ▮

COROLLARY. *Let* $\{Z_n, n \geqslant 1\}$ *be a sequence of* r.r.v.'s *such that* $0 \leqslant Z_n \leqslant 1$. *Then* $\{\sum_n Z_n < \infty\} \underset{\text{a.s.}}{=} \{\sum_n E^{\mathscr{A}_{n-1}}(Z_n) < \infty\}$. *In particular, if* $\{A_n, n \geqslant 1\}$ *is a sequence of events and if the* $\mathscr{A}_n$ *are the* σ*-algebras generated by the* $\{A_m, m \leqslant n\}$, *we have*

$$\limsup_{n\to\infty} A_n \underset{\text{a.s.}}{=} \left\{\sum_n E^{\mathscr{A}_{n-1}}(1_{A_n}) = \infty\right\}.$$

PROOF. The $Y_n = Z_n - E^{\mathscr{A}_{n-1}}(Z_n)$ form a centered sequence of r.r.v.'s such that $|Y_n| \leqslant 1$ and $-E^{\mathscr{A}_{n-1}}(Z_n) \leqslant Y_n \leqslant Z_n$. Since the convergence of the series $\sum Z_m$ implies that

$$\limsup_n \left(\sum_1^n Y_m\right) \leqslant \sum_n Z_n < \infty,$$

the preceding proposition shows that $\lim_{n\to\infty} (\sum_1^n Y_m)$ exists and is finite on the set where $\sum Z_n < \infty$, hence that

$$\sum_n E^{\mathscr{A}_{n-1}}(Z_n) = \sum_n Z_n - \lim_n \left(\sum_1^n Y_m\right)$$

converges on this set. A symmetric argument shows that $\sum Z_n < \infty$ on the set where $\sum E^{\mathscr{A}_{n-1}}(Z_n) < \infty$. ▮

Complements and problems

IV.6.1. If $\{Y_n, n \geqslant 1\}$ is a sequence of independent r.r.v.'s, show that the condition $\sup_n |Y_n| \in L_p$ for a real $p \in [1, \infty)$ is equivalent to the existence of a real positive a such that $\sum_n \int_{\{|Y_n| > a\}} |Y_n|^p < \infty$. [Show first that an arbitrary positive r.r.v. Y is integrable if and only if the infinite product

$$\prod_{m \geqslant m_0} P(Y \leqslant m)$$

converges; here m runs through the integers $\geqslant m_0$ and m_0 denotes an integer such that $P(Y \leqslant m_0) > 0$.] Deduce from this that if the r.r.v.'s Y_n $(n \geqslant 1)$ are independent and identically distributed, the condition $\sup_n |Y_n| \in L_p$ is satisfied if and only if $Y_1 \in L_\infty$, and hence does not depend on p.

Now restate the results of the preceding section, considering only sequences of independent r.r.v.'s, and taking into account that

$$E^{\mathscr{A}_{n-1}}(Y_n^2) = E(Y_n^2)$$

for such sequences.

IV.6.2. If $\{X_n, n \geqslant 1\}$ is a submartingale, show that lim a.s. X_n exists and is $<\infty$ a.s. on the set where the series $\sum_n (E^{\mathscr{A}_{n-1}}(X_n^+) - X_{n-1}^+)$ converges; moreover if $\sup (X_n - X_{n-1})^+ \in L_1$, the preceding set coincides a.s. with the set on which the sequence $\{X_n\}$ converges to a limit $<\infty$.

If $\{X_n, n \geqslant 1\}$ is a martingale or a positive submartingale, show that lim a.s. X_n exists and is finite a.s. on the set

$$\Omega_p \doteq \left\{\sum_n (E^{\mathscr{A}_{n-1}}|X_n|^p - |X_{n-1}|^p) < \infty\right\}$$

if $p \geqslant 1$; moreover if $\sup |X_n - X_{n-1}| \in L_p$, then Ω_p coincides a.s. with the set on which the sequence $\{X_n\}$ converges to a finite limit. Show in addition that the subsets Ω_p decrease as p increases. [Use the technique developed in the proof of Proposition IV.6.2.]

IV.6.3. Deduce from the corollary of Proposition IV.6.3 a new proof of Proposition IV.4.4. [Observe that

$$E^{\mathscr{A}_{n-1}}(1_{A_n}) = P(A_n/A_1^c \cap A_2^c \cap \cdots \cap A_{n-1}^c) \qquad \text{a.s.} \quad \text{on} \quad \bigcap_{m \geqslant 1} A_m^c.]$$

IV.7. SEQUENCES OF INDEPENDENT RANDOM VARIABLES

In this section we are going to derive, from the martingale theorem and from Proposition IV.6.1 which follows from it, two classical theorems of the theory of the addition of independent r.r.v.'s. Other results of this theory are included in the preceding section (see Problem IV.6.1).

PROPOSITION IV.7.1. (*Law of large numbers.*) *If* $\{Y_n, n \geqslant 1\}$ *is a sequence of independent identically distributed* r.r.v.'s, *the condition* $E(|Y_1|) < \infty$ *implies that*

$$\lim_{n\to\infty} \text{a.s.} \frac{1}{n} \sum_1^n Y_m = E(Y_1).$$

More generally, for every real $p \in (0, 2)$, the condition $E(|Y_1|^p) < \infty$ implies that

$$\lim_{n\to\infty} \text{a.s. } n^{-1/p} \sum_1^n (Y_m - a) = 0,$$

where $a = E(Y_1)$ if $p \geqslant 1$, and is evidently an arbitrary real number if $p < 1$. Conversely, if $E(|Y_1|^p) = \infty$, then

$$\limsup_{n\to\infty} n^{-1/p} \left| \sum_1^n (Y_m - a) \right| = +\infty \quad \text{a.s.}$$

for every $a \in R$.

PROOF. Let $\{Y_n, n \geqslant 1\}$ be a sequence of independent identically distributed r.r.v.'s such that $E(|Y_1|^p) < \infty$; in the case where $p \geqslant 1$ we shall assume in addition that $E(Y_1) = 0$ (which is meaningful), as the general case is easily reduced to this special case by subtracting the constant $E(Y_1)$ from the Y_n. We now define a new sequence $\{Z_n, n \geqslant 1\}$ of bounded independent r.r.v.'s by putting $Z_n = Y_n 1_{\{|Y_n| \leqslant n^{1/p}\}}$. An easy calculation will show us, shortly,

(a) that $\sum_{n \geqslant 1} P(Y_n \neq Z_n) < \infty$;

(b) that the series $\sum_{n \geqslant 1} n^{-1/p} E(Z_n)$ is absolutely convergent if $p \neq 1$ and that $\lim_{n\to\infty} E(Z_n) = 0$ if $p = 1$;

(c) that $\sum_{n \geqslant 1} n^{-2/p} E(Z_n^2) < \infty$.

Since $E[(Z_n - EZ_n)^2] = E(Z_n^2) - [E(Z_n)]^2 \leqslant E(Z_n^2)$, we can now deduce, from property (c) and from the second part of Proposition IV.6.1, applied to the centered sequence $\{Z_n - E(Z_n), n \geqslant 1\}$ and to the sequence of real numbers $u_n = n^{1/p}$, that $\lim \text{a.s.}_{n\to\infty} n^{-1/p} \sum_1^n [Z_m - E(Z_m)] = 0$. Property (b) above and, when $p \neq 1$, Kronecker's lemma (p. 147) show next that $\lim_{n\to\infty} n^{-1/p} \sum_1^n E(Z_m) = 0$ and, consequently, that

$$\lim_{n\to\infty} \text{a.s. } n^{-1/p} \sum_1^n Z_m = 0.$$

Finally, property (a) implies that for almost every ω, $Y_n(\omega) = Z_n(\omega)$ if n is sufficiently large. Since $n^{-1/p} \downarrow 0$ as $n \uparrow \infty$, we deduce from this that $\lim \text{a.s.}_{n\to\infty} n^{-1/p} \sum_1^n Y_m = 0$.

To establish (a)–(c), we note first that for every real $y \geqslant 0$ and every real $q \in [0, 1)$ we easily obtain the inequality

$$y^{pq} \sum_{n \geqslant 1} n^{-q} 1_{\{y > n^{1/p}\}} = y^{pq} \sum_{n \geqslant 1} n^{-q} 1_{\{y^p > n\}}$$
$$\leqslant y^{pq} \int_0^{y^p} x^{-q}\, dx = (1 - q)^{-1} y^p.$$

(Here $1_{\{y>n^{1/p}\}}$ is to be understood as 1 when $y > n^{1/p}$, and 0 otherwise.)

This inequality implies property (a) on taking $q = 0$, since we have

$$\sum_{n\geqslant 1} P(Y_n \neq Z_n) = \sum_{n\geqslant 1} E[1_{\{|Y_1|>n^{1/p}\}}] \leqslant E(|Y_1|^p) < \infty.$$

It also implies property (b) when $p > 1$, since we then have, taking into account that $E(Y_1) = 0$,

$$\begin{aligned} |E(Z_n)| &= |E(Y_1 1_{\{|Y_1|\leqslant n^{1/p}\}})| = |E[Y_1 1_{\{|Y_1|>n^{1/p}\}}]| \\ &\leqslant E(|Y_1| 1_{\{|Y_1|>n^{1/p}\}}) \end{aligned}$$

and therefore, on taking $q = 1/p < 1$ in the inequality above,

$$\begin{aligned} \sum_{n\geqslant 1} n^{-1/p}|E(Z_n)| &\leqslant E\left[|Y_1| \sum_{n\geqslant 1} n^{-1/p} 1_{\{|Y_1|>n^{1/p}\}}\right] \\ &\leqslant \left(1 - \frac{1}{p}\right)^{-1} E(|Y_1|^p) < \infty. \end{aligned}$$

On the other hand, for every real $y \geqslant 0$ and every real $q > 1$ we have

$$\begin{aligned} y^{pq} \sum_{n\geqslant 1} n^{-q} 1_{\{y\leqslant n^{1/p}\}} &= y^{pq} \sum_{n\geqslant 1} n^{-q} 1_{\{y^p\leqslant n\}} \\ &\leqslant y^{pq}\left[(y^p)^{-q} + \int_{y^p}^{\infty} x^{-q}\,dx\right] = 1 + (q-1)^{-1} y^p. \end{aligned}$$

This second inequality implies, to begin with, the validity of property (b) above when $p < 1$; in fact, setting $q = 1/p$, we have

$$\begin{aligned} \sum_{n\geqslant 1} n^{-1/p}|E(Z_n)| \leqslant \sum_{n\geqslant 1} n^{-1/p} E(|Z_n|) &= E\left[|Y_1| \sum_{n\geqslant 1} n^{-1/p} 1_{\{|Y_1|\leqslant n^{1/p}\}}\right] \\ &\leqslant 1 + \left(\frac{1}{p} - 1\right)^{-1} E(|Y_1|^p) < \infty. \end{aligned}$$

The preceding inequality also implies property (c); setting in it $q = 2/p > 1$, we in fact find that

$$\begin{aligned} \sum_{n\geqslant 1} n^{-2/p} E(Z_n^2) &= E\left[|Y_1|^2 \sum_{n\geqslant 1} n^{-2/p} 1_{\{|Y_1|\leqslant n^{1/p}\}}\right] \\ &\leqslant 1 + \left(\frac{2}{p} - 1\right)^{-1} E(|Y_1|^p) < \infty. \end{aligned}$$

Finally, the validity of property (b) when $p = 1$ is immediate:

$$E(Z_n) = E[|Y_1| 1_{\{|Y_1|\leqslant n\}}] \to E(Y_1) = 0 \quad \text{as} \quad n \to \infty,$$

and the direct part of the proposition is thus completely proved.

For every sequence $\{Y_n, n \geqslant 1\}$ of independent identically distributed r.r.v.'s, the r.r.v. $\limsup_{n\to\infty} n^{-1/p}|\sum_1^n (Y_m - a)|$ is asymptotic, hence a.s. constant. Suppose that for a $p \in (0, 2)$ and some real a, this constant r.r.v. is not infinite. The equality

$$n^{-1/p}(Y_n - a) = n^{-1/p}\sum_1^n (Y_m - a) - \left(\frac{n-1}{n}\right)^{1/p}\left[(n-1)^{-1/p}\sum_1^{n-1}(Y_m - a)\right]$$

then shows also that the r.r.v. $\limsup_{n\to\infty} n^{-1/p}|Y_n|$, which is asymptotic and hence constant, is equal a.s. to a finite constant, say c. Since the independent events $\{|Y_n| > n^{1/p}(1 + c)\}$ therefore have a limit superior which is a.s. empty, we have

$$\sum_{n\geqslant 1} P(|Y_n| > (1 + c)n^{1/p}) < \infty.$$

The elementary inequality

$$\sum_{n\geqslant 1} 1_{\{y > n^{1/p}\}} = \sum_{n\geqslant 1} 1_{\{y^p > n\}} \geqslant y^p - 1 \qquad (y \geqslant 0)$$

applied to the r.r.v. $|Y_1|/(1 + c)$ now shows that

$$E(|Y_1|^p) \leqslant (1 + c)^p\left[1 + \sum_{n\geqslant 1} P(|Y_1| > (1 + c)n^{1/p})\right] < \infty,$$

which suffices to prove the last part of the proposition. ∎

PROPOSITION IV.7.2. *Let* $\{Y_n, n \geqslant 1\}$ *be a sequence of independent* r.r.v.'s *and let* $\varphi_n(t) = E(e^{itY_n})$ $(n \geqslant 1)$ *be their characteristic functions defined on* R. *In order that the series* $\sum_n Y_n$ *converge* a.s., *it is sufficient that the product* $\prod_n \varphi_n(t)$ *converge, to a limit different from* 0, *on a* t*-set of positive Lebesgue measure.*

PROOF. For every $n \geqslant 0$ we put $X_n = \sum_1^n Y_m$ and define $\mathscr{A}_n$ as the σ-algebra generated by the Y_m $(m \leqslant n)$. Then $E(e^{itX_n}) = E(\prod_1^n e^{itY_m}) = \prod_1^n \varphi_m(t)$ by virtue of the independence of the Y_m, and we recall that $|\varphi_n(t)| \leqslant E(|e^{itY_n}|) = 1$ for every $t \in R$ and every $n \geqslant 1$. For any real t such that $\prod_n |\varphi_n(t)| > 0$, the sequence

$$\{e^{itX_n}/E(e^{itX_n}), \mathscr{A}_n; n \geqslant 0\}$$

is a bounded martingale with values in the complex plane. Since Proposition IV.4.2 implies that $E^{\mathscr{A}_n}(e^{itY_{n+1}}) = \varphi_{n+1}(t)$, the martingale property is in fact obtained by taking the quotient of the terms on the right and left sides of the following two equalities:

$$E^{\mathscr{A}_n}(e^{itX_{n+1}}) = e^{itX_n}E^{\mathscr{A}_n}(e^{itY_{n+1}}) = e^{itX_n}\varphi_{n+1}(t),$$

$$E(e^{itX_{n+1}}) = E[E^{\mathscr{A}_n}(e^{itX_{n+1}})] = E(e^{itX_n})\varphi_{n+1}(t).$$

On the other hand, the variables of the martingale are bounded from above in absolute value by the constant $(\prod_m \varphi_m(t))^{-1} < \infty$, since

$$|E(e^{itX_n})| = \prod_1^n |\varphi_m(t)| \downarrow \prod_m |\varphi_m(t)|$$

as $n \uparrow \infty$. The martingale theorem (p. 139) applied to the real and imaginary parts of the above martingale then shows that this martingale converges a.s. as $n \to \infty$.

We next denote by T the Borel set of those t for which the product $E(e^{itX_n}) = \prod_1^n \varphi_m(t)$ converges to a nonzero limit as $n \to \infty$; for such t we have $\prod_m |\varphi_m(t)| > 0$, and we then deduce from the foregoing and from the convergence of $\{E(e^{itX_n})\}$ that for every $t \in T$ the sequence $\{e^{itX_n}, n \geqslant 0\}$ converges a.s. By hypothesis the set T has positive Lebesgue measure; we are going to deduce from this that $\limsup_{n\to\infty} |X_n| < \infty$ a.s. It will follow from this that the sequence $\{X_n, n \geqslant 0\}$ is a.s. convergent, since T, having positive Lebesgue measure, contains at least two real numbers t, t' whose ratio t'/t is irrational, and since every *bounded* sequence $\{x_n, n \geqslant 0\}$ of real numbers converges whenever the two sequences $\{e^{itx_n}, n \geqslant 0\}$ and $\{e^{it'x_n}, n \geqslant 0\}$, corresponding to real numbers t, t' with t'/t irrational, converge.

With every Borel set S of R with finite and strictly positive Lebesgue measure $\lambda(S)$ we associate the complex function of the real variable $x: f_S(x) = \int_S e^{itx}\lambda(dt)$. By a classical lemma, this continuous and bounded function vanishes at infinity (in fact, a direct calculation shows this when S is a finite union of bounded disjoint intervals; since

$$\sup_x |f_S(x) - f_{S'}(x)| \leqslant \lambda(S \triangle S'),$$

we deduce that $\lim_{|x|\to\infty} f_S(x) = 0$ in the general case by approximating S in measure by finite unions of intervals). If S is moreover contained in T, the sequence $\{f_S(X_n), n \geqslant 0\}$ converges a.s. In fact, the measurable subset D of $S \times \Omega$ consisting of those (t, ω) such that $\{e^{itX_n(\omega)}\}$ does not converge as $n \to \infty$ has sections D_t ($t \in S$) which, by the foregoing, are all of probability zero. Fubini's theorem now shows that

$$\int \lambda(D_\omega)P(d\omega) = [\lambda \times P](D) = \int_S \lambda(dt)P(D_t) = 0,$$

i.e., $\lambda(D_\omega) = 0$ a.s.; but for every ω such that $\lambda(D_\omega) = 0$ the sequence $\{e^{itX_n(\omega)}\}$ converges for almost all $t \in S$ and $f_S(X_n(\omega)) = \int_S \lambda(dt)\, e^{itX_n(\omega)}$ now converges by Lebesgue's theorem.

The event $\{\limsup_n |X_n| < \infty\}$ is an asymptotic event whose probability, therefore, can only equal 0 or 1. If it equalled 0, we would have $\limsup_n |X_n| = \infty$, and the limits a.s. of the sequences $\{f_S(X_n), n \geqslant 0\}$ which exist, by the foregoing, for every Borel set $S \subset T$ of finite Lebesgue measure, would equal 0 since the functions f_S vanish at infinity. Using Lebesgue's theorem twice, taking into account that

$$|f_S(\cdot)| \leqslant \lambda(S), \qquad \left|\prod_1^n \varphi_m(\cdot)\right| \leqslant 1,$$

we would deduce from

$$E[f_S(X_n)] = \int_S \lambda(dt)E(e^{itX_n}) = \int_S \lambda(dt)\prod_1^n \varphi_m(t),$$

on letting $n \to \infty$, that

$$0 = \lim_n E[f_S(X_n)] = \lim_n \int_S \lambda(dt)\prod_1^n \varphi_m(t) = \int_S \lambda(dt)\prod_m \varphi_m(t)$$

for every Borel subset S of T having finite Lebesgue measure. This would imply that $\prod_m \varphi_m(t) = 0$ a.s. on T, in contradiction with the definition of T. We have thus shown that $\limsup_n |X_n| < \infty$ a.s. ∎

COROLLARY 1. *For every sequence* $\{Y_n, n \geqslant 1\}$ *of independent* r.r.v.'s *with the respective characteristic functions* φ_n, *the following convergences are equivalent:*

(a) *the convergence* a.s. *of the series* $\sum Y_n$;

(b) *the convergence in probability of the series* $\sum Y_n$;

(c) *the convergence of the products* $\prod_1^n \varphi_m(t)$ *as* $n \to \infty$, *uniformly in* t *on every compact subset of* R;

(d) *the convergence of the products* $\prod_1^n \varphi_m(t)$ *as* $n \to \infty$ *to a nonzero limit on some* t*-set of positive Lebesgue measure.*

PROOF. It is clear that (a) implies (b). From the convergence in probability of the $X_n = \sum_1^n Y_m$ to a r.r.v. X and from the inequality $|e^{itx'} - e^{itx}| \leqslant |t|\,|x' - x|$, we easily deduce that for every $\epsilon > 0$ and every fixed $u > 0$,

$$P[|e^{itX_n} - e^{itX}| > \epsilon] \leqslant P\left[|X_n - X| \geqslant \frac{\epsilon}{u}\right] \to 0 \qquad (|t| \leqslant u);$$

since the r.v.'s e^{itX_n} are of modulus 1, hence bounded, we deduce from this that $E(e^{itX_n}) = \prod_1^n \varphi_m(t)$ converges to $E(e^{itX})$ uniformly on every interval $|t| \leqslant u$.

Since $\prod_1^n \varphi_m(0) = 1$, condition (c) implies the convergence of $\prod_1^n \varphi_m(t)$ to a limit which is nonzero at least on a neighborhood of 0; therefore, the convergence (c) clearly implies the convergence (d). Finally, the preceding proposition establishes that (d) implies (a). ∎

COROLLARY 2. *Let $\{Y_n, n \geqslant 1\}$ be a sequence of independent* r.r.v.'s *with the respective characteristic functions φ_n. Then in order that there exist a sequence $\{a_n, n \geqslant 1\}$ of real numbers such that the series $\sum_n (Y_n - a_n)$ converges* a.s. (*one then says that the series $\sum Y_n$ is quasi-convergent* a.s.), *it suffices that the infinite product $\prod_n |\varphi_n(t)|$ be >0 on a set of positive Lebesgue measure.*

PROOF. Let $(\Omega', \mathscr{A}', P')$ and $\{Y_n', n \geqslant 1\}$ be respectively a probability space and a sequence of independent r.r.v.'s defined on $(\Omega', \mathscr{A}', P')$, isomorphic to $(\Omega, \mathscr{A}, P)$ and $\{Y_n, n \geqslant 1\}$ respectively. The r.r.v.'s Z_n, defined on the product probability space $(\Omega, \mathscr{A}, P) \times (\Omega', \mathscr{A}', P')$ by $Z_n(\omega, \omega') = Y_n(\omega) - Y_n'(\omega')$, form a sequence of independent r.r.v.'s (by virtue of the corollary of Proposition IV.4.1) whose characteristic functions are given by

$$\int_{\Omega \times \Omega'} e^{itZ_n}\, d(P \times P') = \int_\Omega e^{itY_n}\, dP \int_{\Omega'} e^{-itY_n'}\, dP'$$
$$= \varphi_n(t)\varphi_n(-t) = |\varphi_n(t)|^2.$$

The hypothesis thus assures that the product of the characteristic functions of the Z_n converges to a nonzero limit on a set of positive Lebesgue measure; by Proposition IV.7.2., the convergence set of the series $\sum Z_n$ is equal a.s. to the entire space $\Omega \times \Omega'$. By Fubini's theorem, for almost every ω' the convergence set (subset of Ω) of the series $\sum_n Z_n(\cdot, \omega')$ is then equal a.s. to Ω. Setting $a_n = Y_n'(\omega')$ for such an ω', we see that the series $\sum_n (Y_n - a_n)$ converges a.s. on $(\Omega, \mathscr{A}, P)$. ∎

Complements and problems

IV.7.1. Show that for every sequence $\{c_n, n \geqslant 1\}$ of complex numbers, the condition $\sum_n |c_n|^2 < \infty$ is both necessary and sufficient for the a.s. convergence of the series $\sum_{n \geqslant 1} c_n \epsilon_n$, where $\{\epsilon_n, n \geqslant 1\}$ denotes a sequence of independent r.r.v.'s with the same distribution law: $P(\epsilon_n = \pm 1) = 1/2$. It is, similarly, necessary and sufficient for the a.s. convergence of the series $\sum_{n \geqslant 1} c_n e^{2\pi i \varphi_n}$, where $\{\varphi_n, n \geqslant 1\}$ is a sequence of independent r.r.v.'s uniformly distributed over $[0, 1)$. (Observe that the stronger condition $\sum_n |c_n| < \infty$ is necessary and sufficient for the convergence of the series $\sum c_n e^{2\pi i \varphi_n}$ for *every* choice of φ_n with values in $[0, 1)$, and also, at least in the case of real c_n, for the convergence of the series $\sum c_n \epsilon_n$ for every choice of the $\epsilon_n = \pm 1$.)

Let $\{Y_n, n \geqslant 1\}$ be a sequence of independent r.r.v.'s with symmetric probability laws (Definition: Y_n and $-Y_n$ have the same probability law) which we shall assume defined as the sequence of coordinates of the space $(R, \mathscr{R})^N$. Show that the series $\sum Y_n$ converges a.s. in R if and only if the series $\sum Y_n^2$ converges a.s. in R. [For every sequence $\{\delta_n\}$ of real numbers equalling ± 1, the transformation θ in $(R, \mathscr{R})^N$ defined by $\theta(\{y_n\}) = \{\delta_n y_n\}$ is measurable and probability preserving; therefore the series $\sum Y_n$ converges a.s. if one of the series $\sum \delta_n Y_n$ converges a.s. and only if all of these series converge a.s. On the other hand, if $\{\epsilon_n, n \geqslant 1\}$ is a sequence of independent r.r.v.'s with the same law $P(\epsilon_n = \pm 1) = 1/2$, defined on a probability space $(\Omega', \mathscr{A}', P')$, one can derive from the foregoing that the series $\sum Y_n^2$ converges a.s. on R^N if and only if $\sum \epsilon_n Y_n$ converges a.s. on $R^N \times \Omega'$.]

IV.7.2. If $\{Y_n, n \geqslant 1\}$ is a sequence of independent identically distributed r.r.v.'s and if ν is a stopping time relative to the increasing sequence $\{\mathscr{A}_n = \mathscr{B}(Y_m, m \leqslant n)\}$ of σ-algebras, show that $\{Y_{\nu+n}, n \geqslant 1\}$ is a sequence of independent r.r.v.'s with the same law as that of the Y_n and independent of $\mathscr{A}_\nu$. [It is not assumed here that $\Omega_\nu = \Omega$; thus the definition of the preceding properties has to be made precise.]

IV.7.3. We consider, in the topological vector space of (equivalence classes of) finite r.r.v.'s defined on a probability space $(\Omega, \mathscr{A}, P)$, taken with the topology of convergence in probability, the vector subspace L generated by the terms of a sequence $\{Y_n, n \geqslant 1\}$ of independent (a.s. nonconstant) r.r.v.'s; we wish to describe the closure $\bar{L}$ of L.

Show that for every n there exists a unique continuous linear functional on $\bar{L}$, denoted by c_n, such that $c_n(Y_m) = 1$ if $m = n$ and 0 otherwise. [The functional c_n is unambiguously defined on L and is continuous on L, for, as one should show,

$$\lim_{p \to \infty} \sum_m a_m^{(p)} Y_m = 0 \text{ in probability} \Rightarrow \lim_{p \to \infty} \varphi_n(a_n^{(p)} t) = 1 \qquad (t \in R)$$

$$\Rightarrow \lim_{p \to \infty} a_n^{(p)} = 0.]$$

Show next, for every r.r.v. $Z \in \bar{L}$, the existence of a sequence $\{b_n, n \geqslant 1\}$ in R such that $Z = \lim \text{a.s.}_{n \to \infty} (\sum_1^n c_m(Z) Y_m - b_n)$; if, moreover, the constant 1 does not belong to $\bar{L}$, which is in particular the case when the Y_n have symmetric probability laws, the b_n can be taken equal to 0.

[Show that $Z - \sum_1^n c_m(Z) Y_m$ is independent of $Y_1, \ldots, Y_n$ and hence that $\prod_1^n |\varphi[c_m(Z)t]| \geqslant |E(e^{itZ})|$; deduce from this the existence of real a_n $(n \geqslant 1)$ such that $\sum_1^n c_m(Z) Y_m - a_n$ converges a.s. to a limit which differs from Z only by an asymptotic r.r.v. Finally, if for a sequence $\{n_j\}$ tending to infinity, $\lim_j b_{n_j}$ exists in $\bar{R}$ and is nonzero, we have

$$1 = \lim_j b_{n_j}^{-1} \left[Z - \sum_1^{n_j} c_m(Z) Y_m\right] \in \bar{L}.]$$

CHAPTER V

ERGODIC THEORY AND MARKOV PROCESSES

V.1. A THEOREM OF IONESCU TULCEA AND A THEOREM ON PRODUCT SPACES

This section is devoted to a generalization of Proposition III.2.1 which is interesting in that it yields a construction of the probability spaces associated with discrete time random processes; this construction is particularly natural in the case of Markov processes.

The point of view adopted in carrying out this construction differs from that of Section III.3 in the manner in which randomness is introduced on the space of trajectories. We shall consider a process as represented at each instant t by a point (or state) x_t of a measurable space $(E_t, \mathscr{F}_t)$; we shall suppose throughout this chapter that the index t varies in the half-line N of nonnegative integers (discrete time processes). To make these processes random, we shall assume that we are given, at every instant t, the probability law of the process at the instant $t + 1$ (that is, of x_{t+1}), conditioned upon the evolution of the process up to the instant t (that is, conditioned upon $[x_0, \ldots, x_t]$) in the form of a transition probability. In order to be able to construct a probability on the space

$$(\Omega, \mathscr{A}) = \left(\prod_t E_t, \bigotimes_t \mathscr{F}_t\right)$$

of trajectories, it is still necessary to give the probability law of the process at the initial instant $t = 0$. We shall prefer in the following proposition to construct the probabilities P_{x_0} on $(\Omega, \mathscr{A})$ corresponding to the various possible initial states $x_0 \in E_0$; we shall then show that it is permissible to integrate these probabilities with respect to an arbitrary initial probability law P_0 on $(E_0, \mathscr{F}_0)$ by establishing what will thus be a crucial formula for the rest of this chapter (see Corollary 2).

We remark also that the results of the present section are the most general actually known which permit one to construct probabilities on a product space without having recourse to hypotheses of a topological nature (as was done, for example, in the theorem of Section III.3).

PROPOSITION V.1.1. (Ionescu Tulcea.) *Let $\{(E_t, \mathscr{F}_t);\, t \in N\}$ be an infinite sequence of measurable spaces, and for every $t \in N$ let $P_{t+1}^{0\cdots t}$ be a transition probability defined with respect to the spaces $(\prod_0^t E_s, \bigotimes_0^t \mathscr{F}_s)$ and $(E_{t+1}, \mathscr{F}_{t+1})$. Then for every $x_0 \in E_0$ there exists a unique probability P_{x_0} on*

$$(\Omega, \mathscr{A}) = \prod_t (E_t, \mathscr{F}_t)$$

whose value for every measurable rectangle $\prod_t F_t$ is given by

$$P_{x_0}\left[\prod_t F_t\right] = 1_{F_0}(x_0) \int_{x_1 \in F_1} P_1^0(x_0; dx_1) \int_{x_2 \in F_2} P_2^{01}(x_0, x_1; dx_2) \cdots \int_{x_T \in F_T} P_T^{0\cdots T-1}(x_0 \cdots x_{T-1}; dx_T)$$

as long as T is sufficiently large so that $F_t = E_t$ if $t > T$ (the right side is then independent of the T chosen). For any positive r.r.v. *Y on $(\Omega, \mathscr{A})$ which only depends upon the coordinates up to index T, we have*

$$\int_\Omega P_{x_0}(d\omega') Y(\omega') = \int_{E_1} P_1^0(x_0, dx_1) \int_{E_2} P_2^{01}(x_0, x_1; dx_2) \cdots \int_{E_T} P_T^{0\cdots T-1}(x_0 \cdots x_{T-1}; dx_T)\, Y(x_0 \cdots x_T).$$

Moreover, for any positive r.r.v. *Y on $(\Omega, \mathscr{A})$, the expression*

$$\int P_{x_0}(d\omega')\, Y(\omega')$$

is an $\mathscr{F}_0$-measurable function of x_0.

The formula defining P_{x_0} (whose right side should be read backwards) is intuitive despite its apparent complexity: put into an "infinitesimal" form, it says that the probability of successively visiting the ensembles $dx_1 \cdots dx_T$ of states, starting from the initial state x_0, is given by the product of the conditional probabilities of visiting dx_t after having passed through $x_0 \cdots x_{t-1}$ $(0 < t \leqslant T)$. The last part of the proposition says that $\{P_{x_0}[A];\, x_0 \in E_0,\, A \in \mathscr{A}\}$ is a transition probability defined relative to $(E_0, \mathscr{F}_0)$ and $(\Omega, \mathscr{A})$.

Proof. We shall begin by proving that the proposition is true in the case of a finite sequence of spaces $\{(E_t, \mathscr{F}_t);\, 0 \leqslant t \leqslant T\}$ and transition probabilities $\{P_{t+1}^{0\cdots t},\, 0 \leqslant t < T\}$. Let us define successively, for decreasing t, probabilities $P_{x_0\cdots x_t}$ on the product space $\prod_{s\leqslant T} (E_s, \mathscr{F}_s)$ by setting

(1) $P_{x_0\cdots x_T}[A] = 1_A(x_0 \cdots x_T)$

$$P_{x_0\cdots x_t}[A] = \int_{E_{t+1}} P_{t+1}^{0\cdots t}(x_0 \cdots x_t;\, dx_{t+1}) P_{x_0\cdots x_t x_{t+1}}[A].$$

These definitions are justified by the results of Section III.2 which show that at each step $P_{x_0\cdots x_t}$ is a probability on $\bigotimes_{s\leqslant T} \mathscr{F}_s$ and that $P_{x_0\cdots x_t}[A]$ is, for every fixed A, a $\bigotimes_{s\leqslant t} \mathscr{F}_s$-measurable function of $(x_0, \ldots, x_t)$ and an $\mathscr{F}_t$-measurable function of x_t (for $x_0, \ldots, x_{t-1}$ fixed). It is then evident that for every positive r.r.v. Y on $\prod_{s\leqslant T} (E_s, \mathscr{F}_s)$ and for every $t \leqslant T$ we have

$$\int_\Omega P_{x_0\cdots x_t}[d\omega'] Y(\omega') = \int_{E_{t+1}} P_{t+1}^{0\cdots t}(x_0 \cdots x_t;\, dx_{t+1})$$

$$\cdots \int_{E_T} P_T^{0\cdots T-1}(x_0 \cdots x_{T-1};\, dx_T)\, Y(x_0 \cdots x_T).$$

We pass next to the infinite case; as above, we are going to define probabilities $P_{x_0\cdots x_t}$ rather than only P_{x_0}. For every finite T, the preceding argument shows the existence of probabilities $P_{x_0\cdots x_t}^{(T)}$ on $\bigotimes_{s\leqslant T} \mathscr{F}_s$ which have some of the desired properties on these σ-subalgebras of $\mathscr{A}$. But as T varies, it is easy to verify that these probabilities are mutually compatible; consequently, there exist set functions $P_{x_0\cdots x_t}$ defined on the union $\mathscr{B} = \bigcup_T \bigotimes_{s\leqslant T} \mathscr{F}_s$ whose restrictions to $\bigotimes_{s\leqslant T} \mathscr{F}_s$ are the probabilities $P_{x_0\cdots x_t}^{(T)}$. Moreover, $\mathscr{B}$ is a Boolean algebra of subsets of Ω which generates $\mathscr{A}$ and the $P_{x_0\cdots x_t}$ are additive on $\mathscr{B}$; to show that they can be extended to probabilities on $\mathscr{A}$ it thus suffices, by the theorem of Section I.5, to show that they are continuous at $\varnothing$ on $\mathscr{B}$.

Let $\{B_n, n \geqslant 1\}$ be a sequence in $\mathscr{B}$ decreasing to $\varnothing$, and suppose that there exists a $t \geqslant 0$ and $x_0^*, \ldots, x_t^*$ such that $\lim_n \downarrow P_{x_t^*\cdots x_0^*}(B_n) > 0$.

By the monotone convergence properties of the integral, we have

$$\lim_n \downarrow P_{x_0^*\cdots x_t^*}(B_n) = \int_{E_{t+1}} P_{t+1}^{0\cdots t}(x_0^*\cdots x_t^*; dx_{t+1}) \lim_n \downarrow P_{x_0^*\cdots x_t^* x_{t+1}}(B_n);$$

since the left side is strictly positive, there exists an x_{t+1}^* such that

$$\lim_n \downarrow P_{x_0^*\cdots x_t^* x_{t+1}^*}(B_n) > 0.$$

By induction we can then show the existence of $\omega^* = \{x_0^*, \ldots\}$ such that for every $u \geqslant t$ one has $\lim_n \downarrow P_{x_0^*\cdots x_u^*}(B_n) > 0$. On the other hand, for every fixed n, if u is so large that $B_n \in \bigotimes_0^u \mathscr{F}_s$, we have

$$P_{x_0\cdots x_u}(B_n) = 1_{B_n}(x_0, \ldots, x_u);$$

thus the foregoing shows that $\omega^* \in B_n$ for every n, which is impossible. We conclude that the functions $P_{x_0\cdots x_t}$ are all probabilities on $\mathscr{B}$.

Finally, since we have shown above that $P_{x_0\cdots x_t}[B]$ is a measurable function of $(x_0, \ldots, x_t)$ when $B \in \mathscr{B}$, it follows that $\int P_{x_0\cdots x_t}(d\omega')\, Y(\omega')$ is a measurable function of $(x_0, \ldots, x_t)$ for every positive r.r.v. Y on $(\Omega, \mathscr{A})$. ∎

The significance of the formulas of the following corollary will be clear if one considers the interpretation of the $P_{x_0\cdots x_t}$ as probability laws of the process, conditioned on $(x_0, \ldots, x_t)$.

COROLLARY 1. *The probabilities $P_{x_0\cdots x_t}$ on $(\Omega, \mathscr{A})$ introduced above satisfy the following relations:*

$$\text{(a)} \int_{\omega' \in \Omega} P_{x_0\cdots x_t}(d\omega')\, Y(\omega')$$

$$= \int_{\omega' \in \Omega} P_{x_0\cdots x_s}(d\omega') \int_{\omega'' \in \Omega} P_{x_0'\cdots x_t'}(d\omega'')\, Y(\omega'')$$

if $s \leqslant t$, for any positive r.r.v. *Y;*

$$\text{(b)} \int_{\omega' \in \Omega} P_{x_0\cdots x_t}(d\omega')\, Y(\omega') Z(\omega') = Z(x_0 \cdots x_t) \int_{\omega' \in \Omega} P_{x_0\cdots x_t}(d\omega')\, Y(\omega')$$

for any t and any positive r.r.v. *Y, if Z is a positive $\bigotimes_{s \leqslant t} \mathscr{F}_s$-measurable* r.r.v. (*that is, depends only on the coordinates up to index t*).

We remark that in the right side of formula (a), the integral

$$\int_{\omega'' \in \Omega} P_{x_0' \cdots x_t'}(d\omega'')\, Y(\omega'')$$

defines a function of $(x_0', \ldots, x_t')$, and thus of $\omega' = (x_0', \ldots, x_t', \ldots)$.

PROOF. It suffices to verify these relations when Y and Z are indicator r.r.v.'s; in this case these relations can be written as

$$\text{(a) } P_{x_0 \cdots x_s}[A] = \int P_{x_0 \cdots x_s}(d\omega') P_{x_0' \cdots x_t'}[A] \qquad (s \leqslant t,\ A \in \mathscr{A}),$$

$$\text{(b) } P_{x_0 \cdots x_t}[AB] = 1_B(x_0 \cdots x_1) P_{x_0 \cdots x_t}[A] \quad (A \in \mathscr{A},\ B \in \textstyle\bigotimes_{s \leqslant t} \mathscr{F}_s).$$

It is even enough to verify these relations when A and B are measurable rectangles, which can be done immediately from the defining formulas. ▮

COROLLARY 2. *Let $\{(E_t, \mathscr{F}_t);\ t \in N\}$ be a sequence of measurable spaces. For every $t \in N$, let $P_{t+1}^{0 \cdots t}$ be a transition probability defined relative to $(\prod_0^t E_s, \bigotimes_0^t \mathscr{F}_s)$ and $(E_{t+1}, \mathscr{F}_{t+1})$. Finally, let P_0 be a probability on $(E_0, \mathscr{F}_0)$. Then there exists a unique probability P on the space $(\Omega, \mathscr{A}) = \prod_t (E_t, \mathscr{F}_t)$ whose value on every measurable rectangle is given by*

$$P\left[\prod_t F_t\right] = \int_{F_0} P_0(dx_0) \int_{F_1} P_1^0(x_0, dx_1) \int_{F_2} P_2^{01}(x_0, x_1; dx_2) \cdots \int_{F_T} P_T^{0 \cdots T-1}(x_0 \cdots x_{T-1}; dx_T)$$

as long as T is chosen so that $F_t = E_t$ if $t > T$.

This probability is given by

$$P(A) = \int_{E_0} P_0(dx_0) P_{x_0}(A) \qquad (A \in \mathscr{A}).$$

For every positive (P-quasi-integrable) r.r.v. Y on $(\Omega, \mathscr{A})$, the function $\int P_{x_0}(d\omega') Y(\omega')$ of x_0 which is defined everywhere (P_0-almost everywhere) is a version of the conditional expectation $E^{\mathscr{F}_0}(Y)$ defined on $(\Omega, \mathscr{A}, P)$.

PROOF. It is clear that the set function

$$\int P_0(dx_0) P_{x_0}(A)$$

is a probability (see Section III.2) having the desired values on the semi-algebra $\mathscr{P}$ of measurable rectangles. Since $\mathscr{P}$ generates $\mathscr{A}$, the uniqueness and the representation of P are proved. By Corollary 1, the $\mathscr{F}_0$-measurable r.r.v. defined by $U(x_0) = \int P_{x_0}(d\omega')\,Y(\omega')$ satisfies the relation

$$\int_\Omega P(d\omega')\,Y(\omega')Z(\omega') = \int_{E_0} P_0(dx_0) \int_\Omega P_{x_0}(d\omega')\,Y(\omega')Z(\omega')$$

$$= \int_{E_0} P_0(dx_0)Z(x_0)U(x_0) = \int_\Omega P(d\omega')Z(\omega')U(\omega')$$

for any positive $\mathscr{F}_0$-measurable r.r.v. Z (observe that P_0 is equal to the restriction of P to $\mathscr{F}_0$, as $P_{x_0}(A) = 1_A(x_0)$ if $A \in \mathscr{F}_0$).

By virtue of the definition of the conditional expectation, we conclude that $U(\omega) = E^{\mathscr{F}_0}(Y)$. ∎

Similarly, $\int P_{x_0 \cdots x_t}(d\omega')\,Y(\omega')$ is a version of $E^{\otimes_{s \leqslant t} \mathscr{F}_s}(Y)$ on $(\Omega, \mathscr{A}, P)$. The properties of the $P_{x_0 \cdots x_s}$ stated in Corollary 1 thus appear as two fundamental properties of the conditional expectations $E^{\otimes_{s \leqslant t} \mathscr{F}_s}$; we observe, however, that the relations (a) and (b) hold everywhere on Ω, while relations between conditional expectations are relations between equivalence classes (which by definition hold only almost everywhere).

The following special case of the preceding results leads to the notion of products of probabilities and of probability spaces.

PROPOSITION V.1.2. *Let $\{(E_t, \mathscr{F}_t, P_t); t \in T\}$ be an arbitrary nonempty family of probability spaces. Then there exists a unique probability P on $(\Omega, \mathscr{A}) = (\prod_t E_t, \bigotimes_t \mathscr{F}_t)$ such that*

$$P\Big(\prod_T A_t\Big) = \prod_T P(A_t)$$

for every measurable rectangle. This probability is the unique probability on $(\Omega, \mathscr{A})$ with respect to which the family $\{\mathscr{F}_t, t \in T\}$ of σ-subalgebras of $\mathscr{A}$ is independent and which, restricted to $\mathscr{F}_t$, is equal to P_t $(t \in T)$.

PROOF. In the case where T is countable, we identify T and N and take $P_{t+1}^{0 \cdots t} = P_{t+1}$ (independent of $\omega_0, \ldots, \omega_t$) in Corollary 2 of Proposition V.1.1; the existence and uniqueness of P are thus proved. In the general case, this shows the existence of product probabilities P_S on every σ-algebra $\bigotimes_S \mathscr{F}_t$ for S a countable subset of T. These probabilities are mutually compatible; using Proposition III.3.2, we then see that the set function P defined on $\mathscr{A} = \bigotimes_T \mathscr{F}_t = \bigcup_S (\bigotimes_S \mathscr{F}_t)$, where S runs through the countable subsets of T, is a probability, and therefore the desired one. ∎

Complements and problems

V.1.1. Let $(\Omega, \mathscr{A})$ be a measurable space and let $\{\mathscr{B}_i, i \in I\}$ be a countable family of σ-subalgebras of $\mathscr{A}$ which generates $\mathscr{A}$ and which has the following property: for every choice of $B_i \neq \varnothing$ in $\mathscr{B}_i$ $(i \in I)$ one has $\bigcap_I B_i \neq \varnothing$. Show that there exists a unique probability P on $(\Omega, \mathscr{A})$ whose restrictions to the $\mathscr{B}_i$ are arbitrary given probabilities P_i $(i \in I)$ and such that

$$P\left(\bigcap_I B_i\right) = \prod_I P_i(B_i)$$

for every choice of the $B_i \in \mathscr{B}_i$ $(i \in I)$. [Show that if φ denotes the mapping of Ω into Ω^I defined by $\varphi(\omega) = (\omega, \omega, \ldots)$, the mapping φ^{-1} is an isomorphism of $\otimes_I \mathscr{B}_i$ onto $\mathscr{A}$; then set $P \circ \varphi^{-1} = \prod_I P_i$.] Extend this result to an uncountable family $\{\mathscr{B}_i\}$.

V.1.2. Let $\{(\Omega_n, \mathscr{A}_n, P_n); n \geqslant 1\}$ be a sequence of probability spaces. For every $n \geqslant 1$ let $Q_n = f_n \cdot P_n$ be a probability on $(\Omega_n, \mathscr{A}_n)$ which is absolutely continuous with respect to P_n, and let $\rho_n = \int \sqrt{f_n}\, dP_n$. Show that the probability $Q = \prod_n Q_n$ on the product of the $(\Omega_n, \mathscr{A}_n)$ is absolutely continuous with respect to $P = \prod_n P_n$ or singular with respect to P according as $\prod_n \rho_n > 0$ or $\prod_n \rho_n = 0$. [In the case where $\prod_n \rho_n > 0$, show first that $g_N = \prod_{n \leqslant N} \sqrt{f_n}$ is a Cauchy sequence in $L_2(P)$. In the case where $\prod_n \rho_n = 0$, show that there exist sets $A_N \in \otimes_{n \leqslant N} \mathscr{A}_n$ such that $P(A_N) \to 0$ and $Q(A_N) \to 1$ as $N \to \infty$.]

V.2. CONSTRUCTION OF CANONICAL MARKOV PROCESSES (DISCRETE TIME)

A random process given by a sequence of transition probabilities defined as in Proposition V.1.1 is called a *Markov process* if at each instant t the probability law of the process at the next instant $t + 1$ depends upon the evolution of the system up to the instant t only through the position *at* the instant t; in other words, a random process is *Markovian* if one can set $P_{t+1}^{0\cdots t}(x_0 \cdots x_t; F) = P_{t+1}^{t}(x_t, F)$. By the results of Section V.1, one can construct, at each instant t and for every state x_t, the probability law of the evolution of the process starting from the instant t; this probability, which we shall denote by P_{t,x_t}, is defined on the σ-algebra

$$\mathscr{A}_\infty^t = \bigotimes_{s \geqslant t} \mathscr{F}_s$$

of events not preceding the instant t (we shall consider $\mathscr{A}^t_\infty$ as a σ-algebra of subsets of $\Omega = \prod_s E_s$ rather than of $\prod_{s \geq t} E_s$; evidently these subsets do not depend upon the coordinates whose indices are less than t). In all that follows we shall denote by X_t the coordinate mapping of Ω onto E_t; thus $\omega = \{X_0(\omega), X_1(\omega), \ldots\}$. Under the preceding hypotheses, we shall say, regarding the r.f. $\{X_t, t \geq 0\}$ defined on $(\Omega, \mathscr{A})$, that it is Markovian.

PROPOSITION V.2.1. *Let $\{(E_t, \mathscr{F}_t); t \in N\}$ be a sequence of measurable spaces. For every t, let P^t_{t+1} be a transition probability defined with respect to $(E_t, \mathscr{F}_t)$ and $(E_{t+1}, \mathscr{F}_{t+1})$. Then for every t and for every $x_t \in E_t$ there exists a unique probability P_{t,x_t} on $(\Omega, \mathscr{A}^t_\infty)$ whose value on every measurable rectangle $\prod_s F_s$ ($F_s = E_s$ if $s < t$) is given by*

$$P_{t,x_t}\Big[\prod_s F_s\Big] = 1_{F_t}(x_t) \int_{F_{t+1}} P^t_{t+1}(x_t, dx_{t+1}) \int_{F_{t+2}} P^{t+1}_{t+2}(x_{t+1}, dx_{t+2}) \cdots \int_{F_T} P^{T-1}_T(x_{T-1}, dx_T)$$

as long as T is such that $F_s = E_s$ if $s > T$. For every $\mathscr{A}^t_\infty$-measurable positive r.r.v. *Y, the function $\int P_{t,x_t}(d\omega')Y(\omega')$ of x_t is $\mathscr{F}_t$-measurable.*

The family of probabilities P_{t,x_t} satisfies the following property, called the

MARKOV PROPERTY. *If $0 \leq s \leq t$, then for any positive* r.r.v.'s *Y and Z which are measurable with respect to $\mathscr{A}^s_t = \bigotimes_{s \leq u \leq t} \mathscr{F}_u$ and $\mathscr{A}^t_\infty = \bigotimes_{u \geq t} \mathscr{F}_u$, respectively, one has*

$$\int_{\omega' \in \Omega} P_{s,x_s}(d\omega')Y(\omega')Z(\omega') = \int_{\omega' \in \Omega} P_{s,x_s}(d\omega')Y(\omega') \int_{\omega'' \in \Omega} P_{t,X_t(\omega')}(d\omega'')Z(\omega'').$$

If P_0 is a probability on $(E_0, \mathscr{F}_0)$, the formula

$$P(A) = \int_{E_0} P_0(dx_0)P_{x_0}[A]$$

defines a probability on $(\Omega, \mathscr{A}) = \prod_t (E_t, \mathscr{F}_t)$. For every positive $\mathscr{A}^t_\infty$-measurable r.r.v. *Y defined on $(\Omega, \mathscr{A}, P)$, the conditional expectations $E^{\mathscr{A}^0_t}[Y]$ and $E^{\mathscr{F}_t}[Y]$ are equal, and the function $\int P_{t,X_t(\omega)}(d\omega')Y(\omega')$ of ω is one version of them.*

PROOF. The first part of the proposition is obtained by applying Proposition V.1.1 to the sequence of spaces $\{(E_s, \mathscr{F}_s); s \geqslant t\}$ and transition probabilities $\{P_{s+1}^{t,t+1,\ldots,s} = P_{s+1}^s; s \geqslant t\}$.

We next consider the probabilities $P_{x_0 \cdots x_t}$ constructed at the beginning of this section, starting from the sequences $\{(E_s, \mathscr{F}_s), s \geqslant 0\}$ and

$$\{P_{s+1}^{0 \cdots s} = P_{s+1}^s; s \geqslant 0\}.$$

By the definition of these probabilities, we see at once that for every measurable rectangle A of $\bigotimes_{s \geqslant t} \mathscr{F}_s$ one has $P_{x_0 \cdots x_t}(A) = P_{t,x_t}(A)$. This equality extends to all of the σ-algebra $\mathscr{A}_\infty^t$ and, consequently, the probability P_{t,x_t} is simply the restriction of $P_{x_0 \cdots x_t}$ to the σ-algebra $\mathscr{A}_\infty^t$ of events not preceding t; this result is the essential point of the proof. The Markov property is now deduced from Corollary 1 of Proposition V.1.1; in fact, if Y and Z are positive r.r.v.'s measurable with respect to $\mathscr{A}_t^s$ and $\mathscr{A}_\infty^t$, respectively, this corollary shows that if $x_0' = X_0(\omega'), \ldots, x_t' = X_t(\omega')$, then

$$\begin{aligned}
&\int_{\omega' \in \Omega} P_{x_0 \cdots x_s}(d\omega')\, Y(\omega') Z(\omega') \\
&\qquad = \int_{\omega' \in \Omega} P_{x_0 \cdots x_s}(d\omega') \int_{\omega'' \in \Omega} P_{x_0' \cdots x_t'}(d\omega'')\, Y(\omega'') Z(\omega'') \\
&\qquad = \int_{\omega' \in \Omega} P_{x_0 \cdots x_s}(d\omega')\, Y(\omega') \int_{\omega'' \in \Omega} P_{x_0' \cdots x_t'}(d\omega'') Z(\omega'')
\end{aligned}$$

when $s \leqslant t$, and we can replace in this formula $P_{x_0 \cdots x_s}$ by P_{s,x_s} and $P_{x_0' \cdots x_t'}$ by $P_{t,X_t(\omega')}$.

The existence of the probability P is assured by Corollary 2 of Proposition V.1.1; moreover, we know that for every positive r.r.v. Y defined on $(\Omega, \mathscr{A}, P)$ the function $\int P_{x_0 \cdots x_t}(d\omega')\, Y(\omega')$ of $(x_0 \cdots x_t)$ is a version of $E^{\mathscr{A}_t^0}[Y]$. Hence if Y is $\mathscr{A}_\infty^t$-measurable, the function

$$\int P_{t,x_t}(d\omega')\ Y(\omega')$$

of $x_t = X_t(\omega)$ is a version of $E^{\mathscr{A}_t^0}[Y]$; since this function is indeed $\mathscr{F}_t$-measurable, it follows that the identity $E^{\mathscr{F}_t}[Y] = E^{\mathscr{F}_t}(E^{\mathscr{A}_t^0}[Y])$ reduces to $E^{\mathscr{F}_t}[Y] = E^{\mathscr{A}_t^0}[Y]$. ▮

COROLLARY. *Under the hypotheses of the preceding proposition, there exists a unique family of transition probabilities* P_t^s *defined when* $0 \leqslant s < t$

with respect to $(E_s, \mathscr{F}_s)$ *and* $(E_t, \mathscr{F}_t)$, *respectively, which are equal to the given transition probabilities when* $t = s + 1$ *and which satisfy the (generalized semigroup) relations* $P_t^s P_u^t = P_u^s$ *if* $s < t < u$, *that is,*

$$\int_{x_t \in E_t} P_t^s(x_s, dx_t) P_u^t(x_t, F) = P_u^s(x_s, F) \qquad (x_s \in E_s, F \in \mathscr{F}_u, s < t < u).$$

For every probability $P = \int \mu_0(dx_0) P_{x_0}$ *constructed on* $(\Omega, \mathscr{A})$ *by means of an initial probability* μ_0 *and for any real positive measurable function* h *defined on* $(E_u, \mathscr{F}_u)$, *the conditional expectations*

$$E^{\mathscr{A}_t^0}[h(X_u)] \qquad \text{and} \qquad E^{\mathscr{F}_t}[h(X_u)]$$

are equal when $t < u$; *moreover, the* r.r.v. $P_u^t(h(X_t))$ *is a version of them, if* $P_u^t h$ *denotes the real positive measurable function defined on* $(E_t, \mathscr{F}_t)$ *by the formula*

$$P_u^t h(x_t) = \int_{F_u} P_u^t(x_t, dx_u) h(x_u) \qquad (t < u).$$

The probability laws μ_t *of the variables* X_t, *induced by* P *on* $(E_t, \mathscr{F}_t)$ *for every* $t \geqslant 0$, *are obtained from* μ_0 *by the formula*

$$\mu_t = \int \mu_0(dx_0) P_t^0(x_0, \cdot)$$

which can also be written as $\mu_t = \mu_0 P_t^0$; *more generally, these probabilities satisfy the relations* $\mu_t = \mu_s P_t^s$ $(0 \leqslant s < t)$.

PROOF. For every $s \geqslant 0$ let us define the transition probabilities P_{s+h}^s by induction on $h > 0$ by setting $P_{s+h+1}^s = P_{s+h}^s P_{s+h+1}^{s+h}$; the P_t^s $(0 \leqslant s < t)$ thus obtained obviously satisfy the generalized semigroup relations. On the other hand, the restriction of the probability P_{t,x_t} defined on $\mathscr{A}_\infty^t$ to the σ-subalgebra $\mathscr{F}_u$ $(t < u)$ is equal to $P_u^t(x_t, \cdot)$, as is easily verified from the formula defining P_{t,x_t}; the Markov property applied to the r.r.v. $Y = h(X_u)$ now shows that

$$P_u^t h(X_t) = \int P_{t,X_t}(d\omega') h[X_u(\omega')]$$

is a version of $E^{\mathscr{A}_t^0}[h(X_u)] = E^{\mathscr{F}_t}[h(X_u)]$. Finally, for every $s < t$ and every real positive measurable function h defined on $(E_t, \mathscr{F}_t)$ we have

$$\begin{aligned} \mu_s P_s^t(h) &= \mu_s(P_s^t h) = E[P_s^t h(X_s)] \\ &= E(E^{\mathscr{F}_t}[h(X_t)]) = E[h(X_t)] = \mu_t(h); \end{aligned}$$

it follows that $\mu_s P_s^t = \mu_t$ on $(E_t, \mathscr{F}_t)$. ∎

Given a Markov process, we define the σ-algebra $\mathscr{A}_\infty$ of *asymptotic events* by $\mathscr{A}_\infty = \lim_{t\uparrow\infty} \downarrow \mathscr{A}^t_\infty$; a random variable Z will be said to be asymptotic if it is $\mathscr{A}_\infty$-measurable (example: $Z = \limsup_t Z_t$ if Z_t is $\mathscr{A}^t_\infty$-measurable). Two asymptotic random variables Z and Z' will be said to be *equivalent* if the set $\{Z \neq Z'\}$ is negligible for each of the probabilities P_{t,x_t} ($t \geqslant 0$, $x_t \in E_t$); two asymptotic events F and F' will be said to be equivalent, in particular, if $P_{t,x_t}(F \triangle F') = 0$ for every $t \geqslant 0$ and $x_t \in E_t$.

Proposition V.2.2. *The formulas*

$$g_t(x_t) = \int_\Omega P_{t,x_t}(d\omega')Z'(\omega')$$

establish a one-to-one correspondence between, on the one hand, equivalence classes of bounded (positive) asymptotic random variables Z and, on the other hand, families $\{g_t, t \geqslant 0\}$ of (positive) measurable functions defined on the $(E_t, \mathscr{F}_t)$ and such that

$$g_t = P^t_{t+1} g_{t+1}, \qquad \sup_t \sup_{x_t} |g_t(x_t)| < \infty.$$

In addition we have

$$\lim_{t\to\infty} \text{a.s. } g_t(X_t) = Z$$

with respect to every probability P_{s,x_s}.

Proof. Let Z be a bounded asymptotic random variable. Then the functions $g_t(x_t)$ defined in the proposition are $\mathscr{F}_t$-measurable and such that $|g_t(x_t)| \leqslant \sup_\omega |Z(\omega)|$; moreover, they only depend upon the equivalence class of Z. The Markov property and the fact that Z is $\mathscr{A}^t_\infty$-measurable for every t show that $g_s = P^s_t g_t$ when $s < t$. It is clear that the functions g_t are positive whenever the equivalence class of Z is.

Conversely, if $\{g_t, t \geqslant 0\}$ is a family of functions of the type described in the proposition, the random variable $Z(\omega) = \liminf_{t\to\infty} g_t(X_t(\omega))$ defined on Ω is $\mathscr{A}_\infty$-measurable; moreover, on each of the probability spaces $(\Omega, \mathscr{A}^s_\infty, P_{s,x'_s})$ the sequence $\{g_t(X_t), \mathscr{A}^s_t; t \geqslant s\}$ is a bounded martingale, as

$$E^{\mathscr{A}^s_t}[g_{t+1}(X_{t+1})] = P^t_{t+1} g_{t+1}[X_t] = g_t[X_t].$$

Consequently (see Section IV.5) the variable Z is also the limit a.s. of

$g_t(X_t)$ when $t \to \infty$. Moreover, the variables Z and $g_t(X_t)$, where $t \geqslant s$, have the same expectation; thus

$$\int P_{s,x_s'}(d\omega)Z(\omega) = \int P_{s,x_s'}(d\omega)g_s[X_s(\omega)] = g_s(x_s').$$

The proposition is completely proved. ∎

In the sequel we shall denote by G the vector space of families $\{g_t, t \geqslant 0\}$ of functions described in the preceding proposition.

COROLLARY. *The following two conditions are equivalent for every Markov process:*

(a) *The σ-algebra of equivalence classes of asymptotic events is finite;*
(b) *the space G defined above is finite dimensional.*

If these conditions are satisfied, there exist N positive elements of G, say $g^{(n)} = \{g_t^{(n)}, t \geqslant 0\}$ $(1 \leqslant n \leqslant N)$, such that every (positive) element g of G has a unique representation $g = \sum_{n=1}^N c_n g^{(n)}$, where the c_n are real (positive). Moreover, one can choose the $g^{(n)}$ so that $1 = \sum_1^N g^{(n)}$, in which case they are uniquely determined (up to a permutation).

PROOF. The equivalence of conditions (a) and (b) follows at once from the proposition. Let us suppose that these conditions are satisfied, and denote by $\{A_n, 1 \leqslant n \leqslant N\}$ a partition of Ω consisting of atoms of $\mathscr{A}_\infty$ (see Section I.2); we also denote by $g^{(n)} = \{g_t^{(n)}, t \geqslant 0\}$ the element of G associated by the preceding proposition with the equivalence class of 1_{A_n}. Then the second part of the corollary is immediately deduced from the fact that every (positive) asymptotic r.r.v. Z has the representation $Z = \sum_1^N c_n 1_{A_n}$ which is unique up to equivalence, where the real (positive) numbers c_n are uniquely determined. ∎

Definition V.2.1. A MARKOV PROCESS AS DEFINED AT THE BEGINNING OF THIS SECTION IS SAID TO HAVE STATIONARY TRANSITION PROBABILITIES, IF ALL THE SPACES $(E_t, \mathscr{F}_t)$ ARE ISOMORPHIC TO A SINGLE SPACE $(E, \mathscr{F})$ AND IF ALL THE TRANSITION PROBABILITIES P_{t+1}^t ARE IDENTICAL WITH A SINGLE TRANSITION PROBABILITY P DEFINED ON $(E, \mathscr{F})$.

In the rest of this chapter we shall consider only such Markov processes. We shall reformulate Propositions V.2.1 and V.2.2 for these Markov processes after introducing the following auxiliary notion.

The translation (of coordinates) operator θ is defined on the space $\Omega = E^N$ by the following formula, where $\omega = \{x_t, t \geqslant 0\}$:

$$\theta(\{x_t, t \geqslant 0\}) = \{x_{t+1}, t \geqslant 0\}.$$

The positive integer powers θ_s ($s \geqslant 1$) of this operator can similarly be defined by $\theta_s(\{x_t, t \geqslant 0\}) = \{x_{t+s}, t \geqslant 0\}$. These transformations θ_s are measurable on $(\Omega, \mathscr{A} = \mathscr{A}^0_\infty)$; more precisely, $(\theta_s)^{-1}$ maps $\mathscr{A}^0_\infty$ one-to-one onto $\mathscr{A}^s_\infty$. Consequently, the mapping $Z \to Z\theta_s$ is a one-to-one mapping of the family of random variables Z which are $\mathscr{A}^0_\infty$-measurable onto the family of random variables which are $\mathscr{A}^s_\infty$-measurable; let us agree to write $Z \to Z\theta_{-s}$ for the inverse mapping which maps the set of $\mathscr{A}^s_\infty$-measurable random variables Z onto the set of $\mathscr{A}^0_\infty$-measurable random variables. (Observe that $\theta_{-s}(\omega)$ can only be "defined," when $\omega \in \Omega$ and $s > 0$, as $(\theta_s)^{-1}\{\omega\}$, that is, as the cylinder in Ω whose first s coordinates are arbitrary and whose $(s + t)$-th coordinate is equal to the t-th coordinate of $\omega (t \geqslant 0)$; nevertheless, if Z is $\mathscr{A}^s_\infty$-measurable and hence does not depend upon the first s coordinates, $Z\theta_{-s}(\omega)$ is a well-defined real number.)

Given that the transition probabilities P^t_{t+1} are identical, we easily see that the various probabilities $P_{t,x}$ constructed in Proposition V.2.1 are isomorphic for every fixed x; more precisely, one can write

$$\int_\Omega P_{t,x}(d\omega')Z\theta_t(\omega') = \int_\Omega P_{0,x}(d\omega')Z(\omega')$$

for every $\mathscr{A}^0_\infty$-measurable random variable Z, or, what is equivalent,

$$\int_\Omega P_{t,x}(d\omega')Z(\omega') = \int_\Omega P_{0,x}(d\omega')Z\theta_{-t}(\omega')$$

for every $\mathscr{A}^t_\infty$-measurable r.v. Z. In the following proposition, we write P_x in place of $P_{0,x}$.

PROPOSITION V.2.3. *Let $(E, \mathscr{F})$ be a measurable space and let*

$$P = \{P(x, F)\}$$

be a transition probability defined on this space. Then for every $x \in E$ there exists a unique probability P_x on $(\Omega, \mathscr{A}) = (E, \mathscr{F})^N$ whose value on every measurable rectangle $\prod_s F_s$ is given by

$$P_x\left[\prod_s F_s\right] = 1_{F_0}(x) \int_{F_1} P(x, dx_1) \int_{F_2} P(x_1, dx_2) \cdots \int_{F_T} P(x_{T-1}, dx_T),$$

where T is such that $F_s = E_s$ if $s > T$. For every positive r.r.v. *X defined on $(\Omega, \mathscr{A})$, the function $\int P_x(d\omega)X(\omega)$ of x is $\mathscr{F}$-measurable.*

Markov property. *For any* $s > 0$, *any positive* $\mathscr{A}_s^0$*-measurable* r.r.v. Y *and any positive* $\mathscr{A}$*-measurable* r.r.v. Z, *we have*

$$\int_\Omega P_x(d\omega')\,Y(\omega')Z(\theta_s\omega') = \int_\Omega P_x(d\omega')\,Y(\omega')\int_\Omega P_{x'_s}(d\omega'')Z(\omega'').$$

If P_0 *is a probability on* $(E, \mathscr{F})$, *the formula*

$$P(A) = \int_E P_0(dx_0)P_{x_0}(A)$$

defines a probability on $(\Omega, \mathscr{A})$. *For every positive* r.r.v. Z *defined on* $(\Omega, \mathscr{A})$, *the conditional expectations* $E^{\mathscr{A}_t^0}(Z\theta_t)$ *and* $E^{\mathscr{F}_t}(Z\theta_t)$ *are equal, and the function* $\int P_{X_t(\omega)}(d\omega')Z(\omega')$ *is a version of them.*

This proposition, being nothing more than a reformulation of Proposition V.2.1 for the case of Markov processes with stationary transition probabilities, does not require a new proof.

COROLLARY 1. *Under the hypotheses of the preceding proposition, the iterates* P^t *of the transition probability* P, *which satisfy the semigroup relation* $P^tP^s = P^{t+s}$ $(s, t \geqslant 1)$, *that is,*

$$\int_E P^t(x, dy)P^s(y, F) = P^{t+s}(x, F) \qquad (x \in E, F \in \mathscr{F}; s, t \geqslant 1),$$

are such that for every probability $P = \int \mu_0(dx)P_x$ *constructed on* $(\Omega, \mathscr{A})$ *from an initial probability* μ_0 *and for every real positive measurable function* h *defined on* $(E, \mathscr{F})$, *the* r.r.v. $P^{u-t}h(X_t)$ *is a version of the conditional expectations* $E^{\mathscr{A}_t^0}[h(X_u)]$ *and* $E^{\mathscr{F}_t}[h(X_u)]$, *which are equal* $(t < u)$. *The probability laws* μ_t *of the variables* X_t, *induced by* P *on* $(E, \mathscr{F})$, *are connected by the relations* $\mu_t = \mu_s P^{t-s}$ $(s < t)$, *which suffice to define them from* μ_0.

Let τ be a stopping time defined on all of $(\Omega, \mathscr{A})$ with respect to the increasing family $\{\mathscr{A}_t^0, t \geqslant 0\}$ of σ-algebras; we recall that the σ-algebra $\mathscr{A}_\tau^0$ of events preceding τ is then defined by $\mathscr{A}_\tau^0 = \{A; A\{\tau = t\} \in \mathscr{A}_t^0\}$. We define the operator θ_τ on Ω by setting

$$\theta_\tau(\omega) = \{x_{t+\tau(\omega)}(\omega), \quad t \geqslant 0\};$$

this transformation is measurable, as

$$\theta_\tau^{-1}(A) = \sum_t \theta_\tau^{-1}(A) \cap \{\tau = t\}.$$

COROLLARY 2. STRONG MARKOV PROPERTY. *Under the hypotheses of the preceding proposition, if τ is a stopping time defined on all of $(\Omega, \mathscr{A})$ with respect to the increasing family $\{\mathscr{A}_t^0, t \geqslant 0\}$, then for every $x \in E$ we have*

$$\int_\Omega P_x(d\omega')\, Y(\omega')Z(\theta_\tau\omega') = \int_\Omega P_x(d\omega')\, Y(\omega') \int_\Omega P_{x'_\tau}(d\omega'')Z(\omega'')$$

whenever Y is a positive $\mathscr{A}_\tau^0$-measurable r.r.v. *and whenever Z is a positive* r.v. *on $(\Omega, \mathscr{A})$.*

PROOF. The Markov property applied to the variable $Y \cdot 1_{\{\tau = t\}}$, which is $\mathscr{A}_\tau^0$-measurable, and to the variable Z, shows that

$$\int_{\{\tau(\omega')=t\}} P_x(d\omega')\, Y(\omega')Z(\theta_t\omega') = \int_{\{\tau(\omega')=t\}} P_x(d\omega')\, Y(\omega') \int_\Omega P_{x'_t}(d\omega'')Z(\omega'');$$

the corollary is obtained by summing both sides over t. ∎

Definition V.2.2. AN EVENT A OF $(\Omega, \mathscr{A})$ IS SAID TO BE STATIONARY IF $\theta^{-1}(A) = A$. MORE GENERALLY, A r.v. Z ON $(\Omega, \mathscr{A})$ IS SAID TO BE STATIONARY IF $Z\theta = Z$.

The class $\mathscr{I}$ of stationary events is obviously a σ-algebra; moreover, a r.v. Z is stationary if and only if it is $\mathscr{I}$-measurable (this follows from the identity $\{Z\theta \in S\} = \theta^{-1}\{Z \in S\}$, which holds for every r.v. Z and every Borel set S on the real line). Two stationary random variables Z and Z' will be said to be equivalent if the set $\{Z \neq Z'\}$ is negligible for each of the probabilities P_x $(x \in E)$; in particular, two stationary events F and F' are said to be equivalent if $P_x(F \triangle F') = 0$ for every $x \in E$.

The σ-algebra $\mathscr{I}$ is a σ-subalgebra of the σ-algebra $\mathscr{A}_\infty$ of asymptotic events (in fact, if F is stationary, then $F = \theta_s^{-1}(F) \in \mathscr{A}_\infty^s$ for every $s \geqslant 0$). We observe as well that the equivalence which we have just defined on the stationary events (random variables) is identical with that induced by the equivalence defined earlier on the asymptotic events (random variables). The following proposition is then a corollary of Proposition V.2.2:

PROPOSITION V.2.4. *Under the hypotheses of Proposition* V.2.3, *the formula*

$$g(x) = \int P_x(d\omega')Z(\omega')$$

establishes a one-to-one correspondence between the equivalence classes of (positive) stationary bounded random variables Z and (positive) measurable bounded functions g, defined on $(E, \mathscr{F})$ and such that $Pg = g$ on E. Moreover, we have

$$\lim_{t\to\infty} \text{a.s. } g(X_t) = Z,$$

where lim a.s. *is with respect to P_x, for every $x \in E$.*

PROOF. If Z is a stationary random variable, and therefore asymptotic, the functions g_t which are associated with it by Proposition V.2.2 are all identical, as

$$g_t(x) = \int P_{t,x}(d\omega')Z(\omega') = \int P_x(d\omega')Z\theta_{-t}(\omega') = \int P_x(d\omega')Z(\omega') = g_0(x).$$

Conversely, if g is a bounded measurable function on $(E, \mathscr{F})$ which is invariant under P, the variable $Z(\omega) = \liminf_{t\to\infty} g[X_t(\omega)]$ is stationary; the second part of the proof of Proposition V.2.2 is now applicable. ∎

The corollary of Proposition V.2.2 can be substantially improved in the case of Markov processes with stationary transition probabilities.

PROPOSITION V.2.5. *For every Markov process with stationary transition probabilities, the following two conditions are equivalent:*

(a) *the σ-algebra of equivalence classes of asymptotic events is finite;*
(b) *the space G is finite dimensional.*

If these conditions are satisfied, there exists a finite number $\sum_1^r d_\rho$ of positive measurable functions, denoted by $u_{\rho,\delta}$ where δ is an integer mod d_ρ *(d_ρ is an integer $\geqslant 1$) and where ρ is an integer varying between* 1 *and r, such that every (positive) element $g = \{g_t, t \geqslant 0\}$ of G has a unique representation*

$$g_t = \sum_{\rho=1}^{r} \sum_{\delta=1}^{d_\rho} c_{\rho,\delta} u_{\rho,\delta+t},$$

where the $c_{\rho,\delta}$ are (positive) real numbers, and such also that every bounded (positive) g which is invariant under P has the unique representation

$$g = \sum_{\rho=1}^{r} b_\rho u_\rho,$$

where the b_ρ are real (positive) numbers and where we have put

$$u_\rho = \sum_{\delta=1}^{d_\rho} u_{\rho,\delta}.$$

Moreover, one can so choose the $u_{\rho,\delta}$ that

$$1 = \sum_{\rho=1}^{r} \sum_{\delta=1}^{d_\rho} u_{\rho,\delta},$$

in which case the family of these functions is uniquely determined.

PROOF. By what was said following the definition of the translation operators, we can associate, with every asymptotic ($= \mathscr{A}_\infty$-measurable) r.r.v. Z, r.r.v.'s $Z\theta_s$ (s integer >0 or <0) which are again asymptotic. The operators θ_s obviously form a group of transformations on the space of asymptotic r.r.v.'s. If $\{g_t, t \geqslant 0\}$ is the element of G associated, by Proposition V.2.2, with the equivalence class of Z, it follows from the stationarity of the process that

$$\int Z\theta_s \, dP_{t+s,x} = g_t(x) \qquad (t \geqslant 0, t + s \geqslant 0),$$

and hence that the element of G associated with the equivalence class of $Z\theta_s$ is $\{P_s g_t, t \geqslant 0\}$ if $s \geqslant 0$, and $\{g_{t-s}, t \geqslant 0\}$ if $s \leqslant 0$, since one has

$$\int Z\theta_s \, dP_{t,x} = \int dP_{t,x} \int Z\theta_s \, dP_{t+s,\, X_{t+s}}$$
$$= \int dP_{t,x} \, g_t(X_{t+s}) = P_s g_t(x) \qquad (s \geqslant 0)$$

and

$$\int Z\theta_s \, dP_{t,x} = \int Z\theta_s \, dP_{(t-s)+s,x} = g_{t-s}(x) \qquad (s \leqslant 0).$$

We conclude that if Z and Z' are equivalent asymptotic r.r.v.'s, so are the r.r.v.'s $Z\theta_s$ and $Z'\theta_s$ ($s \gtrless 0$); in other words, the θ_s act on equivalence classes of asymptotic r.r.v.'s. We also note that the equivalence classes of stationary r.r.v.'s are simply the equivalence classes of asymptotic r.r.v.'s which are invariant with respect to the θ_s.

Let us suppose, then, that conditions (a) and (b) of the proposition are satisfied (the equivalence of these two conditions follows from the corollary of Proposition V.2.2) and consider a finite partition $\mathscr{P}$ of Ω consisting of atoms of $\mathscr{A}_\infty$. For every atom A, the indicator function $1_A\theta_s$ is that of an atom (otherwise $1_A = (1_A\theta_s)\theta_{-s}$ could not be the indicator function of an atom!), that is, of an element of $\mathscr{P}$, up to equivalence; consequently the group $\{\theta_s\}$ induces a one-to-one group of transformations on the finite set $\mathscr{P}$, that is, a group of permutation on $\mathscr{P}$. We can then label the elements of $\mathscr{P}$ as $A_{\rho,\delta}$ ($\rho = 1, 2, \ldots, r$; δ an integer modulo d_ρ) in such a way that $1_{A_{\rho,\delta}}\theta_s = 1_{A_{\rho,\delta-s}}$.

Let $\{g_t^{\rho,\delta}, t \geqslant 0\}$ be the positive elements of G corresponding to the equivalence classes of the $1_{A_{\rho,\delta}}$; the preceding equation therefore implies that $g_t^{\rho,\delta-s} = g_{t-s}^{\rho,\delta}$, since

$$g_t^{\rho,\delta-s}(x) = P_{t,x}(A_{\rho,\delta-s}) = P_{t,x}(\theta_s^{-1} A_{\rho,\delta}) = P_{t-s,x}(A_{\rho,\delta}) = g_{t-s}^{\rho,\delta}(x).$$

We then set $u_{\rho,\delta} = g_0^{\rho,\delta}$, so that $g_t^{\rho,\delta} = u_{\rho,\delta+t}$. By virtue of the corollary of Proposition V.2.2, every element of G admits the representation announced in the proposition. Moreover, the stationary random variables are (up to equivalence) those which are constant on the sets $\bigcup_\delta A_{\rho,\delta}$; similarly, the sequences $\{g_t, t \geqslant 0\}$ of G which are constants in t can be expressed in terms of the $u_\rho = \sum_\delta u_{\rho,\delta}$. ∎

Complements and problems

V.2.1. Let $\mathscr{P}$ be a transition probability defined on $(E, \mathscr{F})$ and suppose that the conditions of Proposition V.2.5 are satisfied. If

$$\lambda_{\rho,k} = \exp\left(\frac{2\pi ik}{d_\rho}\right) \qquad \text{and} \qquad f_{\rho,k} = \sum_\delta (\lambda_{\rho,k})^\delta u_{\rho,\delta},$$

where k is an integer defined modulo d_ρ and where $\rho = 1, \ldots, r$, then we have: $Pf_{\rho,k} = \lambda_{\rho,k}\cdot f_{\rho,k}$. Show that for every complex number λ of modulus 1, the space of bounded measurable functions f which are solutions of $Pf = \lambda f$ is finite dimensional and admits as a basis the $f_{\rho,k}$ corresponding to those of the $\lambda_{\rho,k}$ equal to λ. (Make use of the fact that $g_t = \lambda^{-t}f$ belongs to G if $Pf = \lambda f$ and $|\lambda| = 1$.)

V.2.2. Consider a Markov process with stationary transition probabilities defined on the state space $(E, \mathscr{F})$. A set $F \in \mathscr{F}$ is said to be *almost closed* if $\lim_{t\to\infty} \{X_t \in F\}$ exists almost surely with respect to every probability P_x; show that these sets form a subalgebra of $\mathscr{F}$. (A closed set, in the sense that $X_t \in F \Rightarrow X_s \in F$ ($s < t$) a.s. P_x ($x \in E$), is evidently almost closed.) Two almost closed sets F and F' are said to be equivalent if

$$\overline{\lim_n} \{X_n \in F \triangle F'\} = \varnothing \quad \text{a.s.} \quad P_x \qquad (x \in E).$$

Show that the Boolean algebra of equivalence classes of almost closed sets and the Boolean algebra of equivalence classes of stationary events are isomorphic. (Associate, with the almost closed set F, the stationary event $\overline{\lim}_n \{X_n \in F\}$; if $g(x) = P_x(A)$, where A is a stationary event, show that $F = \{g > a\}$ is almost closed and that $A \underset{\text{a.s.}}{=} \lim_n \{X_n \in F\}$ whenever $0 < a < 1$.) Note that the almost closed sets do not in general form a σ-subalgebra of $\mathscr{F}$.

V.3. STRONG ERGODIC THEOREM

Let P be a transition probability defined on a measurable space $(E, \mathscr{F})$. We intend in this section to give a theorem on the convergence in norm of the iterates of P and to describe the class of asymptotic events of the associated Markov process, when the transition probability P satisfies a quasi-compactness hypothesis which will be specified below.

Given an arbitrary transition probability P on $(E, \mathscr{F})$, the formula

$$Pf(x) = \int P(x; dy)f(y)$$

defines a positive endomorphism on the Banach space $B(E, \mathscr{F})$ of bounded measurable functions on $(E, \mathscr{F})$ with the norm $\|f\| = \sup_E |f(x)|$; this positive endomorphism is, moreover, such that $P1 = 1$ and therefore $\|P\| = 1$. On the other hand, the formula

$$\mu P(F) = \int \mu(dx)P(x, F),$$

where F varies in $\mathscr{F}$, defines a positive endomorphism (operating to the left) on the Banach space $\mathscr{M}(E, \mathscr{F})$ of bounded measures on $(E, \mathscr{F})$. In addition, under the duality between the spaces B and $\mathscr{M}$ established by the bilinear form $\mu(f) = \int \mu(dx)f(x)$, the operators P are transposes of one another: $\mu(Pf) = \mu P(f)$ for any $f \in B$ and $\mu \in \mathscr{M}$.

Definition V.3.1. AN ENDOMORPHISM Q DEFINED ON A BANACH SPACE B IS SAID TO BE COMPACT IF THE IMAGE UNDER Q OF THE UNIT BALL B_1 OF B IS RELATIVELY COMPACT. AN ENDOMORPHISM P IS SAID TO BE QUASI-COMPACT IF THERE EXISTS A SEQUENCE $\{Q_t, t \geqslant 1\}$ OF COMPACT ENDOMORPHISMS Q_t ON B SUCH THAT THE ITERATES P^t OF P SATISFY

$$\lim_{t \to \infty} \|P^t - Q_t\| = 0.$$

It is possible to give a definition of quasi-compactness which is in appearance weaker, by using

LEMMA V.3.1. *In order that the endomorphism P be quasi-compact on B, it is (necessary and) sufficient that there exist an integer* $t_0 \geqslant 1$ *and a compact endomorphism Q such that* $\|P^{t_0} - Q\| < 1$.

PROOF. The condition is clearly necessary. Before proving that it is sufficient, let us recall the following elementary result concerning compact endomorphisms: if Q_1 and Q_2 are compact endomorphisms on B, and P_1 and P_2 are arbitrary endomorphisms on B, then the endomorphisms $Q_1 + Q_2$ and $P_1Q_1P_2$ are again compact.

Let us suppose, then, that the endomorphism P is such that $P^{t_0} = Q + U$ for some integer $t_0 \geqslant 1$, where Q is a compact endomorphism and $\|U\| < 1$. We set $Q_t = 0$ if $t < t_0$ and $Q_t = P^t - P^lU^m$, where l and m are defined by $t = mt_0 + l$, $0 \leqslant l < t_0$, $1 \leqslant m$; the operators Q_t can be written in the form $P^l[(Q + U)^m - U^m]$ when $t \geqslant t_0$ and are, by the binomial expansion, sums of products of endomorphisms all containing Q as a factor. Hence the Q_t are compact. On the other hand,

$$\|P^t - Q_t\| = \|P^lU^m\| \leqslant C\|U\|^m \to 0$$

if t and thus $m \to \infty$, where $C = \sup_{l<t_0} \|P^l\| < \infty$. ∎

Given a transition probability P on $(E, \mathscr{F})$, we have denoted by G the space of sequences $g = \{g_t, t \geqslant 0\}$ in $B(E, \mathscr{F})$ such that

$$|||g||| \doteq \sup_t \|g_t\| < \infty \qquad \text{and} \qquad g_t = Pg_{t+1}$$

for every $t \geqslant 0$. It is clear that the space G is a vector space and a Banach space for the norm $|||g|||$; moreover, since $\|P\| = 1$, the function $\|g_t\|$ of t is nondecreasing and $|||g||| = \lim_{t\uparrow\infty} \uparrow \|g_t\|$. On the other hand, Proposition V.2.2 shows that the study of the space G is equivalent to the study of the space of bounded asymptotic random variables.

PROPOSITION V.3.1. *If P is a transition probability on* $(E, \mathscr{F})$ *and if the operator, on the space* $B(E, \mathscr{F})$, *associated with P is quasi-compact, then the Banach space G defined above is finite dimensional.*

PROOF. By virtue of a classical theorem of the theory of Banach spaces, it suffices to prove that the unit ball G_1 of G is precompact, that is, can be covered for any $\epsilon > 0$ by a finite number of balls of radius less than ϵ. This is the same as showing that one cannot find, for any $\epsilon > 0$, more than a finite number r_ϵ of elements of G_1 such that the distance between every pair of distinct elements is greater than ϵ.

For $\epsilon > 0$ fixed, let t be an integer such that $\|P^t - Q_t\| \leqslant \epsilon/4$; since Q_t is compact, we can find a finite number, say N, of balls with centers f_n $(n = 1, \ldots, N)$ and radius $\epsilon/4$ which cover the image $Q_t(B_1)$ of the unit ball B_1 of B. Therefore the N balls with centers f_n $(n = 1, \ldots, N)$ and radius $\epsilon/2$ cover $P^t(B_1)$ and it is not possible to find more than N points of $P^t(B_1)$ whose pairwise distances are all greater than ϵ. Therefore, there cannot exist more than N points of G_1 whose pairwise distances are all greater than ϵ; in fact, if there existed $N + 1$, say $g^{(0)}, g^{(1)}, \ldots, g^{(N)}$, we could choose s large enough so that $\| g_s^{(n)} - g_s^{(n')}\| > \epsilon$ if $n \neq n'$; but this is impossible, as $g_s^{(n)} = P^t g_{s+t}^{(n)} \in P^t(B_1)$. ∎

ERGODIC THEOREM. *Let P be a transition probability on the measurable space $(E, \mathscr{F})$ such that the operator on $B(E, \mathscr{F})$ which is associated with P is quasi-compact. Then there exist integers $d_\rho \geqslant 1$ $(\rho = 1, \ldots, r)$, $\sum_\rho d_\rho$ bounded positive measurable functions and $\sum_\rho d_\rho$ probabilities on $(E, \mathscr{F})$, denoted respectively by $u_{\rho,\delta}$ and $\Pi_{\rho,\delta}$ (where δ is an integer modulo d_ρ), such that*

$$u_{\rho,\delta} = P u_{\rho,\delta+1}, \qquad \Pi_{\rho,\delta} = \Pi_{\rho,\delta-1} P,$$

$$\int_E \Pi_{\rho',\delta'}(dx) u_{\rho,\delta}(x) = \begin{cases} 1 & \text{if} \quad \rho' = \rho \text{ and } \delta' \equiv \delta (\operatorname{mod} d_\rho) \\ 0 & \text{otherwise} \end{cases}$$

$$\sum_\rho \sum_\delta u_{\rho,\delta} = 1,$$

and such that if d denotes the least common multiple of the d_ρ, then

$$\lim_{n\to\infty} \left\| P^{nd+t} - \sum_{\rho=1}^{r} \sum_{\delta=1}^{d_\rho} u_{\rho,\delta-t} \otimes \Pi_{\rho,\delta} \right\| = 0.$$

It follows from this convergence that

$$\lim_{t\to\infty} \left\| \frac{1}{t} \sum_{1}^{t} P^s - \sum_{\rho=1}^{r} u_\rho \otimes \Pi_\rho \right\| = 0,$$

where we have put

$$u_\rho = \sum_{\delta=1}^{d_\rho} u_{\rho,\delta} \qquad \text{and} \qquad \Pi_\rho = \frac{1}{d_\rho} \sum_{\delta=1}^{d_\rho} \Pi_{\rho,\delta}.$$

PROOF. We start by showing that the sequence $\{P^t f, t \geqslant 1\}$ is relatively compact in $B(E, \mathscr{F})$ for every function $f \in B$; we can restrict ourselves to the case of a function f of norm $\|f\| \leqslant 1$. Given any $\epsilon > 0$, we choose an integer $s > 0$ and a compact endomorphism Q such that

$$\|P^s - Q\| < \epsilon/2.$$

The image $Q(B_1)$ of the unit ball B_1 of B can be covered by a finite number of balls of radius $\epsilon/2$; the balls with the same centers and of radius ϵ will then cover the set $\{P^t f, t \geqslant s\}$, since

$$\|P^t f - Q(P^{t-s} f)\| = \|(P^s - Q)P^{t-s} f\| < \epsilon/2$$

where $P^{t-s} f \in B_1$ $(t \geqslant s)$. It follows that the sequence $\{P^t f, t \geqslant 1\}$ can also be covered by a finite number of balls of radius ϵ.

By Proposition V.3.1, the representation of the elements of G given in Proposition V.2.5 is valid. Let therefore d be the least common multiple of the d_ρ $(\rho = 1, \ldots, r)$. For every $f \in B$ we can, by the relative compactness of the sequence $\{P^t f, t \geqslant 1\}$, and using the diagonal procedure, find an increasing sequence $\{n_j\}$ of integers such that $g_t = \lim_j P^{n_j d - t} f$ exists for every $t \geqslant 0$ in the sense of convergence in the norm in B. It is easy to see that $\{g_t\}$ is an element of G. As we have $g_{t+md} = g_t$ for every integer $m > 0$ by the representation given by Proposition V.2.5, we can write $P^{md-t} g_0 = P^{md-t} g_{md} = g_t$ as long as $md \geqslant t \geqslant 0$; consequently, if $nd \geqslant n'_j d + t$, then

$$\|P^{nd-t} f - g_t\| = \|P^{(n-n'_j)d-t}(P^{n'_j d} f - g_0)\| \leqslant \|P^{n'_j d} f - g_0\|.$$

Letting $n \to \infty$ and then $n'_j \to \infty$, we obtain $g_t = \lim_{n\to\infty} P^{nd-t} f$ in the sense of the norm in B, for every $t \geqslant 0$.

By the preceding, setting $Sf = \lim_{n\to\infty} P^{nd} f$ when $f \in B$ defines an endomorphism S of norm $= 1$ on B; moreover, $SP^{md} = P^{md} S = S$ for every integer $m \geqslant 0$. We now show that the convergence of P^{nd} to S holds in the norm in the algebra of operators, or, what is equivalent, that the convergence $\lim_{n\to\infty} P^{nd} f = Sf$ is uniform on the unit ball B_1 of B. To this end, given $\epsilon > 0$, we choose an integer $m > 0$ and a compact operator Q such that $\|P^{md} - Q\| < \epsilon$. For every $f \in B_1$ we can write

$$\|P^{(m+n)d} f - Sf\| = \|(P^{nd} - S)P^{md} f\| \leqslant 2\epsilon + \|(P^{nd} - S)Qf\|,$$

since $\{Qf, f \in B_1\}$ is relatively compact in B. The convergence

$$\lim_{n\to\infty} \|(P^{nd} - S)Qf\| = 0$$

is uniform on B_1; it follows upon letting $n \to \infty$ and then $\epsilon \downarrow 0$ that the convergence $\lim_{n\to\infty} P^{nd} f = Sf$ is uniform on B_1.

For every $f \in B$ there exist uniquely determined coefficients $c_{\rho,\delta}(f)$ such that $Sf = \sum_{\rho=1}^{r} \sum_{\delta=1}^{d_\rho} c_{\rho,\delta}(f) u_{\rho,\delta}$. The mappings $f \to c_{\rho,\delta}(f)$ are defined by measures on $(E, \mathscr{F})$. In fact, since the endomorphisms P^{nd} of $B(E, \mathscr{F})$ converge in norm to the endomorphism S, the measures

$P^{nd}(x, \cdot)$ also converge in norm in $\mathscr{M}(E, \mathscr{F})$, for every fixed x, since one has

$$\|P^{nd}(x, \cdot) - P^{n'd}(x, \cdot)\|_{\mathscr{M}(E,\mathscr{F})} \leqslant \|P^{nd} - P^{n'd}\|$$

(see Problem IV.1.6). If we now denote this limit measure by $S(x, \cdot)$, then for every $f \in B(E, \mathscr{F})$ we have

$$\int S(x, dy) f(y) = Sf(x) = \sum_{\rho=1}^{r} \sum_{\delta=1}^{d_\rho} u_{\rho,\delta}(x) c_{\rho,\delta}(f);$$

since the functions $u_{\rho,\delta}$ are linearly independent, we conclude that the mappings $c_{\rho,\delta}(\cdot)$ are linear combinations of the measures

$$S(x_1, \cdot), \ldots, S(x_n, \cdot)$$

for suitable $x_1, \ldots x_n$ with $n = \sum_{\rho=1}^{r} d_\rho$. We shall denote these linear combinations by $\Pi_{\rho,\delta}$; they are probabilities since $\int f\, d\Pi_{\rho,\delta} = c_{\rho,\delta}(f)$ is positive if f is positive, and equals 1 if $f = 1$. We have thus obtained the representation (in which the meaning of $\otimes$ is now clear)

$$S = \sum_{\rho=1}^{r} \sum_{\delta=1}^{d_\rho} u_{\rho,\delta} \otimes \Pi_{\rho,\delta}.$$

It follows from $P^d u_{\rho,\delta} = u_{\rho,\delta}$ that $S u_{\rho,\delta} = u_{\rho,\delta}$; consequently $\Pi_{\rho'\delta'}(u_{\rho,\delta}) = 1$ or 0 according as $\rho = \rho'$ and $\delta = \delta'$ (mod d_ρ) or not. The commutativity of P and S permits us to write

$$\begin{aligned}\sum_\rho \sum_\delta u_{\rho,\delta} \otimes \Pi_{\rho,\delta} P^t = SP^t = P^t S &= \sum_\rho \sum_\delta P^t u_{\rho,\delta} \otimes \Pi_{\rho,\delta} \\ &= \sum_\rho \sum_\delta u_{\rho,\delta-t} \otimes \Pi_{\rho,\delta} \\ &= \sum_\rho \sum_\delta u_{\rho,\delta} \otimes \Pi_{\rho,\delta+t},\end{aligned}$$

from which we deduce that $\Pi_{\rho,\delta} P^t = \Pi_{\rho,\delta+t}$ for every $t \geqslant 0$. The first part of the proposition is thus proved, since the convergence of P^{nd} to S at once implies that of P^{nd+t} to SP^t.

To prove the second part of the theorem, we first note that by the preceding results we have, for every $t \geqslant 0$,

$$\frac{1}{N} \sum_{n=0}^{N-1} P^{nd+t} \to \sum_\rho \sum_\delta u_{\rho,\delta-t} \otimes \Pi_{\rho,\delta}.$$

From the decomposition

$$\sum_1^s P^u = \sum_{t=1}^{s'} \sum_{n=0}^{N} P^{nd+t} + \sum_{t=s'+1}^{d} \sum_{n=0}^{N-1} P^{nd+t},$$

which is valid when $s = Nd + s', 0 < s' \leqslant d$, we deduce that

$$\frac{1}{d}\sum_{1}^{s} P^{u} \rightarrow \frac{1}{d}\sum_{t=1}^{d}\sum_{\rho}\sum_{\delta} u_{\rho,\delta-t}\otimes \Pi_{\rho,\delta}$$

as $s \rightarrow \infty$. To complete the proof of the theorem, it remains only to observe that

$$\frac{1}{d}\sum_{t=1}^{d}\sum_{\delta} u_{\rho,\delta-t}\otimes \Pi_{\rho,\delta} = \frac{1}{d_\rho}\left(\sum_{\delta} u_{\rho,\delta}\right)\otimes\left(\sum_{\delta}\Pi_{\rho,\delta}\right) = u_\rho \otimes \Pi_\rho. \quad \blacksquare$$

COROLLARY. *Under the conditions of the ergodic theorem, the sets* $E_{\rho,\delta} = \{u_{\rho,\delta} = 1\}$ *are pairwise disjoint and are, respectively, the supports of the* $\Pi_{\rho,\delta}$. *Moreover,* $P(x, E_{\rho,\delta+1}) = 1$ *if and only if* $x \in E_{\rho,\delta}$; *consequently,*

$$P_x[X_t \in E_{\rho,\delta+t} \quad (t \in N)] = 1 \qquad \textit{if} \qquad x \in E_{\rho,\delta}.$$

If we denote by $A_{\rho,\delta}$ *the pairwise disjoint asymptotic events*

$$A_{\rho,\delta} = \underline{\lim}_{t}\{X_t \in E_{\rho,\delta+t}\},$$

then we have

$$P_x(A_{\rho,\delta}) = u_{\rho,\delta}(x) \qquad (x \in E)$$

and besides $A_{\rho,\delta} = \lim \text{a.s.}_{t\rightarrow\infty}\{X_t \in E_{\rho,\delta+t}\}$ *for every* P_x. *Moreover, every asymptotic event is equivalent to a sum of events* $A_{\rho,\delta}$; *in particular,* $\sum_\rho \sum_\delta A_{\rho,\delta} = \Omega$ a.s. P_x $(x \in E)$.

PROOF. Since $0 \leqslant u_{\rho,\delta} \leqslant 1$ and since $\Pi_{\rho,\delta}$ is a probability, it is clear that $\Pi_{\rho,\delta}(E_{\rho,\delta}) = 1$ follows from $\int \Pi_{\rho,\delta}(dx)u_{\rho,\delta}(x) = 1$. Since

$$1 - u_{\rho,\delta}(x) = \int P(x, dy)[1 - u_{\rho,\delta+1}(y)],$$

we see at once that $E_{\rho,\delta} = \{x\colon P(x, E_{\rho,\delta+1}) = 1\}$, that is, $P_x[X_1 \in E_{\rho,\delta+1}] = 1$ if $x \in E_{\rho,\delta}$; repeating the argument, we see that

$$P_x[X_t \in E_{\rho,\delta+t}(t \in N)] = 1$$

as long as $x \in E_{\rho,\delta}$.

The preceding results also imply that for every $x \in E$

$$P_x[X_t \in E_{\rho,\delta+t}(t \geqslant s)] = P_x(X_s \in E_{\rho,\delta+s}) = P^s(x, E_{\rho,\delta+s});$$

moreover, the term on the right equals 1 if $x \in E_{\rho,\delta}$, and is majorized by

$$P^s u_{\rho,\delta+s}(x) = u_{\rho,\delta}(x)$$

for any $x \in E$. When $s \uparrow \infty$, the first term tends to $P_x[A_{\rho,\delta}]$ by the definition of $A_{\rho,\delta}$; since $A_{\rho,\delta}$ is an asymptotic event, the function $P_x(A_{\rho,\delta})$ of x is necessarily a convex combination of the functions $u_{\rho',\delta'}$. As this function equals 1 on the nonempty set $E_{\rho,\delta}$, we necessarily have

$$P_x[A_{\rho,\delta}] = u_{\rho,\delta}(x)$$

for every $x \in E$. Finally, Proposition V.2.5 implies that every asymptotic event is equivalent to a sum of the $A_{\rho,\delta}$. ▮

Complements and problems

V.3.1. In order that the operator P on $B(E, \mathscr{F})$ associated with a transition probability defined on $(E, \mathscr{F})$ be quasi-compact, show that it is necessary and sufficient that there exist an integer $d \geqslant 1$ such that the limit $\lim_{t\to\infty} P^{td}$ exists in the sense of the norm and is an operator of finite rank.

V.3.2. **(Doeblin's condition.)** A transition probability P defined on $(E, \mathscr{F})$ is said to satisfy the condition (D) if there exists an integer $t \in N$, two real numbers $\theta < 1$ and $\eta > 0$, and a probability μ on $(E, \mathscr{F})$ such that

$$\mu(F) \geqslant \theta \Rightarrow P^t(\cdot, F) \geqslant \eta \qquad \text{on} \quad E \quad (F \in \mathscr{F}).$$

By making use of the ergodic theorem, show that the quasi-compactness of the operator P on $B(E, \mathscr{F})$ implies the validity of the condition (D). (Take for μ a convex combination of the measures $\Pi_{\rho,\delta}$.) Conversely, Doeblin has shown that the validity of the condition (D) implies the validity of the strong ergodic theorem, and therefore the quasi-compactness of the operator P (see the preceding problem); one can, incidentally, also show this last result directly. Show that if the condition (D) is satisfied, the total number of cyclic classes is restricted by the relation $\sum d_\rho < 1/1 - \theta$ by observing that one necessarily has $\Pi_{\rho,\delta}(F) \geqslant \eta$ when $\mu(F) \geqslant \theta$ $(F \in \mathscr{F})$.

V.3.3. If P is a transition probability on $(E, \mathscr{F})$, show that in order that the iterates P^n of the operator P converge in norm to an operator of the form $1 \otimes \Pi$, where Π is a probability on $(E, \mathscr{F})$, it is necessary and sufficient that there exist a $t \in N$, a constant $c > 0$ and a probability μ on $(E, \mathscr{F})$ such that

$$P^t(x, f) \geqslant c\mu(F) \qquad (x \in E;\ F \in \mathscr{F}).$$

[To prove this without calling upon the results of this chapter, first deduce from the hypothesis that the measures $[P^t(x, \cdot) - P^t(y, \cdot)]^+$ $(x, y \in E)$ all have total mass $\leqslant 1 - c$. Next, use the relation

$$P^{t+u}(x, \cdot) - P^{t+u}(y, \cdot) = [P^t(x, \cdot) - P^t(y, \cdot)]P^u$$

to show that $\sup_{x,y} \|P^s(x, \cdot) - P^s(y, \cdot)\| \to 0$ when $s \uparrow \infty$.]

V.4. SUB-MARKOVIAN OPERATORS

The rest of this chapter is devoted to the study of the *pointwise ergodic theorem* in the context of the theory of Markov processes.

We have shown earlier that with every transition probability $P = \{P(x, F)\}$ defined on $(E, \mathscr{F})$ there are associated two operators, denoted again by P and defined below, the first of which operates on the space $B(E, \mathscr{F})$ of bounded measurable functions, and the second of which operates on the space $\mathscr{M}(E, \mathscr{F})$ of bounded measures on $(E, \mathscr{F})$:

$$Pf(x) = \int_E P(x, dy)f(y);$$

$$\mu P(F) = \int_E \mu(dx)P(x, F).$$

In its full generality, the pointwise ergodic theorem is a theorem involving the operator P defined on $\mathscr{M}(E, \mathscr{F})$ or, more precisely, its restrictions to the subspaces $L^1_1(E, \mathscr{F}, \Pi)$† of $\mathscr{M}(E, \mathscr{F})$ which are invariant under P. [Nevertheless, when there exists a measure μ which is invariant under P, an elementary transformation allows one to obtain, from the preceding theorem, an ergodic theorem for the operator P operating on functions.]

The present section is devoted to an account of the preliminaries. We shall consider two measurable spaces $(E_i, \mathscr{F}_i)_{i=1,2}$, each with a positive measure Π_i. These measures Π_i, which are fixed once and for all, will enter essentially in the sequel only by way of the classes of negligible sets which they define (we are in fact going to study operators defined on the spaces $L^1(E, \mathscr{F}, \Pi)$, and it is easily shown (Problem IV.1.2) that two spaces $L^1(E, \mathscr{F}, \Pi)$ and $L^1(E, \mathscr{F}, \Pi')$ are isometric if (and only if) the measures Π and Π' admit the same family of negligible sets in $(E, \mathscr{F})$). We can therefore suppose without loss of generality that the measures Π_i are probabilities.

A *sub-Markovian operator* mapping the space $L^1(E_1, \mathscr{F}_1, \Pi_1)$ into the space $L^1(E_2, \mathscr{F}_2, \Pi_2)$ is by definition a positive linear transformation, of norm $\leqslant 1$, of the first space into the second. If T denotes such an operator, we shall denote the image in $L^1(E_2, \mathscr{F}_2, \Pi_2)$ of $f \in L^1(E_1, \mathscr{F}_1, \Pi_1)$ by T as fT; we thus let T operate to the left. The adjoint of T which maps $L^\infty(E_2, \mathscr{F}_2, \Pi_2)$ into $L^\infty(E_1, \mathscr{F}_1, \Pi_1)$ will again be denoted by T, but we will let it operate to the right: if $g \in L^\infty(E_2, \mathscr{F}_2, \Pi_2)$, the image Tg of g by

† For notational convenience, we shall henceforth write L^p for L_p.

the adjoint operator T is thus the unique element of $L^\infty(E_1, \mathscr{F}_1, \Pi_1)$ such that

$$\int_{E_1} f\cdot Tg\, d\Pi_1 = \int_{E_2} fT\cdot g\, d\Pi_2$$

for every $f \in L^1(E_1, \mathscr{F}_1, \Pi_1)$.† This adjoint operator is positive. Its norm is equal to that of the operator T on L^1 and is consequently $\leqslant 1$; since the operator T is positive, the hypothesis $\|T\|_\infty \leqslant 1$ is, by the way, equivalent to the condition $T1 \leqslant 1$.

The sub-Markovian operator T is said to be *Markovian* if $T1 = 1$ or, equivalently, if for every $f \in L^1(E_1, \mathscr{F}_1, \Pi_1)$

$$\int fT\, d\Pi_2 = \int f\, d\Pi_1$$

(in the case of a sub-Markovian operator, only the inequality

$$\int fT\, d\Pi_2 \leqslant \int f\, d\Pi_1,$$

when $f \geqslant 0$, is valid).

PROPOSITION V.4.1. *If T is a positive linear operator mapping*

$$L^1(E_1, \mathscr{F}_1, \Pi_1)$$

into $L^1(E_2, \mathscr{F}_2, \Pi_2)$, then

$$(\lim_n \uparrow f_n)T = \lim_n \uparrow (f_nT)$$

for every increasing sequence $\{f_n, n \geqslant 1\}$ in $L^1_+(E_1, \mathscr{F}_1, \Pi_1)$ such that

$$\lim_n \uparrow f_n \in L^1_+,$$

and

$$T(\lim_n \uparrow h_n) = \lim_n \uparrow (Th_n)$$

† We remark that the notation adopted for the operator T and its adjoint is compatible with the usual notation for the product of two operators. In fact, the product of the operators T and T' mapping, respectively, $L^1(E_1, \mathscr{F}_1, \Pi_1)$ into $L^1(E_2, \mathscr{F}_2, \Pi_2)$ and $L^1(E_2, \mathscr{F}_2, \Pi_2)$ into $L^1(E_3, \mathscr{F}_3, \Pi_3)$ is defined as the operator associating with $f \in L^1(E_1, \mathscr{F}_1, \Pi_1)$ the element $(fT)T'$ of $L^1(E_3, \mathscr{F}_3, \Pi_3)$; the adjoint of this product maps $L^\infty(E_3, \mathscr{F}_3, \Pi_3)$ into $L^\infty(E_1, \mathscr{F}_1, \Pi_1)$ and associates with $h \in L^\infty(E_3, \mathscr{F}_3, \Pi_3)$ the element $T(T'h) \in L^\infty(E_1, \mathscr{F}_1, \Pi_1)$, since

$$\langle f, T(T'h)\rangle = \langle fT, T'h\rangle = \langle (fT)T', h\rangle.$$

If the product of the operators being considered is denoted by TT', one thus has the "natural formulas"

$$f(TT') = (fT)T', \qquad (TT')h = T(T'h).$$

for every increasing sequence $\{h_n, n \geq 1\}$ *in* $L_+^\infty(E_2, \mathscr{F}_2, \Pi_2)$ *such that*

$$\lim_n \uparrow h_n \in L_+^\infty.$$

PROOF. Since the operator T is positive, the sequence $\{f_n T, n \geq 1\}$ is an increasing sequence in $L_+^1(E_2, \mathscr{F}_2, \Pi_2)$ whenever $\{f_n, n \geq 1\}$ is an increasing sequence in $L_+^1(E_1, \mathscr{F}_1, \Pi_1)$. Moreover, if the limit $f = \lim_n \uparrow f_n$ is integrable, the sequence $\{f_n\}$ converges to f in L^1, as

$$\|f - f_n\| = \int (f - f_n) \downarrow 0;$$

the operator T being continuous, the sequence $\{f_n T\}$ converges to fT in L^1 and, consequently, $\lim_n \uparrow f_n T = fT$.

If $\{h_n, n \geq 1\}$ is an increasing sequence in $L_+^\infty(E_2, \mathscr{F}_2, \Pi_2)$, the sequence $\{Th_n, n \geq 1\}$ is an increasing sequence in $L_+^\infty(E_1, \mathscr{F}_1, \Pi_1)$. Passing to the limit under the integral in the equality

$$\int fT \cdot h_n \, d\Pi_2 = \int f \cdot Th_n \, d\Pi_1, \qquad \text{where} \qquad f \in L_+^1(E_1, \mathscr{F}_1, \Pi_1),$$

we obtain

$$\int fT \cdot \lim h_n \, d\Pi_2 = \int f \cdot \lim Th_n \, d\Pi_1;$$

hence, if $\lim_n \uparrow h_n \in L_+^\infty$ we have $T(\lim_n \uparrow h_n) = \lim_n \uparrow Th_n$. ▮

COROLLARY. *Every positive linear operator* T *which maps a space* $L^1(E_1, \mathscr{F}_1, \Pi_1)$ *into a space* $L^1(E_2, \mathscr{F}_2, \Pi_2)$ *can be extended in a unique way to a mapping of the cone of positive measurable functions, finite or not, on* $(E_1, \mathscr{F}_1)$ *into the cone of positive measurable functions, finite or not, on* $(E_2, \mathscr{F}_2)$*, which is linear and positive, and has the monotone continuity property* $(\lim_n \uparrow f_n)T = \lim_n \uparrow f_n T$*. An analogous result holds for the adjoint operator; moreover, these extensions are such that*

$$\int fT \cdot g \, d\Pi_2 = \int f \cdot Tg \, d\Pi_1.$$

PROOF. This corollary can be proved directly by appealing to an argument similar to that of Section II.3. Alternatively, one can define fT for every positive measurable function, finite or not, on $(E_1, \mathscr{F}_1, \Pi_1)$ from the formula $\int_F fT = \int f \cdot T1_F$ by making use of the Radon-Nikodym theorem; it is then easy to verify the properties of this extension of T. A similar procedure applies to the adjoint of T. ▮

PROPOSITION V.4.2. *Let* $P = \{P(x_1, F_2)\}$ *be a transition probability defined on* $(E_1, \mathscr{F}_1)$ *and* $(E_2, \mathscr{F}_2)$. *If* Π_1 *and* Π_2 *are two probabilities on* $(E_1, \mathscr{F}_1)$ *and* $(E_2, \mathscr{F}_2)$, *respectively, and if* $P(\cdot, F_2) = 0$ Π_1-a.s. *when* $\Pi_2(F_2) = 0$ (*that is, the probability* $\Pi_1 P$ *is absolutely continuous with respect to* Π_2), *there exists a unique Markovian operator* T *mapping* $L^1(E_1, \mathscr{F}_1, \Pi_1)$ *into* $L^1(E_2, \mathscr{F}_2, \Pi_2)$ *such that the measures* $(f\cdot\Pi_1)P$ *and* $(fT)\cdot\Pi_2$ *are equal for any* $f \in L^1(E_1, \mathscr{F}_1, \Pi_1)$. *Moreover, if* h *is a bounded measurable function on* $(E_2, \mathscr{F}_2, \Pi_2)$ *and* $\tilde{h}$ *denotes its equivalence class in* $L^\infty(E_2, \mathscr{F}_2, \Pi_2)$, *the adjoint* T *is such that* $\widetilde{Ph} = T(\tilde{h})$.

PROOF. Since the measure $(f\cdot\Pi_1)P$ by definition equals

$$\int f(x)P(x, F_2)\Pi_1(dx)$$

on a set $F_2 \in \mathscr{F}_2$, the hypothesis implies that $(f\cdot\Pi_1)P$ is absolutely continuous with respect to Π_2 on $(E_2, \mathscr{F}_2)$ and therefore of the form $(fT)\cdot\Pi_2$ for some element, denoted by fT, of $L^1(E_2, \mathscr{F}_2, \Pi_2)$. We verify at once that the correspondence $f \to fT$ defines a positive linear operator from $L^1(E_1, \mathscr{F}_1, \Pi_1)$ into $L^1(E_2, \mathscr{F}_2, \Pi_2)$. Moreover, the duality formulas

$$\int (f\cdot\Pi_1)P(dy)h(y) = \int f(x)\cdot Ph(x)\cdot\Pi_1(dx)$$

and

$$\int fT\cdot\tilde{h}\cdot d\Pi_2 = \int f\cdot T(\tilde{h})\, d\Pi_1$$

show that $\widetilde{Ph} = T(\tilde{h})$ and, in particular, that $T1 = 1$. ∎

In the case where $(E_1, \mathscr{F}_1) = (E_2, \mathscr{F}_2)$, the preceding proposition shows that every transition probability induces a Markovian endomorphism of the space $L^1(E, \mathscr{F}, \Pi)$, provided that $\Pi P \ll \Pi$. Let us remark that there exist many probabilities on $(E, \mathscr{F})$ which satisfy this condition and, more precisely, that for every probability μ on $(E, \mathscr{F})$ there exists at least one probability Π such that $\mu \ll \Pi$, which satisfies the hypothesis $\Pi P \ll \Pi$; to see this, it suffices to take $\Pi = \sum_{n\geqslant 0} a_n \mu P^n$, where the a_n are constants >0 such that $\sum_{n\geqslant 0} a_n = 1$.

In Section V.2 we associated with every transition probability P on a measurable space $(E, \mathscr{F})$ a Markov process (with stationary transition probabilities) defined on the product space $(\Omega, \mathscr{A}) = (E, \mathscr{F})^N$. The probability law of this process at the instant n, that is, of X_n, is given by

μP^n, when μ is the probability law of the process at the initial instant (that is, of X_0), if P^n denotes the n-th iterate of the transition probability P. Let us take, therefore, a probability Π on $(E, \mathscr{F})$ such that $\Pi P \ll \Pi$ and denote by T the endomorphism of $L^1(E, \mathscr{F}, \Pi)$ induced by P; it is easily seen that $\Pi P^n \ll \Pi$ for every $n > 0$ and that P^n induces the iterates T^n of T, that is, that $(f \cdot \Pi)P^n = fT^n \cdot \Pi$. For every initial law μ of the process which is absolutely continuous with respect to Π, that is, of the form $\mu = f \cdot \Pi$ where $f \geqslant 0$ and $\int f\, d\Pi = 1$, fT^n is thus the probability density (with respect to Π) of X_n $(n \geqslant 0)$.

The pointwise ergodic theorem concerns a sub-Markovian endomorphism of a space $L^1(E, \mathscr{F}, \Pi)$. Its validity does not in any way require that this endomorphism be induced by a transition probability on $(E, \mathscr{F})$ and therefore that it be possible to associate a Markov process with it; nevertheless, the results which we shall obtain in the course of proving it are of greater interest for Markov processes, and, in addition, the proof of it which we shall give is based in part on the notion of waiting times, which is fundamental in the study of Markov processes.

On the other hand, reasonable hypotheses on the probability space $(E, \mathscr{F}, \Pi)$ (which are fulfilled, for example, if $(E, \mathscr{F})$ is a Polish space with the σ-algebra of its Borel sets) enable us to show that every Markovian endomorphism defined on $L^1(E, \mathscr{F}, \Pi)$ can be induced by a transition probability. The rest of this section, whose results will not be used in the rest of the chapter, is devoted to the proof of this result under a slightly more general form.

PROPOSITION V.4.3. *The formula*

$$\int_F fT\, d\Pi_2 = \int_{E_1} f \cdot T(\cdot, F)\, d\Pi_1 \qquad (F \in \mathscr{F}_2),$$

where f is an arbitrary element of $L^1(E_1, \mathscr{F}_1, \Pi_1)$, establishes a one-to-one correspondence between sub-Markovian operators T mapping $L^1(E_1, \mathscr{F}_1, \Pi_1)$ into $L^1(E_2, \mathscr{F}_2, \Pi_2)$ and "sub-Markovian kernels" defined on $(E_1, \mathscr{F}_1, \Pi_1)$ and $(E_2, \mathscr{F}_2, \Pi_2)$, that is, families $\{T(\cdot, F), F \in \mathscr{F}_2\}$ of elements of

$$L^\infty(E_1, \mathscr{F}_1, \Pi_1)$$

satisfying the following relations in $L^\infty(E_1, \mathscr{F}_1, \Pi_1)$:

(a) $0 \leqslant T(\cdot, F) \leqslant 1$ *for every* $F \in \mathscr{F}_2$,

(b) $T(\cdot, F) = 0$ *if* $\Pi_2(F) = 0$,

(c) *for every countable family $\{F_i, i \in I\}$ of pairwise disjoint measurable sets in $(E_2, \mathscr{F}_2)$, the series $\sum_I T(\cdot, F_i)$ converges* a.s. *to* $T(\cdot, \sum_I F_i)$.

(We observe that properties (b) and (c) imply that $T(\cdot, F)$ depends upon F only through the equivalence class of F.)

PROOF. If T is a sub-Markovian operator and if $F \in \mathscr{F}_2$, let $T(\cdot, F)$ be the image (also denoted by $T1_F$) of 1_F under the adjoint of T. Since this adjoint is a positive operator of norm $\leqslant 1$, we have

$$0 \leqslant T(\cdot, F) \leqslant 1 \qquad \text{in} \quad L^\infty(E_1, \mathscr{F}_1, \Pi_1).$$

It is clear that $T(\cdot, F)$ depends upon F only through the equivalence class of F, and in particular that $T(\cdot, F) = 0$ if $\Pi_2(F) = 0$. To show that $\{T(\cdot, F)\}$ satisfies property (c) of countable additivity in $L^\infty(E_1, \mathscr{F}_1, \Pi_1)$, note that for every $f \in L^1(E_1, \mathscr{F}_1, \Pi_1)$ we have

$$\int fT\Big(\cdot, \sum_I F_i\Big)\, d\Pi_1 = \int_{\sum_I F_i} fT\, d\Pi_2 = \sum_I \int_{F_i} fT\, d\Pi_2$$
$$= \sum_I \int fT(\cdot, F_i)\, d\Pi_2,$$

which implies that $T(\cdot, \sum_I F_i) = \sum_I T(\cdot, F_i)$ in $L^\infty(E_1, \mathscr{F}_1, \Pi_1)$.

Conversely, if $T(\cdot, F)$ is a sub-Markovian kernel and if

$$f \in L^1(E_1, \mathscr{F}_1, \Pi_1),$$

the set function $\varphi_f(F) = \int fT(\cdot, F)\, d\Pi_1$ is σ-additive on $(E_2, \mathscr{F}_2)$ and absolutely continuous with respect to Π_2. If fT denotes the element of $L^1(E_1, \mathscr{F}_1, \Pi_1)$ which is the Radon-Nikodym derivative of φ_f with respect to Π_2, it is easily verified that the mapping $f \to fT$ defines a sub-Markovian operator T such that $T1_F = T(\cdot, F)$. ∎

If T is a sub-Markovian operator and $\{T(\cdot, F), F \in \mathscr{F}_2\}$ is the associated kernel, let us choose in each of the equivalence classes $T(\cdot, F)$ a measurable function on $(E_1, \mathscr{F}_1)$ which we shall denote by $\bar{P}(\cdot, F)$. The family of functions $\{\bar{P}(\cdot, F), F \in \mathscr{F}_2\}$ has the following almost sure properties, by virtue of the definition of a sub-Markovian kernel:

(a) $0 \leqslant \bar{P}(x, F) \leqslant 1$ for Π_1-almost every x, if $F \in \mathscr{F}_2$; if T is Markovian, $\bar{P}(x, E_2) = 1$ for Π_1-almost every x;

(b) $\bar{P}(x, F) = 0$ for Π_1-almost every x, if $\Pi_2(F) = 0$;

(c) $\bar{P}(x, \sum_I F_i) = \sum_I \bar{P}(x, F_i)$ for Π_1-almost every x if $\{F_i, i \in I\}$ is a countable family of pairwise disjoint sets in $(E_2, \mathscr{F}_2)$.

This family of functions differs from a transition probability only in that each of the preceding relations holds only outside of a negligible set.

To find a transition probability which induces T therefore reduces to choosing the functions $\bar{P}(\cdot, F)$ $(F \in \mathscr{F}_2)$ within their equivalence classes $T(\cdot, F)$ in such a way that the preceding relations (a), (b), (c) shall hold everywhere, not only outside of negligible sets; such a choice is not possible in general, the difficulty being to satisfy condition (c) for every family $\{F_i, i \in I\}$. Nevertheless, the following result holds:

PROPOSITION V.4.4. *Let $(E_i, \mathscr{F}_i, \Pi_i)_{i=1,2}$ be two probability spaces. Suppose that $\mathscr{F}_2$ is a σ-algebra of countable type and that there exists a compact subclass $\mathscr{C}$ of $\mathscr{F}_2$ having the approximation property*

$$\Pi_2(F) = \sup\{\Pi_2(C); C \in \mathscr{C}, C \subset F\} \qquad (F \in \mathscr{F}_2).$$

Then with every (sub-) Markovian operator T mapping $L^1(E_1, \mathscr{F}_1, \Pi_1)$ into $L^1(E_2, \mathscr{F}_2, \Pi_2)$ one can associate at least one (sub-) transition probability $P = \{P(x_1, F_2)\}$ such that

$$\int_F fT\, d\Pi_2 = \int_{E_1} fP(\cdot, F)\, d\Pi_1$$

for every $f \in L^1(E_1, \mathscr{F}_1, \Pi_1)$ and every $F \in \mathscr{F}_2$ (that is, inducing the operator T in the sense of Proposition V.4.2).

A sub- (transition) probability is by definition a (transition) probability which is not required to have total mass equal to 1, but only $\leqslant 1$.

By Proposition II.7.3, the hypothesis concerning $(E_2, \mathscr{F}_2, \Pi_2)$ is satisfied for every probability Π_2 if $(E_2, \mathscr{F}_2)$ is a Polish space with the σ-algebra of its Borel sets.

PROOF. Let $\{B_n, n \geqslant 1\}$ be an enumeration of a countable Boolean algebra $\mathscr{B}$ which generates $\mathscr{F}_2$. If the class $\mathscr{C}$ is closed under finite union, which we may suppose by virtue of Lemma I.6.1, for every $n \geqslant 1$ there exists an increasing sequence of subsets of B_n in $\mathscr{C}$, say $\{C_n^k, k \geqslant 1\}$, such that $\Pi_2(B_n) = \lim_{k \uparrow \infty} \uparrow \Pi_2(C_n^k)$. The Boolean algebra $\mathscr{D}$ generated by the B_n and the C_n^k $(n \geqslant 1, k \geqslant 1)$ is a countable subalgebra of $\mathscr{F}_2$.

By what was said earlier, every family $\{\bar{P}(\cdot, F), F \in \mathscr{F}_2\}$ of measurable functions chosen, respectively, in the equivalence classes $T1_F = T(\cdot, F)$ has the following properties:

(1) For every $D \in \mathscr{D}$ we have $0 \leqslant \bar{P}(\cdot, D) \leqslant 1$ outside a negligible set in $\mathscr{F}_1$; moreover, if T is Markovian, then $\bar{P}(\cdot, E_2) = 1$ outside a negligible set of $\mathscr{F}_1$;

(2) For every pair D, D' of disjoint sets in $\mathscr{D}$,

$$\bar{P}(\cdot, D + D') = \bar{P}(\cdot, D) + \bar{P}(\cdot, D')$$

outside a negligible set of $\mathscr{F}_1$;

(3) For every $n \geqslant 1$ there exists a negligible set of $\mathscr{F}_1$ outside which the sequence $\{\bar{P}(\cdot, C_n^k), k \geqslant 1\}$ of functions is increasing and converges a.s. to $\bar{P}(\cdot, B_n)$ (in fact, since $1_{C_n^k} \uparrow 1_{B_n}$ Π_2-almost everywhere,

$$T(\cdot, C_n^k) \uparrow T(\cdot, B_n)$$

Π_1-almost everywhere).

These properties introduce only a countable family of negligible sets of $\mathscr{F}_1$; consequently, there exists a negligible set N_1 of $\mathscr{F}_1$ outside which these properties hold everywhere.

If $x \notin N_1$, the set function $\bar{P}(x, \cdot)$ restricted to the algebra $\mathscr{D}$ (and a fortiori to the smaller algebra $\mathscr{B}$) is positive and additive by (1), (2). The argument of the first part of the proof of Proposition I.6.2 shows, next, using property (3) above, that for every sequence $\{B_{n_j}, j \geqslant 1\}$ in $\mathscr{B}$ decreasing to $\varnothing$ we have $\bar{P}(x, B_{n_j}) \downarrow 0$. Consequently, the restriction of $\bar{P}(x, \cdot)$ to $\mathscr{B}$ is a probability in the Markovian case and a sub-probability in the sub-Markovian case; we denote by $P(x, \cdot)$ the unique σ-additive extension of $\{\bar{P}(x, B), B \in \mathscr{B}\}$ to the σ-algebra $\mathscr{F}_2$ (Theorem I.5).

If $x \in N_1$, let $P(x, \cdot) = \Pi_2(\cdot)$. Then it is easily verified that $P = \{P(x, F)\}$ is a (sub-) transition probability on $(E_1, \mathscr{F}_1)$ and $(E_2, \mathscr{F}_2)$ which induces the operator T. In fact, on the one hand $P(x, \cdot)$ is a (sub-) probability on $(E_2, \mathscr{F}_2)$ for every $x \in E_1$; on the other hand $P(\cdot, F)$ is an $\mathscr{F}_1$-measurable function in the equivalence class of $T(\cdot, F)$, for every $F \in \mathscr{B}$ by construction, and therefore for every $F \in \mathscr{F}_2$ by the remark following Definition III.2.1. Finally, the transition probability P satisfies the condition $\Pi_1 P \ll \Pi_2$ since $P(\cdot, F)$ belongs to the equivalence class of $T(\cdot, F)$; it is then clear that P induces T. ▮

In the case where the endomorphism T is a conditional expectation, the preceding proposition can be stated in the following form:

Corollary. *Let $(E, \mathscr{F}, \Pi)$ be a probability space such that the σ-algebra $\mathscr{F}$ is of countable type and such that there exists a compact class $\mathscr{C}$ contained in $\mathscr{F}$, having the approximation property*

$$\Pi(F) = \sup\{\Pi(C); C \in \mathscr{C}, C \subset F\} \qquad (F \in \mathscr{F}).$$

Then for every σ-subalgebra $\mathscr{G}$ of $\mathscr{F}$, there exists at least one "regular conditional probability," that is, a family $\{P(x, F), x \in E, F \in \mathscr{F}\}$ *such that:*

(a) *for every* $x \in E$, $P(x, \cdot)$ *is a probability on* $(E, \mathscr{F})$;

(b) *for every* $F \in \mathscr{F}$, $P(\cdot, F)$ *is a* $\mathscr{G}$*-measurable function in the equivalence class* $E^{\mathscr{G}}(1_F)$. *For every positive* r.r.v. X *defined on* $(E, \mathscr{F})$, *the function* $\int_E P(\cdot, dy)X(y)$ *is* $\mathscr{G}$*-measurable and is a version of* $E^{\mathscr{G}}(X)$.

PROOF. The conditional expectation $E^{\mathscr{G}}$ is a Markovian endomorphism of $L^1(E, \mathscr{F}, \Pi)$ whose adjoint is $E^{\mathscr{G}}$ on $L^\infty(E, \mathscr{F}, \Pi)$. It follows by virtue of the preceding proposition, that there exists a transition probability P defined relative to $(E, \mathscr{F})$ and $(E, \mathscr{F})$ such that $P(\cdot, F)$ is a version of $E^{\mathscr{G}}(1_F)$ and $\int P(\cdot, dy)X(y)$ is a version of $E^{\mathscr{G}}(X)$ if $X \geqslant 0$. This does not imply that $P(\cdot, F)$ is $\mathscr{G}$-measurable, but only that $P(\cdot, F)$ differs from a $\mathscr{G}$-measurable function only on a negligible set of $\mathscr{F}$. Nevertheless, if in the proof of the preceding proposition one takes care to choose the functions $\bar{P}(\cdot, F)$ $\mathscr{G}$-measurable from the beginning, it is easily seen that the functions $P(\cdot, F)$ then obtained will be precisely $\mathscr{G}$-measurable. ∎

V.5. ERGODIC DECOMPOSITION

The following result is known as the *maximal ergodic theorem*; in the general form given here, it is due to E. Hopf. This result will play a fundamental role throughout the remainder of this chapter. The very short proof presented here is due to A. Garsia.

PROPOSITION V.5.1. *Let T be a sub-Markovian endomorphism of the space* $L^1(E, \mathscr{F}, \Pi)$. *For any* $f, g \in L^1_+(E, \mathscr{F}, \Pi)$ *we have the inequality*

$$\int_E f \geqslant \int_{B_{f,g}} g,$$

where

$$B_{f,g} = \bigcup_{n \geqslant 0} \left\{ \sum_{k \leqslant n} fT^k > \sum_{k \leqslant n} gT^k \right\}.$$

Throughout this section, the integrals will be taken with respect to the probability Π.

PROOF. We shall in fact prove the following result: For every $h \in L^1$, we have the inequality $\int_{A_h} h \geqslant 0$, where

$$A_h = \bigcup_{n \geqslant 0} \left\{ \sum_{k \leqslant n} hT^k > 0 \right\}.$$

This result implies that in the statement of the proposition, for, setting $h = f - g$ ($f, g \in L^1_+$), we find that $B_{f,g} = A_h$ and therefore that

$$\int_E f - \int_{B_{f,g}} g \geqslant \int_{B_{f,g}} (f - g) = \int_{A_h} h \geqslant 0.$$

(Conversely, by the way, one can see that the proposition implies the above result by putting $f = h^+$, $g = h^-$; one then has $B_{f,g} = A_h$ and $f = 0$ on $B^c_{f,g}$.)

If $h \in L^1$, we put $h_n = \sup_{0 \leqslant m \leqslant n} (\sum_{k \leqslant m} hT^k)$ for every integer $n \geqslant 0$. We then have $h = h_0 \leqslant h_1 \leqslant \cdots$, and as $n \uparrow \infty$ the sets $\{h_n > 0\}$ increase to A_h. On the other hand, $h_{n+1} \leqslant h + h_n^+ T$ since $h \leqslant h + h_n^+ T$ and $\sum_{k \leqslant m+1} hT^k = h + (\sum_{k \leqslant m} hT^k)T \leqslant h + h_n^+ T$ if $0 \leqslant m \leqslant n$; it follows that $h_n \leqslant h_{n+1} \leqslant h + h_n^+ T$ and therefore that

$$\int_{\{h_n > 0\}} h \geqslant \int_{\{h_n > 0\}} h_n - \int_{\{h_n > 0\}} h_n^+ T \geqslant \int h_n^+ - \int h_n^+ T \geqslant 0$$

since T is a contraction. To prove the assertion, we have only to let $n \uparrow \infty$. ∎

The following technical result will be useful to us in subsequent proofs.

COROLLARY. *Let T be a sub-Markovian endomorphism on $L^1(E, \mathscr{F}, \Pi)$ and let f be an element of L^1_+ such that $\{f > 0\} = E$. If $\{g_p, p \geqslant 1\}$ is a sequence in L^1 which converges to 0 and is either decreasing or such that $\sum_p \|g_p\| < \infty$, then*

$$\limsup_{p \to \infty} \left(\sup_n \left| \frac{\sum_{k \leqslant n} g_p T^k}{\sum_{k \geqslant n} fT^k} \right| \right) = 0.$$

PROOF. We can reduce the proof to the case where the g_p are positive by observing that $\sum_{k \leqslant n} |g_p T^k| \leqslant \sum_{k \leqslant n} |g_p| T^k$ and that $\|g_p\| = \| |g_p| \|$. In this case, it suffices to prove that $\limsup_p B_{p,\epsilon} = \varnothing$ for every $\epsilon > 0$, where

$$B_{p,\epsilon} = \sup_n \left\{ \sum_{k \leqslant n} g_p T^k > \epsilon \sum_{k \leqslant n} fT^k \right\}.$$

But, by the preceding proposition, we have $\int_{B_{p,\epsilon}} f \leqslant \int g_p$. If $\{g_p\}$ is a decreasing sequence, the same is true of the sequence $\{B_{p,\epsilon}, p \geqslant 1\}$ for every $\epsilon > 0$; the preceding inequality then shows that if g_p decreases to 0 in L^1, then

$$\limsup_p B_{p,\epsilon} = \lim_p \downarrow B_{p,\epsilon} = \varnothing \quad \text{a.s.}$$

for the measure $f \cdot \Pi$, and hence for the measure Π if $\{f > 0\} = E$. If $\{g_p\}$ is a sequence in L^1_+ such that $\sum_p \| g_p \| < \infty$, the inequality above shows that the series $\sum_p \int_{B_{p,\epsilon}} f$ is convergent; by Proposition I.4.4, this implies that $\limsup_p B_{p,\epsilon} = \varnothing$ a.s. for the measure $f \cdot \Pi$, and therefore for the measure Π if $\{f > 0\} = E$. ▮

PROPOSITION V.5.2. *For every sub-Markovian endomorphism T of $L^1(E, \mathscr{F}, \Pi)$, there exists a subset C of E ($C \in \mathscr{F}$), unique up to equivalence, such that for every $f \in L^1_+(E, \mathscr{F}, \Pi)$ one has*

$$\sum_k fT^k = 0 \text{ or } +\infty \text{ on } C,$$

$$\sum_k fT^k < +\infty \text{ on the complement of } C.$$

The class $\mathscr{C}$ of subsets $C_f = \{\sum_k fT^k = \infty\}$ of C obtained when f runs through L^1_+ is a σ-algebra of subsets of C.

For every finite and positive measurable function h defined on $(E, \mathscr{F}, \Pi)$, we have the following implications:

$$Th \leqslant h \text{ on } C \Leftrightarrow Th = h \text{ on } C \Leftrightarrow h \text{ is } \mathscr{C}\text{-measurable on } C.$$

In particular, in order that a subset B of C belong to $\mathscr{C}$, it is necessary that $T1_B = 1_B$ on C and it is sufficient that $T1_B = 1_B$ on B.

The subsets C and $D = C^c$ of E are called, respectively, the *conservative part* and the *dissipative part* of E associated with T; the sets of $\mathscr{C}$ are called (when C is not empty) the *invariant sets*.

In the case where the endomorphism T is induced by a transition probability P, the expression $\sum_{k \geqslant 0} fT^k$ represents the "mean density of the number of visits" of the Markovian random function $\{X_k, k \geqslant 0\}$ with initial law $f \cdot \Pi$ and stationary transition probability P; if $N(F)$ denotes the number of visits of $\{X_k, k \geqslant 0\}$ to the measurable set F, i.e., $N(F) = \sum_{k \geqslant 0} 1_F(X_k)$, then we in fact have

$$E[N(F)] = \int_F \Big(\sum_{k \geqslant 0} fT^k \Big) \, d\Pi,$$

since $E[1_F(X_k)] = \int_F fT^k \, d\Pi$. On the other hand, the reader can easily show that a subset B of C belongs to $\mathscr{C}$ if and only if

$$P_x[X_k \in B \quad \text{for every } k \geqslant 0] = 1 \text{ a.s.} \quad \text{in} \quad x \quad \text{on} \quad B.$$

PROOF. (a) We shall show, to begin with, that if $f, g \in L^1_+$, then $\sum_k gT^k = 0$ on

$$A = \left\{\sum_k fT^k = \infty, \sum_k gT^k < \infty\right\}.$$

To this end, we observe first that $A \subset B_{f,ag}$ for any constant $a > 0$ if

$$B_{f,ag} = \bigcup_{n \geqslant 0} \left\{\sum_{k \leqslant n} fT^k > a \sum_{k \leqslant n} gT^k\right\};$$

by Proposition V.5.1, this implies that $a \int_A g \leqslant \int f$ and hence, letting $a \to \infty$, that $g = 0$ on A. But

$$\left\{\sum_k gT^k < \infty\right\} = \left\{\sum_k (gT^m)T^k < \infty\right\} \qquad \text{for every} \quad m \geqslant 0,$$

since the two series differ only by $\sum_{k<m} gT^k < \infty$. The preceding argument now shows also that $gT^m = 0$ on A for every $m \geqslant 0$, and therefore that $\sum_{m \geqslant 0} gT^m = 0$ on A.

Now let p be an element of L^1_+ such that $\{p > 0\} = E$, and let

$$C = \left\{\sum_k pT^k = \infty\right\}.$$

On setting $g = p$ in the preceding, we find that $\sum_k fT^k < \infty$ on $D = C^c$ for every $f \in L^1_+$ since $\sum_k pT^k \geqslant p > 0$ everywhere. Now taking $f = p$ in the result obtained at the beginning of the present proof, we find that $\sum_k gT^k = 0$ or ∞ on C, for every $g \in L^1_+$.

In particular, if $g \in L^1_+$ is such that $\{g > 0\} = E$, we have thus shown that $\sum_k gT^k = \infty$ on C, $< \infty$ on D. It follows that the equivalence class of C does not depend on the strictly positive function p chosen in defining it. Having thus proved the uniqueness of C, we have proved the first sentence of the proposition.

(b) We shall show next that $T(\cdot, C_f^c) = 0$ on C_f for every $f \in L^1_+$. To this end, we put $A_a = \{\sum_k fT^k \leqslant a\}$ and observe that $T(\cdot, A_a) = 0$ on $C_f = \{\sum_k fT^k = \infty\}$, as

$$\int \left(\sum_k fT^k\right) T(\cdot, A_a) = \int_{A_a} \sum_{k \geqslant 1} fT^k \leqslant a\Pi(A_a) < \infty.$$

Since $A_a \uparrow C_f^c$ as $a \uparrow \infty$, the assertion is proved.

It follows, in particular, that for every $g \in L^1_+$ which vanishes on D, we have

$$\sum_k gT^k = 0 \quad \text{on } D.$$

To see this, we show by induction on k that $gT^k = 0$ on D by using the formula

$$\int_D gT^{k+1} = \int gT^{k}T(\cdot, D)$$

and the equality $T(\cdot, D) = 0$ on C.

(c) We now show that every finite and positive measurable function h such that $Th \leqslant h$ on C necessarily satisfies the equality $Th = h$ on C. To this end, we introduce the positive function $g = (1 + h)^{-1}1_C$ which is majorized by 1; this function thus belongs to L^1_+ and $\{g > 0\} = C$. By virtue of results (a) and (b) above, we have $\sum_k gT^k = \infty$ on C, $= 0$ on D. On the other hand,

$$\int_C \Big(\sum_{k<n} gT^k\Big)(h - Th) = \int g(h - T^n h) \leqslant \int gh \leqslant 1;$$

since $h - Th \geqslant 0$ on C, on letting $n \to \infty$ we obtain

$$\int_C \Big(\sum_k gT^k\Big)(h - Th) \leqslant 1,$$

which is possible only if $h - Th = 0$ on C.

The result just obtained shows that $T1 = 1$ on C and that $T1_{C_f^c} = 1_{C_f^c}$ on C, since we have $T1 \leqslant 1$ on E by hypothesis and since it then follows from (b) that $T1_{C_f^c} \leqslant 1_{C_f^c}$. Taking differences, we deduce that $T1_{C_f} = 1_{C_f}$ on C and in particular that $T1_C = 1$ on C.

(d) Finally, let us denote by H the convex cone of finite and positive measurable functions which vanish on D and are such that $Th = h$ on C. This convex cone contains 1_C by (c), and is obviously closed under monotone limits. It is a lattice, for if $h, h' \in H$, then

$$T[\inf(h, h')] \leqslant \inf(Th, Th') = \inf(h, h') \quad \text{on } C,$$

which implies, by (c), that $\inf(h, h') \in H$ (the formula

$$\inf(h, h') + \sup(h, h') = h + h'$$

then shows that $\sup(h, h') \in H$). These properties of H imply that the class $\mathscr{H} = \{B: B \subset C, T1_B = 1_B \text{ on } C\}$ is a σ-algebra of subsets of C.

Conversely, a positive and finite measurable function h which vanishes on D belongs to H if and only if it is $\mathscr{H}$-measurable. In fact, the condition is sufficient, for if h is $\mathscr{H}$-measurable, it is the limit of an increasing sequence of sums of characteristic functions of sets of $\mathscr{H}$ and hence belongs to H. The condition is necessary, on the other hand, for if $h \in H$, the formula

$$1_{\{h>a\}} = \lim_{n \uparrow \infty} \uparrow \inf [1, n(h-a)^+]$$

shows that $1_{\{h>a\}} \in H$ for every constant $a > 0$, and hence that h is $\mathscr{H}$-measurable [compare with Problem II.2.1].

The σ-algebra $\mathscr{H}$ and the class $\mathscr{C}$ are identical. In fact, it follows from (b) that every set C_f of $\mathscr{C}$ belongs to $\mathscr{H}$. Conversely, if $B \in \mathscr{H}$ and if an $f \in L^1_+$ is chosen such that $\{f > 0\} = B$, it follows from $C - B \in \mathscr{H}$ that $\sum_k fT^k = 0$ on $C - B$, since

$$\int_{C-B} fT^k = \int_{C-B} f = 0.$$

On the other hand, $\sum_k fT^k \geqslant f > 0$ on B implies that $\sum_k fT^k = \infty$ on B since $B \subset C$. We have thus shown that $B = \{\sum_k fT^k = \infty\} \in \mathscr{C}$.

To complete the proof of the proposition, it now suffices to observe that for every finite and positive measurable function h we have

$$Th = h \quad \text{on} \quad C \Leftrightarrow h1_C \in H.$$

In fact, the equality $T(\cdot, D) = 0$ on C, established in paragraph (b), implies that for every function h we have $Th = T(h1_C)$ on C. ∎

COROLLARY 1. *Let T be a sub-Markovian endomorphism of*

$$L^1(E, \mathscr{F}, \Pi)$$

and let C' be a nonempty invariant set (= subset of C in $\mathscr{C}$). Then the formula

$$f'T' = fT, \quad \text{where} \quad f = \begin{cases} f' & \text{on} \quad C', \\ 0 & \text{on} \quad E - C' \end{cases}$$

defines an endomorphism T' of $L^1[C', C' \cap \mathscr{F}, \Pi(C' \cap \cdot)]$ whose powers T'^k are given by a similar formula: $f'T'^k = fT^k$. The transpose of T', defined on $L^\infty[C']$, and its powers have the property

$$T'^k h' = T^k h \quad \text{on} \quad C' \quad \text{whenever} \quad h = h' \quad \text{on} \quad C'.$$

It follows, in particular, that $T^k h = 0$ on C' whenever $h = 0$ on C'. The *endomorphism T' is Markovian and conservative, and the σ-algebra of its invariant sets is equal to $C' \cap \mathscr{C}$.*

When $C' = C$, we shall call T' the *conservative part* of T.

PROOF. This corollary results from the two equalities: $T1_{C'} = 1$ on C', $T1_{E-C'} = 0$ on C', established in the preceding proposition. In fact, the second equality shows that $fT = 0$ on $E - C'$ whenever $f = 0$ on $E - C'$; the formula concerning the powers of the endomorphism T' is immediately deduced from this. The duality formulas

$$\int_{C'} f'T'^k \cdot h' = \int_{C'} f' \cdot T'^k h', \qquad \int_E fT^k \cdot h = \int_E f \cdot T^k h,$$

whose left sides are equal by the foregoing whenever $f = f'$ on C', $= 0$ on $E - C'$ and $h = h'$ on C' (h arbitrary on $E - C'$), now show that $T^k h = T'^k h'$ on C' whenever $h = h'$ on C'.

The equality $T1_{C'} = 1$ on C' shows that T' is Markovian. Finally, it follows from the equality $\sum_k f'T'^k = \sum_k fT^k$ that the conservative part of T' is equal to C' and that the σ-algebra of its invariant sets coincides with the trace $C' \cap \mathscr{C}$. ∎

COROLLARY 2. *If T is a sub-Markovian endomorphism defined on $L^1(E, \mathscr{F}, \Pi)$, then for every positive function h,*

$$\sum_k T^k h = \infty \quad \textit{on} \quad H, \qquad = 0 \quad \textit{on} \quad C - H,$$

where H denotes the smallest subset of C in $\mathscr{C}$ containing the set $C \cap \{h > 0\}$.

PROOF. Since $h = 0$ on $C - H$, it follows from the preceding corollary that $\sum_k T^k h = 0$ on $C - H$.

If a is a positive constant and if $f \in L^1_+(E, \mathscr{F}, \Pi)$ is chosen so that $\{f > 0\} = C \cap \{\sum_k T^k h \leqslant a\}$, then we have, for every $n \geqslant 0$,

$$\int \Big(\sum_{k \geqslant 0} fT^k\Big) T^n h = \int f \Big(\sum_{k \geqslant n} T^k h\Big) \leqslant a \int f < \infty.$$

It follows that $\sum_n T^n h = 0$ on $\{\sum_k fT^k = \infty\}$, that is, by the preceding proposition, on a subset of C in $\mathscr{C}$ containing $\{f > 0\}$. If H'_a denotes this set, we therefore have

$$C \cap \Big\{\sum T^n h = 0\Big\} \supset H'_a \supset C \cap \Big\{\sum T^k h \leqslant a\Big\}.$$

In view of the form of the two extreme terms, this double inclusion is an equality; consequently, the set $C \cap \{\sum T^k h = 0\}$ belongs to $\mathscr{C}$ and coincides with the set $C \cap \{\sum T^k h < \infty\}$, as is seen by letting $a \uparrow \infty$. On the other hand, this set is obviously disjoint from

$$C \cap \{h > 0\}$$

and hence, since it belongs to $\mathscr{C}$, it is disjoint from H; this shows that $\sum_k T^k h = \infty$ on H. ▮

Complements and problems

V.5.1. If T is an *idempotent* ($T^2 = T$) sub-Markovian endomorphism of $L^1(E, \mathscr{F}, \Pi)$, show that the dissipative part D is the largest subset (actually, equivalence class of subsets) of $(E, \mathscr{F}, \Pi)$ such that $T1_D = 0$, and that the σ-algebra $\mathscr{C}$ is the smallest σ-algebra of subsets of $C = D^c$ with respect to which the functions $T1_F$ ($F \in \mathscr{F}$) are measurable on C.

V.5.2. Let $(E, \mathscr{F})$ be a countable space taken with the σ-algebra of all its subsets, and let Π be a probability on $(E, \mathscr{F})$ such that $\Pi(x) > 0$ for every $x \in E$. Then the formula

$$\sum_y fT(y) \cdot \Pi(y) = \sum_x \Pi(x) f(x) P(x, y)$$

establishes a one-to-one correspondence between the (sub-) Markovian endomorphisms T of $L^1(E, \mathscr{F}, \Pi)$ and the (*sub-*) *Markovian matrices* P defined on E, i.e., matrices such that $P(x, y) \geqslant 0$, $\sum_z P(x, z) = 1$ ($\leqslant 1$) for every $x, y \in E$.

If $\{C_1, C_2, \ldots\}$ is the countable partition of the conservative part C of E which generates the σ-algebra $\mathscr{C}$, show that:

(1) $\sum_k P^k(x, y) < \infty$ $(=0)$ if $y \notin C$, for any $x \in E$ $(x \in C)$;

(2) $\sum_k P^k(x, y) = \infty$ or 0 when $x \in C_i$ and $y \in C_j$, according as $i = j$ or $i \neq j$.

Note that these properties completely characterize C and the C_i. Show that the idempotent sub-Markovian matrices P are the matrices of the following form:

There exists a finite or infinite sequence of probabilities Π_n whose supports C_n are pairwise disjoint, and a mapping p of $D = (\sum C_n)^c$ into $[0, 1]$ such that:

$$P(x, y) = \begin{cases} \Pi_n(y) & \text{if } \ x \in C_n, \ y \in C_n \quad \text{for some } n, \\ p(x)\Pi_n(y) & \text{if } \ x \in D, \ y \in C_n \quad \text{for some } n, \\ 0 & \text{otherwise.} \end{cases}$$

[Use Problem V.5.1.]

V.5.3. RIESZ DECOMPOSITION. A positive and finite measurable function h defined on a space $(E, \mathscr{F}, \Pi)$ is said to be (*super-*) *regular* with respect to a sub-Markovian endomorphism T if $(Th \leqslant h)Th = h$; it is called the *potential* of the positive function g if $h = \sum_{k \geqslant 0} T^k g$.

Show that every super-regular function h can be decomposed in one and only one way into the sum of a finite potential $\sum_{k \geqslant 0} T^k g$ and a regular function h', and that one necessarily has $g = h - Th$, $h' = \lim_{n \uparrow \infty} \downarrow T^n h$. Show, moreover, that if the function h is majorized by a finite potential, say,

$$h \leqslant \sum_{k \geqslant 0} T^k f < \infty,$$

the function f is itself a potential (namely, the potential of $g = h - Th$). Deduce from this that the convex cone consisting of the regular functions is a complete lattice.

If the operator T is conservative, there exists no finite potential different from 0. If the operator T is dissipative, show that every super-regular function h is the limit of an increasing sequence of potentials. [Consider the functions

$$\min\left(h, \sum_{k \geqslant 0} T^k 1_{D_n}\right),$$

where we have put $D_n = \{\sum_k fT^k \leqslant n\}$ for an $f \in L^1_+$ such that $\{f > 0\} = E$.]

V.6. POINTWISE ERGODIC THEOREM

In this section we shall prove a very general ergodic theorem relative to a sub-Markovian endomorphism T defined on a space $L^1(E, \mathscr{F}, \Pi)$; the proof will be based on a study of the operators ${}^F T$ defined below, which incidentally is of intrinsic interest.

Given a sub-Markovian endomorphism T of a space $L^1(E, \mathscr{F}, \Pi)$, we associate with every set $F \in \mathscr{F}$ the sub-Markovian endomorphism ${}^F T = TI_{F^c}$, where I_{F^c} denotes the operator of multiplication by 1_{F^c}. By definition, we therefore have

$$f\,{}^F T = fT \text{ on } F^c, \quad = 0 \text{ on } F; \qquad {}^F Th = T(h1_{F^c}).$$

We shall also consider the endomorphisms

$${}^F H^{(n)} = \sum_{0 \leqslant k < n} ({}^F T)^k T I_F \qquad (n > 0)$$

which are obviously positive, and even sub-Markovian since the inequality $T1_F = T1 - {}^F T1 \leqslant 1 - {}^F T1$ implies that

$${}^F H^{(n)} 1 = \sum_{0 \leqslant k < n} ({}^F T)^k T 1_F \leqslant \sum_{0 \leqslant k < n} ({}^F T)^k (1 - {}^F T1) = 1 - ({}^F T)^n 1 \leqslant 1.$$

Therefore the limit ${}^F H = \sum_{k \geqslant 0} ({}^F T)^k T I_F$ of the increasing sequence $\{{}^F H^{(n)}\}$ is again a sub-Markovian endomorphism.

In the case where the endomorphism T is induced by a transition probability P, the endomorphisms ${}^FT$, ${}^FH^{(n)}$ and ${}^FH$ are evidently induced by the sub-transition probabilities

$$ {}^FP = \{{}^FP(x, G) = P(x, F^cG)\}, \qquad \sum_{0 \leqslant k < n} ({}^FP)^n PI_F \qquad \text{and} \qquad \sum_{k \geqslant 0} ({}^FP)^n PI_F $$

respectively. If ${}^F\nu$ denotes the first instant $n > 0$ at which a Markovian random function $\{X_n, n \geqslant 0\}$ with stationary transition probability P enters F (we put ${}^F\nu = \infty$ if $X_n \notin F$ for every $n > 0$), we have the formula

$$ P_x[X_n \in G, {}^F\nu > n] = ({}^FP)^n(x, G). $$

This formula can be proved by induction on n, on noting that

$$ \begin{aligned} P_x[X_{n+1} \in G, {}^F\nu > n + 1] &= P_x(X_{n+1} \in F^cG, {}^F\nu > n) \\ &= \int_{y \in E} P_x(X_n \in dy, {}^F\nu > n) P(y, F^cG) \end{aligned} $$

by virtue of the Markov property and of ${}^F\nu$ being a stopping time $(\{{}^F\nu > n\} \in \mathscr{A}_n^0)$.

The preceding formula implies that

$$ P_x[X_k \in G, {}^F\nu = k] = P_x(X_k \in FG, {}^F\nu > k - 1) = ({}^FP)^{k-1}P(x, FG), $$

and by adding over k, that

$$ \begin{aligned} P_x[X_{({}^F\nu)} \in G, {}^F\nu \leqslant n] &= {}^FH^{(n)}(x, G), \\ P_x[X_{({}^F\nu)} \in G, {}^F\nu < \infty] &= {}^FH(x, G). \end{aligned} $$

It is now clear that

$$ {}^FHh(x) = \int_{\{{}^F\nu < \infty\}} dP_x h[X_{({}^F\nu)}] $$

and in particular, that ${}^FH1(x) = P_x[{}^F\nu < \infty]$. Finally, if $\mu_0 = f \cdot \Pi$ is the probability law of X_0, the positive measure $f{}^FH \cdot \Pi$ is the distribution law of $X_{({}^F\nu)}$ on $\{{}^F\nu < \infty\}$.

PROPOSITION V.6.1. *Let T be a sub-Markovian endomorphism defined on the space $L^1(E, \mathscr{F}, \Pi)$ and let $\mathscr{C}$ be the σ-subalgebra of $C \cap \mathscr{F}$ consisting of the subsets of the conservative part C which are invariant under T. If F is a subset of C belonging to $\mathscr{F}$ and if $\bar{F}$ denotes the smallest equivalence class of the sets in $\mathscr{C}$ containing F, then*

$$ {}^FHh = h1_{\bar{F}} \quad \text{on} \quad C, $$

for every function $h \geqslant 0$ which is $\mathscr{C}$-measurable on C.

PROOF. If h is positive and $\mathscr{C}$-measurable, the decomposition $h = Th = T(h1_F) + {}^FTh$ implies that for every $n \geqslant 0$,

$$^FH^{(n)}h = \sum_{k<n} (^FT)^k T(h1_F) = \sum_{k<n} (^FT)^k(h - {}^FTh) = h - (^FT)^n h.$$

Hence

$$h - {}^FHh = \lim_{n\uparrow\infty} \downarrow (h - {}^FH^{(n)}h) = \lim_{n\uparrow\infty} \downarrow (^FT)^n h$$

is a positive function, invariant under ^FT. Since $T = {}^FT + TI_F$, we deduce from this that

$$T(h - {}^FHh) = (h - {}^FHh) + T[1_F(h - {}^FHh)]$$

and, since $h = Th$, that

$$^FHh = T(^FHh) + T[1_F(h - {}^FHh)] \geqslant T(^FHh).$$

By Proposition V.5.2, the function ^FHh is then $\mathscr{C}$-measurable on C and we have $T[1_F(h - {}^FHh)] = 0$ on C. It follows, evidently, that

$$0 = T[1_F(h - {}^FHh)] \leqslant 1_F(h - {}^FHh) \qquad \text{on} \quad C,$$

which, by the same proposition, implies that $1_F(h - {}^FHh) = 0$. But since the function $h - {}^FHh$ is $\mathscr{C}$-measurable, it cannot be zero on F without also being zero on $\bar{F}$, and we have thus proved that $^FHh = h$ on $\bar{F}$.

Since $C - \bar{F} \in \mathscr{C}$, we have $T(h1_{\bar{F}}) = 0$ on $C - \bar{F}$ for any function $h \geqslant 0$, and we easily see, then, that ^FHh vanishes on $C - \bar{F}$. ▮

COROLLARY. *Under the hypotheses of the preceding proposition, the conservative part of the endomorphism ^FT is equal to $C - \bar{F}$, and the σ-algebra of subsets of $C - \bar{F}$ consisting of the sets which are invariant under ^FT is the trace of $\mathscr{C}$ on $C - \bar{F}$.*

PROOF. The preceding proposition shows that $^FH1 = 1_{\bar{F}}$, while the corollary of Proposition V.5.2 applied to ^FT shows that

$$^FH1 = \sum_{k\geqslant 0} (^FT)^k T1_F$$

can only be zero or infinity on the conservative part of ^FT. It follows that the conservative part ^FC of ^FT is disjoint from $\bar{F}$. Since the inequality $^FT \leqslant T$ immediately implies that $^FC \subset C$, we have shown that

$$^FC \subset C - \bar{F}.$$

On the other hand, the restrictions of the operators T and ${}^FT$ to the set $C - \bar{F}$, which is invariant under T, are identical; then the corollary of Proposition V.5.2 implies that ${}^FC = C - \bar{F}$ and that the traces on $C - \bar{F}$ of the σ-algebras of sets invariant under T and ${}^FT$, respectively, are identical. ∎

The following result (due to Doeblin in the case of a countable space E) is a special case of the ergodic theorem which we have in view.

PROPOSITION V.6.2. *Let T be a sub-Markovian endomorphism defined on $L^1(E, \mathscr{F}, \Pi)$ and let $\mathscr{C}$ be the σ-algebra of the subsets of the conservative part C which are invariant under T. If F is a subset of C in $\mathscr{F}$ and if $\bar{F}$ denotes the smallest equivalence class of sets in $\mathscr{C}$ which contains F, then*

$$\lim_{n\to\infty} \text{a.s.} \frac{\sum_{k\leqslant n} (f^F H)T^k}{\sum_{k\leqslant n} fT^k} = 1_{\bar{F}} \qquad on \quad C,$$

for every $f \in L^1_+(E, \mathscr{F}, \Pi)$ such that $\{f > 0\} = E$.

PROOF. (a) For every $k \geqslant 0$, the function $(f^F H)T^k$ is zero on $C - \bar{F}$ since

$$\int_{C-\bar{F}} (f^F H)T^k = \int_{C-\bar{F}} f^F H = 0.$$

The proposition is therefore evident on $C - \bar{F}$.

(b) The rest of the proof is based on the following formula, which we shall establish by induction on n:

$$\sum_{k\leqslant n} T^k = \sum_{k\leqslant n} ({}^FT)^k + \sum_{k+l<n}\sum ({}^FT)^k T I_F T^l \qquad (n \geqslant 0).$$

This formula is evident for $n = 0$. If it is true for n, the following calculation shows that it remains valid for $n + 1$:

$$\begin{aligned}\sum_{k\leqslant n+1} T^k &= I + \Big(\sum_{k\leqslant n} T^k\Big)T \\ &= I + \Big(\sum_{k\leqslant n} {}^FT^k\Big)({}^FT + TI_F) + \sum_{k+l<n}\sum {}^FT^k T I_F T^{l+1} \\ &= \sum_{k\leqslant n+1} {}^FT^k + \sum_{k+l<n+1}\sum {}^FT^k T I_F T^l.\end{aligned}$$

(c) Some evident upper bounds in the preceding formula give the inequalities

$$\sum_{k \leqslant n} fT^k \leqslant \sum_{k \geqslant 0} f^F T^k + \sum_{l \leqslant n} (f^F H)T^l$$

for every $f \in L^1_+(E, \mathscr{F}, \Pi)$. On the other hand, it follows from the corollary of Proposition V.6.1 and from Proposition V.5.1 that

$$\sum_{k \geqslant 0} f^F T^k < \infty$$

on $\bar{F}$ and that $\sum_{k \geqslant 0} fT^k = \infty$ at least on $\{f > 0\} \cap C$. Dividing the second term of the preceding inequality by the first and letting $n \to \infty$, we therefore obtain, for every $f \in L^1_+$ such that $\{f > 0\} = E$,

$$1 \leqslant \liminf_{n \to \infty} \frac{\sum_{k \leqslant n} (f^F H)T^k}{\sum_{k \leqslant n} fT^k} \qquad \text{on} \quad \bar{F}.$$

(d) Evident lower bounds in the formula of part *b* give the inequalities

$$\sum_{k \leqslant n} fT^k + \sum_{l=1}^{m} fT^{n+l} = \sum_{k \leqslant m+n} fT^k \geqslant \sum_{k < m} \sum_{l \leqslant n} f^F T^k T I_F T^l$$
$$= \sum_{l \leqslant n} [f^F H^{(m)}]T^l.$$

Dividing both sides of this inequality by $\sum_{k \leqslant n} fT^k$, we see that it implies, for every $f \in L^1_+$ such that $\{f > 0\} = E$, that

$$1 \geqslant \limsup_{n \to \infty} \frac{\sum_{k \leqslant n} (f^F H^{(m)})T^k}{\sum_{k \leqslant n} fT^k} \qquad (m > 0),$$

if we first show that for such f and for every $l \geqslant 0$ one has

$$\lim_{n \to \infty} \text{a.s.} \frac{fT^{n+l}}{\sum_{k \leqslant n} fT^k} = 0.$$

It suffices, to this end, to show that for every $\epsilon > 0$

$$\limsup_{n \to \infty} \left\{ fT^{n+l} > \epsilon \sum_{k \leqslant n} fT^k \right\} = \varnothing.$$

But, setting $g_n = fT^{n+l} - \epsilon \sum_{k \leqslant n} fT^k$, so that $g_n = g_{n-1}T - \epsilon f$, we have

$$\int g_n^+ = \int_{\{g_n > 0\}} g_{n-1}T - \epsilon \int_{\{g_n > 0\}} f \leqslant \int (g_{n-1}T)^+ - \epsilon \int_{\{g_n > 0\}} f$$
$$\leqslant \int g_{n-1}^+ - \epsilon \int_{\{g_n > 0\}} f.$$

It follows that

$$\sum_n \int_{\{g_n > 0\}} f \leqslant \frac{1}{\epsilon} \sum_n \int (g_{n-1}^+ - g_n^+) \leqslant \frac{1}{\epsilon} \int g_0^+ < \infty$$

and hence (by Proposition I.4.4) that $\limsup_n \{g_n > 0\} = \varnothing$ a.s. for the measure $f \cdot \Pi$, hence also for the measure Π if $\{f > 0\} = E$. Finally, letting $m \to \infty$ in the evident inequality

$$\limsup_{n \to \infty} \frac{\sum_{k \leqslant n} (f^F H) T^k}{\sum_{k \leqslant n} fT^k} \leqslant \limsup_{n \to \infty} \frac{\sum_{k \leqslant n} (f^F H^{(m)}) T^k}{\sum_{k \leqslant n} fT^k} + \sup_n \frac{\sum_{k \leqslant n} [f^F H - f^F H^{(m)}] T^k}{\sum_{k \leqslant n} fT^k}$$

and applying the corollary of Proposition V.5.1 to the sequence of functions $g_m = f^F H - f^F H^{(m)}$ which decreases to zero in L_+^1, we obtain

$$\limsup_{n \to \infty} \frac{\sum_{k \leqslant n} (f^F H) T^k}{\sum_{k \leqslant n} fT^k} \leqslant 1.$$

Comparing this with the result of part (c), we establish the proposition. ∎

ERGODIC THEOREM. (CHACON–ORNSTEIN.) *Let T be a conservative Markovian endomorphism defined on a space $L^1(E, \mathscr{F}, \Pi)$ and let $\mathscr{C}$ be the σ-subalgebra of $\mathscr{F}$ consisting of the invariant sets. Then for every $g \in L^1$ and for every $f \in L_+^1$ such that $\{f > 0\} = E$, we have*

$$\lim_{n \to \infty} \text{a.s.} \frac{\sum_{k \leqslant n} gT^k}{\sum_{k \leqslant n} fT^k} = \frac{E^{\mathscr{C}}(g)}{E^{\mathscr{C}}(f)}.$$

PROOF. When g is of the form $g = f^F H$ for an $F \in \mathscr{F}$, Proposition V.6.2 shows that the limit above exists and equals $1_{\bar{F}}$. The theorem will therefore be established in this special case if we are able to show that $E^{\mathscr{C}}(f^F H) = E^{\mathscr{C}}(f)1_{\bar{F}}$ for any $f \in L^1_+$ and $F \in \mathscr{F}$. But since $C = E$ by hypothesis, this equality is equivalent to the result stated in Proposition V.6.1; in fact, for every $\mathscr{C}$-measurable function $h \geqslant 0$ one has

$$\int E^{\mathscr{C}}(f^F H)\cdot h = \int f^F H\cdot h = \int f^F Hh,$$

$$\int E^{\mathscr{C}}(f)1_{\bar{F}}\cdot h = \int f 1_{\bar{F}} h,$$

and the equality of the right sides now implies the result.

Let Λ_f denote the vector subspace of L^1 generated by the functions $f^F H$, where F runs through $\mathscr{F}$. By the foregoing, the theorem is clearly true when $g \in \Lambda_f$; we shall show that it is true when g belongs to the closure $\overline{\Lambda_f}$ of Λ_f in L^1. To this end, we choose a sequence $\{g_p, p \geqslant 1\}$ in Λ_f such that $\sum_p \|g - g_p\| < \infty$. Letting n and then p tend to $+\infty$ in the inequality

$$\left| \frac{\sum_{k\leqslant n} gT^k}{\sum_{k\leqslant n} fT^k} - \frac{E^{\mathscr{C}}(g)}{E^{\mathscr{C}}(f)} \right| \leqslant \left| \frac{\sum_{k\leqslant n} g_pT^k}{\sum_{k\leqslant n} fT^k} - \frac{E^{\mathscr{C}}(g_p)}{E^{\mathscr{C}}(f)} \right| + \sup_n \left| \frac{\sum_{k\leqslant n} (g - g_p)T^k}{\sum_{k\leqslant n} fT^k} \right| + \frac{|E^{\mathscr{C}}(g - g_p)|}{E^{\mathscr{C}}(f)}$$

establishes the result; in fact, the first term on the right side then tends to 0 since $g_p \in \Lambda_f$, the second term tends to 0 by the corollary of Proposition V.5.1, and the third term tends to 0 a.s. since

$$\sum_p \int |E^{\mathscr{C}}(g - g_p)| \leqslant \sum_p \int |g - g_p| < \infty.$$

Next, we show that $\overline{\Lambda_f} = L^1$, which will complete the proof of the theorem. To this end, it is sufficient to prove that there exists no element $h \neq 0$ of L^∞ such that $\int gh = 0$ for every $g \in \overline{\Lambda_f}$ (Hahn-Banach theorem). But if there were such an element h, we would have $\int f^{F_0} H\cdot h = 0$ if we put $F_0 = \{h > 0\}$. Since $f^{F_0}H = 0$ on F_0^c, and since $f^{F_0}H \geqslant 0$ and $h > 0$ on F_0, this would imply that $f^{F_0}H = 0$ on F_0, hence on E. But since $\int f^{F_0}H = \int_{\overline{F_0}} f$ and $\{f > 0\} = E$, we would deduce from this that $\overline{F_0} = \varnothing$ and hence that $F_0 = \varnothing$. A similar argument would show that $\{h < 0\} = \varnothing$ and therefore that $h = 0$, contrary to hypothesis. ▮

PROPOSITION V.6.3. (E. HOPF.) *Every sub-Markovian endomorphism T of $L^1(E, \mathscr{F}, \Pi)$ having a left-invariant element $f = fT$ in L^1 such that $\{f > 0\} = E$ is necessarily Markovian and conservative. If $\mathscr{C}$ is the σ-subalgebra of $\mathscr{F}$ consisting of the sets which are right-invariant under T, the following ergodic results hold:*

$$\lim_{n\to\infty} \text{a.s.} \frac{1}{n+1} \sum_{k\leqslant n} gT^k = \frac{f}{E^{\mathscr{C}}(f)} \cdot E^{\mathscr{C}}(g) \qquad \text{if} \qquad g \in L^1,$$

$$\lim_{n\to\infty} \text{a.s.} \frac{1}{n+1} \sum_{k\leqslant n} T^k g = \frac{1}{E^{\mathscr{C}}(f)} E^{\mathscr{C}}(fg) \qquad \text{if} \qquad fg \in L^1.$$

Moreover, the limits exist as well in the sense of $L^1(E, \mathscr{F}, \Pi)$ and $L^1(E, \mathscr{F}, f\cdot\Pi)$, respectively, where the latter is the space constructed with respect to the measure $f\cdot\Pi$.

PROOF. The endomorphism T is conservative, hence Markovian (see Proposition V.5.2) since $\sum_k fT^k = \infty \cdot f = \infty$ on E. Since $\sum_{k\leqslant n} fT^k = (n+1)f$, the ergodic theorem implies the first ergodic result stated above.

The formula

$$gT' = f \cdot T\left(\frac{g}{f}\right)$$

defines a Markovian endomorphism T' on $L^1(E, \mathscr{F}, \Pi)$; we observe, in fact, that if g is a positive function, the same is true of gT', and

$$\int gT' = \int T\left(\frac{g}{f}\right)\cdot f = \int \frac{g}{f} \cdot fT = \int g.$$

The transpose of T' can be defined directly by the formula

$$T'\left(\frac{h}{f}\right) = \frac{hT}{f} \qquad (h \geqslant 0).$$

To see this, we write the identities (valid for all $g, h \geqslant 0$)

$$\int T\left(\frac{g}{f}\right)\cdot\left(\frac{h}{f}\right)\cdot f = \int \left(\frac{g}{f}\right)\cdot hT,$$

$$\int gT' \cdot \left(\frac{h}{f}\right) = \int \left(\frac{g}{f}\right)\cdot T'\left(\frac{h}{f}\right)\cdot f$$

and deduce that the equality $T(g/f)\cdot f = gT'$, which is valid for all g, is equivalent to the equality $hT/f = T'(h/f)$ for all h.

We verify at once that $fT' = f$, which implies that T' is conservative. It is also easily verified that $gT'^k = f\cdot T^k(g/f)$ for every $g \in L^1_+$. By

Corollary 2 of Proposition V.5.2, the σ-algebra $\mathscr{C}'$, consisting of the sets $\{\sum_k gT'^k = \infty\} = \{\sum_k T^k(g/f) = \infty\}$ obtained when g runs through L^1, is contained in $\mathscr{C}$. Since $gT = f \cdot T'(g/f)$, we see, by interchanging the roles of T and T' in the preceding argument, that $\mathscr{C} \subset \mathscr{C}'$ and consequently $\mathscr{C} = \mathscr{C}'$. The second ergodic result of the proposition is now obtained by applying the first result to the operator T'.

It remains to show that the preceding convergences also hold in norm in L^1. It will suffice to prove, for example, that when $g \in L^1$ and $g \geqslant 0$, the sequence $g_n = 1/(n+1) \sum_{k \leqslant n} gT^k$ converges in L^1 to g_∞. But we already know that $\lim \text{a.s.}_{n \to \infty} g_n = g_\infty$ and it is easily seen that the functions g_n $(n \geqslant 1)$ and g_∞ are positive and that

$$\int g_n = \int g_\infty = \int g.$$

Consequently, on the one hand, the sequence $\{(g_\infty - g_n)^+\}$ of positive functions tends to 0 a.s. and is bounded by $g_\infty \in L^1$, and on the other hand,

$$\int |g_\infty - g_n| = 2 \int (g_\infty - g_n)^+;$$

therefore the dominated convergence theorem implies that $g_n \to g_\infty$ in L^1 as $n \to \infty$.

COROLLARY. (BIRKHOFF'S THEOREM.) *Let θ be a measurable transformation of the probability space $(E, \mathscr{F}, \Pi)$ into itself which leaves Π invariant, that is, such that $\Pi(\theta^{-1}F) = \Pi(F)$ for all $F \in \mathscr{F}$. We denote by $\mathscr{I}$ the σ-subalgebra of $\mathscr{F}$ consisting of the sets in $\mathscr{F}$ which are invariant under θ, that is*

$$\mathscr{I} = \{I \in \mathscr{F} : \theta^{-1}I \underset{\text{a.s.}}{=} I\}.$$

Then for every $h \in L^1$ we have

$$\lim_{n \to \infty} \text{a.s.} \frac{1}{n+1} \sum_{k \leqslant n} h\theta^k = E^{\mathscr{I}}(h)$$

and this convergence also holds in the sense of L^1.

PROOF. The formula

$$\int_F fT = \int_{\theta^{-1}F} f$$

defines a Markovian endomorphism T of L^1. For every $f \in L^1$, the right side is, in fact, a bounded measure, absolutely continuous with respect to Π. Therefore, it is of the form $\int_F fT$ for some element $fT \in L^1$, by the Radon-Nikodym theorem. Moreover, the correspondence $f \to fT$ is linear, positive, and such that $\int fT = \int f$. We also note that $1T = 1$.

Next, it is easily verified that $Th = h \cdot \theta$ and more generally that $T^k h = h \cdot \theta^k$. The preceding proposition now implies the validity of the corollary. ∎

The ergodic theorem holds for an arbitrary sub-Markovian endomorphism without the requirement that this endomorphism be conservative; this result is established in the following proposition.

PROPOSITION V.6.4. *Let T be a sub-Markovian endomorphism defined on a space $L^1(E, \mathscr{F}, \Pi)$. Then for every $g \in L^1$ and every $f \in L^1_+$ such that $\{f > 0\} = E$, the almost-sure limit*

$$\lim_{n \to \infty} \text{a.s.} \left(\sum_{k \leqslant n} gT^k \Big/ \sum_{k \leqslant n} fT^k \right)$$

exists on E. On the dissipative part D, this limit is equal to the quotient of the a.s. *convergent series $\sum_k gT^k$ and $\sum_k fT^k$. On the conservative part C, it is equal to $E^{\mathscr{C}}(g')/E^{\mathscr{C}}(f')$, where the conditional expectations $E^{\mathscr{C}}$ are taken on the space $(C, C \cap \mathscr{F}, \Pi(C \cap \cdot))$ and the functions g' and f' are defined on C by $g' = g^C H, f' = f^C H$.*

PROOF. It is clear that the limit under consideration exists on D and has there the value indicated. On the other hand, if T' denotes the conservative part of T, Corollary 1 of Proposition V.5.2 and the ergodic theorem above show that

$$\lim_{n \to \infty} \text{a.s.} \left(\sum_{k \leqslant n} g'T'^k \Big/ \sum_{k \leqslant n} f'T'^k \right) = E^{\mathscr{C}}(g')/E^{\mathscr{C}}(f')$$

on C. The proposition now follows from the fact that the quotient

$$\frac{\sum_{k \leqslant n} f'T'^k}{\sum_{k \leqslant n} fT^k} = \frac{\sum_{k \leqslant n} (f^C H)T^k}{\sum_{k \leqslant n} fT^k}$$

defined on C, and the analogous quotient defined with g and g', converge a.s. to 1 on C as $n \to \infty$ (Proposition V.6.2). ∎

Complements and problems

V.6.1. Improve Proposition V.5.1 by showing, under the same conditions, that $\int_{B_{f,g}} f \geqslant \int_{B_{f,g}} g$. [Apply this proposition to the functions $(f - g)^+$ and $(g - f)^+$.] We put

$$h = \sup_{n \geqslant 0} \left(\sum_{k \leqslant n} gT^k \Big/ \sum_{k \leqslant n} fT^k \right).$$

Prove that the inequality

$$\|h\|_p \leqslant \left(\frac{p}{p-1}\right) \left\|\frac{g}{f}\right\|_p$$

holds for every $p > 1$.

[Integrate the inequality $\int_{\{h>a\}} g \geqslant \int_{\{h>a\}} af$ with respect to the measure $pa^{p-1}\, da$ over $(0, \infty)$ and use Hölder's inequality.] Deduce from this that if T is conservative, then

$$\lim_{n\to\infty} \left(\sum_{k \leqslant n} gT^k \Big/ \sum_{k \leqslant n} fT^k \right) = (E^{\mathscr{C}} g / E^{\mathscr{C}} f)$$

in $L^p(f\cdot \Pi)$ whenever $f \in L^1_+$, $\{f > 0\} = E$, and $g/f \in L^p(f \cdot \Pi)$.

V.6.2. If T is a conservative Markovian endomorphism, then $(gh)T = gT\cdot h$ for any $\mathscr{C}$-measurable function $h \geqslant 0$ and for any $g \geqslant 0$. Deduce from this that the ergodic theorem remains true if the hypotheses $f, g \in L^1$ are weakened to $E^{\mathscr{C}} f < \infty$, $E^{\mathscr{C}} g < \infty$. Show, on the other hand, that the hypothesis $\{f > 0\} = E$ can be weakened to $\{E^{\mathscr{C}} f > 0\} = E$ by observing that

$$\{E^{\mathscr{C}} f > 0\} = \left\{ \sum_k fT^k = \infty \right\}.$$

V.6.3. **Generalization of Proposition V.6.3.** Let T be a sub-Markovian endomorphism of the space $L^1(E, \mathscr{F}, \Pi)$ for which there exists an invariant $(f = fT)$ function f such that $\{f > 0\} = E$, but f is not necessarily integrable. Show that the formula $gT' = f\cdot T(g/f)$ defines a Markovian endomorphism of $L^1(E, \mathscr{F}, \Pi)$ which has the same conservative part C and the same σ-algebra $\mathscr{C}$ of invariant sets as T (the dissipative part D is not necessarily empty unless $f \in L^1$). Deduce from this (1) that $T1_c = 1_c$, (2) that $gT = g$ on C if and only if g/f is $\mathscr{C}$-measurable on C.

Show that $\lim \text{a.s.}_{n\to\infty} (\sum_{k \leqslant n} T^k g / \sum_{k \leqslant n} T^k h)$ exists on C and equals $E^{\mathscr{C}}(fg)/E^{\mathscr{C}}(fh)$ there whenever $g, h \in L^1_+(f\cdot \Pi)$ and $\{h > 0\} = E$ (more generally, whenever $E^{\mathscr{C}} g < \infty$, $E^{\mathscr{C}} h < \infty$ and $\{h > 0\} = E$, by Problem V.6.2). Deduce from this that

$$\lim_{n\to\infty} \text{a.s.} \frac{1}{n+1} \sum_{k \leqslant n} T^k g$$

exists and equals $E^{\mathscr{C}}(fg)/E^{\mathscr{C}}(f)$ on C whenever $g \in L^1_+(f\cdot\Pi)$ (more generally, whenever $E^{\mathscr{C}}(fg) < \infty$); in particular, the preceding limit equals 0 on

$\{E^{\mathscr{C}}f = \infty\}$. Show that the preceding convergence holds in the L^1 sense if and only if

$$g = 0 \quad \text{on} \quad \{E^{\mathscr{C}}f = \infty\}.$$

V.6.4. If T is a conservative operator defined on $L^1(E, \mathscr{F}, \Pi)$, every positive function h which is invariant under T is determined on $\bar{F}$ from its values on F (Proposition V.6.1). Show that, conversely, if h is a positive and finite function defined on a set F on which it satisfies $h = {}^F Hh$, the function $h' = {}^F Hh$ extends h to E and is invariant under T. Show that h' is finite (observe that $\{h' = \infty\} \in \mathscr{C}$).

V.6.5. Proposition V.6.3 can be proved directly, appealing only to the maximal ergodic theorem of Section V.5. To prove that under the hypotheses of this proposition one has

$$\lim_{n\to\infty} \text{a.s.} \frac{1}{n+1} \sum_{k\leqslant n} T^k g = \frac{E^{\mathscr{C}}(fg)}{E^{\mathscr{C}}(f)} \quad \text{when} \quad 0 \leqslant g \leqslant 1,$$

one proceeds as follows (this result can then be extended to functions g such that $\int |g| f < \infty$ by using the corollary of Proposition V.5.1).

Show that the function

$$\liminf_{n\to\infty} \frac{1}{n+1} \sum_{k\leqslant n} T^k g$$

satisfies $Th \leqslant h$ and is consequently $\mathscr{C}$-measurable ($0 \leqslant g \leqslant 1$); show next, by using Fatou's lemma, that $h \leqslant E^{\mathscr{C}}(fg)/E^{\mathscr{C}}(f)$. If, for $\epsilon > 0$, C_ϵ denotes the set $\{h + \epsilon < E^{\mathscr{C}}(fg)/E^{\mathscr{C}}(f)\}$, apply the maximal ergodic theorem to the operator T' (defined in the proof of Proposition V.6.3) and to the functions

$$\frac{E^{\mathscr{C}}(fg)}{E^{\mathscr{C}}(f)} 1_{C_\epsilon} f, \qquad (g + \epsilon) 1_{C_\epsilon} f$$

to show that

$$\int_{C_\epsilon} \frac{E^{\mathscr{C}}(fg)}{E^{\mathscr{C}}(f)} f \geqslant \int_{C_\epsilon} (g + \epsilon) f$$

and therefore that $\Pi(C_\epsilon) = 0$. Deduce from this that $h = E^{\mathscr{C}}(fg)/E^{\mathscr{C}}(f)$ and finish by applying the preceding argument to $1 - g$.

V.6.6. **Converse of Proposition V.6.3.** Show that for every sub-Markovian endomorphism T of $L^1(E, \mathscr{F}, \Pi)$, the following two conditions are equivalent:

(a) There exists a function $f \in L^1_+$ satisfying $fT = f$ and $\{f > 0\} = C$.

(b) For every $h \in L^\infty$, the sequence

$$\left\{\frac{1}{n+1} \sum_{k\leqslant n} T^k h\right\}$$

converges a.s.

Deduce from Proposition V.6.3 that (a) $\Rightarrow$ (b). Establish the opposite implication by using the results of Section IV.2; show that the convergence in probability of the sequences

$$\left\{\frac{1}{n+1}\sum_{k\leqslant n} T^k 1_F\right\} \qquad (F\in\mathscr{F})$$

already implies the convergence of the sequence

$$\left\{\frac{1}{n+1}\sum_{k\leqslant n} 1T^n\right\}$$

in the sense of the weak topology in L^1 induced by L^∞, and that the limit f of this last sequence satisfies (a).

V.6.7. **Stationary sequences of r.r.v.'s.** If θ denotes the operator of translation defined on the product space $(\Omega, \mathscr{A}) = (E, \mathscr{F})^N$ by the formula

$$\theta(\{x_n, n \geqslant 0\}) = \{x'_n, n \geqslant 0\}, \qquad \text{where} \qquad x'_n = x_{n+1}, \quad n \geqslant 0,$$

a probability P on $(\Omega, \mathscr{A})$ is said to be stationary when $P\cdot\theta^{-1} = P$ on $\mathscr{A}$. Show that if $\{X_n, n \geqslant 0\}$ is the sequence of the coordinate r.v.'s of $(\Omega, \mathscr{A})$, the probability P on $(\Omega, \mathscr{A})$ is stationary if and only if the probability law induced by $(X_{n_1+h}, \ldots, X_{n_k+h})$ on $(E, \mathscr{F})^k$ is independent of $h \geqslant 0$ for every $k \geqslant 1$ and every choice of $n_1, \ldots, n_k \in N$.

If $\mathscr{I}$ denotes the σ-subalgebra of $\mathscr{A}$ consisting of the events which are invariant under θ (stationary events), show that for every real measurable function f defined on $(E, \mathscr{F})$ such that $\int |f(X_0)|\, dP < \infty$, one has

$$\lim_{n\to\infty}\frac{1}{n+1}\sum_0^n f(X_k) = E^{\mathscr{I}}[f(X_0)]$$

in the sense of a.s. convergence and of convergence in $L^1(P)$.

Show that a Markovian random function with stationary transition probabilities P defined on $(\Omega, \mathscr{A})$ as in Section V.2 is stationary in the preceding sense if and only if the initial probability μ_0 (the probability law of X_0) is invariant under P (that is, $\mu_0 P = \mu_0$).

BIBLIOGRAPHY

The following short bibliography lists various important books and papers relating to the material treated in this book, or to the complements.

E. S. ANDERSEN and B. JESSEN. "On the introduction of measures in infinite product sets," *Danske Vid. Selsk. Mat. Fys Medd.*, **25**, no. 4, 1946.

N. ARONSZAJN. "Theory of reproducing kernels," *Trans. Amer. Math. Soc.*, **68**, 1950, pp. 337–404.

C. B. BELL. "On the structure of stochastic independence," *Illinois J. Math.*, **2**, 1958, pp. 415–424.

G. BIRKHOFF. "*Lattice Theory*," *Amer. Math. Soc. Coll. Publ.*, Vol. 25, Providence, R.I., Rev. ed., 1948.

D. BLACKWELL. "Idempotent Markov chains," *Ann. of Math.*, **43**, 1942, pp. 560–567.

———. "On a class of probability spaces," *Proc. of the Third Berkeley Symp. on Math., Stat. and Prob.*, Vol. II, Univ. of Calif. Press, Berkeley and Los Angeles, 1956, pp. 1–6.

A. BLANC-LAPIERRE and R. FORTET. *Théorie des fonctions aléatoires*, Masson et Cie, Éd., Paris, 1953.

S. BOCHNER. *Harmonic Analysis and the theory of Probability*, Univ. of Calif. Press, Berkeley and Los Angeles, 1955.

N. BOURBAKI. *Éléments de Mathématique*, Hermann et Cie, Paris.

A. BRUNEL. "Sur un lemme ergodique voisin du lemme de E. Hopf," *C.R. Acad. Sci. Paris*, **256**, 1963, pp. 5481–5484.

D. BURKHOLDER. "Sufficiency in the undominated case," *Ann. Math. Stat.*, **32**, 1961, pp. 1191–1200.

R. V. CHACON. "On the ergodic theorem without assumption of positivity," *Bull. Amer. Math. Soc.*, **67**, 1961, pp. 186–190.

——— and D. ORNSTEIN. "A general ergodic theorem," *Illinois. J. Math.*, **4**, 1960, pp. 153–160.

G. CHOQUET. "Theory of capacities," *Ann. Inst. Fourier*, **5**, 1953, pp. 131–295.

G. Choquet. "Forme abstraite du théorème de capacitabilité," *Ann. Inst. Fourier*, **9**, 1959, pp. 83–89.

———. *Topology*, Academic Press, New York, 1966.

Y. S. Chow. "A martingale inequality and the law of large numbers," *Proc. Amer. Math. Soc.*, **11**, 1960, pp. 107–111.

K. L. Chung. *Markov Chains with Stationary Transition Probabilities*, Springer Verlag, Berlin, 1960.

———. "The general theory of Markov processes according to Doeblin," *Z. Wahrscheinlichkeitstheorie und Verw. Gebiete*, **2**, 1964, pp. 230–254.

H. Cramer. *Mathematical Methods of Statistics*, 9th Ed., Princeton Univ. Press, Princeton, 1961.

W. B. Davenport and W. L. Root. *An Introduction to the Theory of Random Signals and Noise*, McGraw-Hill, New York, 1958.

J. Dieudonné. "Sur le théorème de Radon-Nikodym (III)," *Ann. Univ. Grenoble*, **23**, 1948, pp. 25–53.

———. "Sur le théorème de Jessen," *Fund. Math.*, **37**, 1950, pp. 242–248.

———. "Sur les espaces de Köthe," *J. Analyse Math.*, **1**, 1951, pp. 81–115.

J. L. Doob. *Stochastic Processes*, Wiley and Sons, New York, 1953.

L. E. Dubins. "Rises and upcrossings of nonnegative martingales," *Illinois J. Math.*, **6**, 1962, pp. 226–241.

N. Dunford and J. T. Schwartz. *Linear Operators*, Interscience Publ., New York, Vol. 1, 1958; Vol. 2, 1964.

E. B. Dynkin. *Theory of Markov Processes*, Prentice-Hall, Englewood Cliffs, N.J., 1961.

———. *Markov Processes*, Academic Press, New York, 1965.

W. F. Eberlein. "Abstract ergodic theorems and weak almost periodic functions," *Trans. Amer. Math. Soc.*, **67**, 1949, pp. 217–240.

J. Feldman. "Equivalence and perpendicularity of Gaussian processes," *Pacific J. Math.*, **8**, 1958, pp. 699–708.

———. "On the measurability of stochastic processes in product spaces," *Pacific J. Math.*, **14**, 1962, pp. 113–120.

———. "Integral kernels and invariant measures for Markoff transition functions," *Ann. Math. Stat.*, **36**, 1965, pp. 517–523.

W. Feller. *An Introduction to Probability and its Applications*, Wiley and Sons, New York, 1957.

R. Fortet and E. Mourier. "Les fonctions aléatoires comme éléments aléatoires dans les espaces de Banach," *Stud. Math.*, **15**, 1955, pp. 62–79.

A. M. Garsia. "A simple proof of E. Hopf's maximal ergodic theorem," *J. Math. Mech.*, **14**, 1965, pp. 381–382.

I. M. Gelfand. "Generalized random processes," *Dokl. Akad. Nauk SSSR*, **100**, 1955, pp. 853–856.

——— and N. Ya. Vilenkin. *Generalized Functions, Vol. 4, Applications of Harmonic Analysis*, Academic Press, New York, 1964.

B. V. Gnedenko. *Theory of Probability*, Chelsea, New York, 1962.

——— and A. N. Kolmogorov. *Limit Distributions for Sums of Independent Random Variables*, Addison-Wesley, Reading, Mass., 1954.

A. Grothendieck. "Sur les applications linéaires faiblement compactes d'espaces du type C(K)," *Canad. J. Math.*, **5**, 1953, pp. 129–173.

P. R. Halmos. *Measure Theory*, Van Nostrand, Princeton, N.J., 1956.

——— and L. J. Savage. "Application of the Radon-Nikodym theorem to the theory of sufficient statistics," *Ann. Math. Stat.*, **20**, 1949, pp. 225–241.

T. E. Harris. "The existence of stationary measures for certain Markov Processes," *Third Berkeley Symp. on Math., Stat. and Prob.*, Vol. II, Univ. of Calif. Press, Berkeley and Los Angeles, 1956, pp. 113–124.

L. L. Helms. "Mean convergence of martingales," *Trans. Amer. Math. Soc.*, **87**, 1958, pp. 439–446.

E. Hewitt and L. J. Savage. "Symmetric measures on Cartesian products," *Trans. Amer. Math. Soc.*, **80**, 1955, pp. 470–501.

T. Hida. "Canonical representations of Gaussian processes and their applications," *Mem. Coll. Sci. Kyoto*, **23**, 1960, pp. 109–155.

E. Hille and R. S. Phillips. *Functional Analysis and Semi-groups*, *Amer. Math. Soc. Coll. Publ.*, Vol. 31, Providence, R.I., 1957.

E. Hopf. "The general temporally discrete Markov process," *Journal of Rat. Mech. and Anal.*, **3**, 1954, pp. 13–45.

G. A. Hunt. *Théorie des Martingales*, Cours multigraphié, Faculté des Sciences d'Orsay, 1963.

W. Hurewicz. "Ergodic theorem without invariant measure," *Ann. of Math.*, **45**, 1944, pp. 192–206.

C. Ionescu Tulcea. "Mesures dans les espaces produits," *Atti Acad. Naz. Lincei Rend.*, **7**, 1949, pp. 208–211.

A. and C. Ionescu Tulcea. "On the lifting property." I., *J. Math. Anal. Appl.*, **3**, 1961, pp. 537–546. II., *J. Math. Mech.*, **11**, 1962, pp. 773–795.

———. "Abstract ergodic theorems," *Trans. Amer. Math. Soc.*, **107**, 1963, pp. 107–124.

K. Ito. "Multiple Wiener Integral," *J. Math. Soc. Japan*, **3**, 1951, pp. 157–169.

———. "Stationary Random Distributions," *Kyoto Sc. Rep.*, **28** A, 1954, pp. 209–223.

——— and H. P. McKean. *Diffusion Processes and their Sample Paths*, Academic Press, New York, 1965.

K. Jacobs. *Neuere Methoden und Ergebnisse der Ergodentheorie*, Ergebnisse der Mathematik und ihrer Grenzgebiete, Vol. 29, Springer Verlag, Berlin, 1960.

———. *Lecture Notes on Ergodic Theory*, Matematisk Institut, Aarhus Universitet, 1963.

M. Jirina. "On regular conditional probabilities," *Czech. Math. J.*, **84**, 1959, pp. 445–451.

S. Kakutani. "Concrete representation of abstract (M)-spaces," *Ann. of Math.*, **42**, 1941, pp. 994–1024.

———. "On the equivalence of infinite product measures," *Ann. of Math.*, **49**, 1948, pp. 214–224.

D. A. Kappos. *Strukturtheorie der Wahrscheinlichkeitsfelder und -Raüme.* Ergebnisse der Mathematik und ihrer Grenzgebiete, Vol. 24, Springer Verlag, Berlin, 1960.

K. Karhunen. "Uber lineare Methoden in der Wahrscheinlichkeitsrechnung," *Ann. Acad. Sci. Fenn.*, **37**, 1947.

A. N. Kolmogorov. *Foundations of the Theory of Probability*, Chelsea, New York, 1950.

———. "Stationary sequences in Hilbert space," *Bull. Moscow State University*, **2**, no. 6, 1941.

———. "Algèbres de Boole métriques complètes," *VI Zjazd. Mat. Pols. Warsaw*, 1948, pp. 21–30.

K. Krickeberg. "Stochastische Konvergenz von Semi-martingales," *Math. Zeit.*, **66**, 1957, pp. 470–486.

L. Le Cam. "Convergence in distribution of stochastic processes," *Univ. Calif. Publ. Stat.*, Vol. 2, no. 11, 1957, pp. 207–236.

E. L. Lehmann. *Testing Statistical Hypotheses*, Wiley and Sons, New York, 1959.

P. Lévy. *Théorie de l'Addition des Variables Aléatoires*, Gauthier-Villars, Paris, 1937.

———. *Processus Stochastiques et Mouvement Brownien*, Gauthier-Villars, Paris, 1948.

———. "Wiener's random function and other Laplacian random functions," *Proc. of the 2nd Berkeley Symp. on Math., Stat. and Prob.*, Univ. of Calif. Press, Berkeley and Los Angeles, 1951, pp. 171–187.

M. Loève. "Fonctions aléatoires du second ordre," *Rev. Scient.*, **84**, 1946, pp. 195–206.

———. *Probability Theory*, Van Nostrand, Princeton, N.J., 3rd Ed., 1963.

D. Maharam. "On a theorem of Von Neumann," *Proc. Amer. Math. Soc.*, **9**, 1958, pp. 987–994.

E. Marczewski. "On compact measures," *Fund. Math.*, **40**, 1953, pp. 113–124.

——— and C. Ryll-Nardzewski. "Projections in abstract sets," *Fund. Math.*, **40**, 1953, pp. 160–164.

P. A. Meyer. "Théorèmes fondamentaux du calcul des probabilités," *Séminaire de Théorie du Potentiel*, 1960–1961, Paris.

———. "A decomposition theorem for supermartingales," *Illinois J. Math.*, **6**, 1962, pp. 193–205.

E. Mourier. "Éléments aléatoires à valeurs dans un espace de Banach," *Thése de doctorat*, Paris, 1952; *Ann. Inst. H. Poincaré*, **13**, 161–244 (1953).

S. Moy. "Characterizations of conditional expectation as a transformation on function spaces," *Pacific J. Math.*, **4**, 1954, pp. 47–63.

J. Neveu. "Théorie des semi-groupes de Markov," *Univ. Calif. Publ. Stat.*, Vol. 2, no. 14, pp. 319–394.

———. "Sur le théorème ergodique ponctuel," *C.R. Acad. Sci. Paris*, **252**, 1961, pp. 1554–1556.

S. Orey. "Recurrent Markov chains," *Pacific J. Math.*, **9**, 1959, pp. 805–827.

E. Parzen. *Stochastic Processes*, Holden-Day, San Francisco, 1962.

Yu. V. Prohorov. "Convergence of random processes and limit theorems in probability theory," *Theory of Prob. and its Applications*, **1**, 1956, pp. 157–214.

A. Renyi. "A new axiomatic construction of probability," *Mag. Tud. Akad. Mat. Fiz. Oszt. Kozl.*, **4**, 1954, pp. 369–427.

———. "On mixing sequences of sets," *Acta Math. Acad. Sci. Hungar.*, **9**, 1958, pp. 215–228.

S. Rice. "Mathematical analysis of random noise," *Bell System Tech. J.*, **23**, 1944, pp. 282–332, and **24**, 1945, pp. 46–156.

F. Riesz and B. Sz. Nagy. *Functional Analysis*, Ungar, New York, 1955.

S. Saks. *Theory of the Integral*, Hafner Publ. Co., New York, 1937.

L. V. Seregin. "Continuity conditions for stochastic processes," *Theory of Prob. and its Applications*, **6**, 1961, pp. 1–26.

S. Sherman. "On denumerably independent families of Borel fields," *Amer. J. Math.*, **72**, 1950, pp. 612–614.

Z. Sidak. "On relations between strict-sense and wide-sense conditional expectations," *Theory of Prob. and its Applications*, **2**, 1957, pp. 267–272.

R. Sikorski. *Boolean Algebras*, Academic Press, New York, 2nd Ed., 1964.

J. L. Snell. "Applications of martingale system theorems," *Trans. Amer. Math. Soc.*, **73**, 1952, pp. 293–312.

F. Spitzer. *Principles of Random Walk*, Van Nostrand, Princeton, N.J., 1964.

M. H. Stone. *Linear Transformations in Hilbert Space*, *Amer. Math. Soc. Coll. Publ.*, Vol. 15, Providence, R.I., 1932.

———. "The theory of representations for Boolean algebras," *Trans. Amer. Math. Soc.*, **40**, 1936, pp. 37–111.

A. Tortrat. *Calcul des Probabilités*, Masson et Cie, Ed. Paris, 1963.

V. S. Varadarajan. "Weak convergence of measures on separable metric spaces," *Sankhya*, **19**, 1958, pp. 15–22.

K. Yosida and S. Kakutani. "Operator-theoretical treatment of Markov's process and mean ergodic theorem," *Ann. of Math.*, **42**, 1941, pp. 188–228.

INDEX

The numbers in this index refer to chapters and sections; for example, III.2 means Chapter III, Section 2.